How do insects have the "wisdom" to adapt to hostile environments, organize complex societies, evolve, migrate, and reproduce in patterns designed to ensure survival?

❧

The answer, Sir Vincent explains in his engrossing book, can be found in the study of insect physiology. The author describes such physiological functions as reproduction, digestion, hearing, smell, movement, growth and metamorphosis. He discusses methods of attack and defense, the exciting problem of population and migration, the sexual lures of sound, scent, and color (the yellow fever mosquito will try to mate with a tuning fork). Sir Vincent also tells how new species are constantly evolving, and how insects affect the other living inhabitants of the earth.

❧

This unique volume includes an illustrated survey of insect classification, a bibliography, glossary, and many superb drawings and photographs.

❧

"Immense knowledge, deployed with fascinating charm."
—*London Illustrated News*

Other MENTOR AND SIGNET SCIENCE
Books of Related Interest

THE LIFE OF INSECTS

V. B. WIGGLESWORTH
CBE, MD, FRS

Fellow of Gonville and Caius College
Quick Professor of Biology in the University of Cambridge
Director, Agricultural Research Council Unit of Insect Physiology

THE WORLD NATURAL HISTORY

EDITOR: RICHARD CARRINGTON

ASSOCIATE EDITORS:

DR. L. HARRISON MATTHEWS, FRS
PROFESSOR J. Z. YOUNG, FRS

A MENTOR BOOK

Published by The New American Library,
New York and Toronto
The New English Library Limited, London

Published as a MENTOR BOOK
by arrangement with The World Publishing Company,
New York, and Weidenfeld & Nicolson Limited, London, who
have authorized this softcover edition. A hardcover edition is
published in the United States by The World Publishing
Company and in Great Britain by Weidenfeld & Nicolson
Limited.

MENTOR BOOKS are published in the
United States by The New American Library, Inc.,
1301 Avenue of the Americas, New York, New York 10019,
in Canada by The New American Library of Canada Limited,
295 King Street East, Toronto 2, Ontario,
in the United Kingdom by The New English Library Limited,
Barnard's Inn, Holborn, London, E.C. 1, England

PRINTED IN THE UNITED STATES OF AMERICA

Contents

List of Illustrations

ACKNOWLEDGMENTS FOR PHOTOGRAPHS—

Anti-Locust Research Centre, plates 13(a), 33(a) [C. Ashall];
J. W. L. Beament, plate 1(c); S. Beaufoy, plate 32; Colin G.
Butler, plates 30 and 31; H. B. Cott, plates 11, 12, 25, and 26;
K. Daumer, plate 28; Mme M. Dupont-Raabe, plate 13(b);
T. Eisner, plate 8; E. Ernst, plate 9; S. Fukuda, plate 4; H. E.
Hinton, plate 2; H. B. D. Kettlewell, plates 17, 21, 22, and 29;
National Publicity Studios, New Zealand, plate 7(c); J. Pybus,
plate 7(a); S. A. Ramsey and the Department of Scientific and
Industrial Research, New Zealand, plate 7(b); Hon Miriam
Rothschild, plates 18(b), 19, 20, 23, and 24; D. Schneider,
plate 6; P. M. Sheppard, plate 10; Shell, C. Milnes, plate 33(b);
V. B. Wigglesworth and Michael Day, plates 14, 15, and 16(a).

PREFACE

        THIS BOOK about the Natural History of Insects is an attempt to present the problems and complexities of insect life against the background of what is known today about the physiological workings of the insect body. During the past half-century there have been great advances in knowledge about the biochemistry and physiology of insects. The broad outlines of these subjects can readily be grasped by any interested reader, and the object of the present book is to incorporate this knowledge into the everyday story of the life of insects.

    The number of insect species and the amount of information that exists about them are both so vast that it is possible to illuminate this theme only by selected examples. But these examples form a connected story and it is the high ambition of the author that any sympathetic reader who follows this story from the beginning to the end may be left with a new appreciation of the problems that beset the life of insects, and perhaps even a trace of wonder at the means they have discovered by which these problems can be solved.

    I have received much generous assistance in the provision of illustrations. Excellent colour photographs have been put at my disposal by the Hon Miriam Rothschild, Dr H. B. Kettlewell and Mme Dupont-Raabe; and half-tone photographs of equal quality have been lent me by Dr J. W. L. Beament, Dr C. G. Butler, Dr H. B. Cott, Dr P. S. Corbet, Dr K. Daumer of Munich, Dr T. Eisner of Cornell, Dr E. Ernst of Basle, Dr H. E. Hinton, Dr M. Lüscher of Berne, Dr Aola Richards of the University of New South Wales, Dr

P. M. Sheppard, Dr Dietrich Schneider of Munich, Dr Tadao Yokoyama of Tokyo, the Anti-Locust Research Centre, London and Messrs Shell (Chemicals). I am most grateful to all these authors and authorities. Finally, the line drawings have been rendered by my wife Katharine, to whom my warmest thanks are due for the hard work she put in, learning a new group of animals and re-presenting them in a clear and lively style.

Cambridge, January 1964   V.B.W.

Chapter 1

INTRODUCTION

SOMETHING RATHER less than a million different sorts of insects have already been described and named; several thousand new ones are discovered each year; and the total number of species now in existence is variably estimated at figures which lie between two million and five million. Even at the present time at least five-sixths of the named species of animals in the world are insects.

In a particular countryside there are only a few species with a very large number of individuals, whereas there are many more species that are rare. In fact, when the numbers of species are plotted against the numbers of individuals per species, as has been done by C. B. Williams, a constant form of mathematical curve is obtained. Assuming that the same principle applies to the number of insects in the world, Williams has attempted to prepare such a curve and to infer from it the total number of insects and of insect species that probably exist. The procedure involves many assumptions, but it leads to the suggestion that at any moment the insect population of the world is 10^{18}, one million English billions of individuals and that there are perhaps as many as three million species.

The most primitive insects known are to be found as fossils in the rocks of the middle Devonian period, perhaps three hundred and fifty million years ago. They were recognizable then as now by having the body divided into three more or less well defined regions: a head bearing a pair of 'feelers' or antennae, a thorax with three pairs of legs, and a segmented abdomen (figure 1).

The hypothetical ancestor of the insects would be a worm-like creature with its body made up of ring-like segments, each supported by a pair of appendages or limbs. It would move predominantly in one direction and the appendages at the leading end would have become modified by natural selection, some for the purpose of seizing and manipulating the food and conveying it to the mouth, others by the great development of the sense organs they carried. During this evolu-

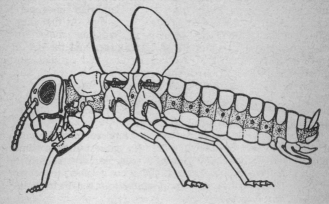

Figure 1.
Diagram showing the general anatomy of an insect (Weber). The body consists of three regions: (1) the *head* with large compound eyes, small simple eyes, feelers or antennae, and mouth-parts with associated sense organs (palps); (2) the *thorax* of three segments, each of which carries a pair of legs, the second and third segments a pair of wings; the legs are always made up of the same set of segments: the 'coxa' attached to the body, a small 'trochanter', a stout thigh or 'femur', a long shank or 'tibia', and a 'tarsus' with about three to five segments, ending in a claw or claws; (3) the *abdomen* with a maximum of eleven segments; the last segment may carry a pair of tail feelers ('cerci'), and the segments near the end carry the structures concerned in reproduction. The 'spiracles' leading to the 'tracheal system' can be seen along the side of the body.

tionary process these leading segments would have become consolidated or fused together to form a 'head'. And since the nervous system in the head region would be abundantly supplied with sensory nerves from the numerous organs of sense developed in this leading part, it would have become enlarged to form a ganglion or primitive brain where all these sensory impressions could be received and integrated and the movements of the whole animal controlled accordingly.

Meanwhile the appendages at the tail end of the body would have become modified also, some to provide for mating and the manipulation of the eggs, others to carry sensory organs. The entire hypothetical creature would resemble a primitive sort of centipede, probably not measuring more than a few millimetres in length.

If we were to trace this ancestral form still further back we should find it took its origin from the terrestrial branch of the arthropods. The origin of the Arthropoda is quite unknown; they must have arisen in pre-Cambrian times, perhaps as much as a thousand million years ago. At first they may have lived along the shore lines and later moved in two directions. A part colonized the open sea and the ocean depths to give rise to the Crustacea, crabs, and shrimps, etc of today; a part colonized the land. Whole classes of the terrestrial line have since died out and are known only as fossils; the survivors are the millepedes and centipedes, the spiders, scorpions, ticks and mites, as well as the restricted class which we call Insecta today.

In the course of the three or four hundred million years, at least, which have passed since the earliest insects came into existence, they have assumed the most diverse forms. It is generally accepted that one form has evolved in course of time from another; but the mechanism by which evolution has been brought about is still a subject for controversy. The theory that is best supported by evidence, and is in fact most widely accepted by biologists, is that of Charles Darwin: the theory of natural selection with the survival of the fittest. During the past sixty years our increased knowledge of genetics has given a much firmer basis to this theory than it had in Darwin's time. For the science of genetics has shown that animals do change or vary, that these variations or mutations are inherited, and that natural selection, even when it favours one variant only a little more than another, is an extremely powerful instrument which leads very rapidly to the predominance of the favoured form.

These notions are not 'proved' in the popular sense of our knowing as a fact that the changes during evolution did happen in that way. Like all scientific theories the 'theory of natural selection' is merely a provisional description of what we believe has happened and is happening. There is at present no other theory which fits the facts so well; it will, therefore, be accepted throughout this book as the basis for thinking about the life of insects.

Among the enthusiastic followers of Darwin in the second half of the last century it became fashionable to construct

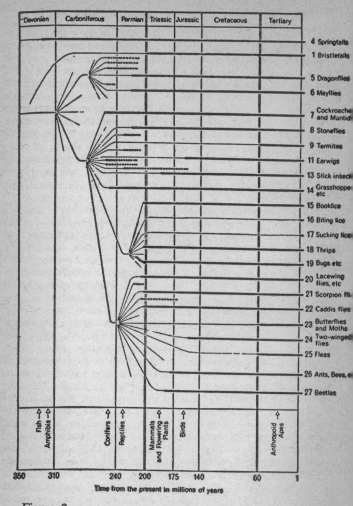

Figure 2.
Diagram showing the fossil history of insects (simplified from chart by J. Smart). To the right are listed the chief 'orders' of insects; the numbers refer to the Appendix (p. 313) where each order is described. The thick continuous lines indicate the periods in geological time during which fossils of each order have been found. The thick broken lines indicate orders which have died out and are known only as fossils. The thin lines show the possible origin of the orders in evolution.

'phylogenetic trees'. These were intended to show the relationship between different groups of animals and how one group had evolved from another. But we realize now that the few animals in existence today are only the rare survivors among the vast hordes of species that have become extinct, and that of the extinct species we have found fossil remains of very few. Family trees of the old sort have, therefore, become discredited. The modern family tree shows each existing group arising from an unknown ancestor. If two groups are thought to be closely related they will be shown as coming from a common stem. A primitive existing animal is no longer regarded as a true ancestor but may be represented as the end of a twig coming off near the base of the stem.

We have come to realize also that the evolution of the different groups of animals has been far more active at some periods in the past than at others. Geologically speaking there have been epochs of 'explosive' evolution when many new types have been produced, most of which have later died out. These explosive periods are perhaps the epochs that have followed some 'new invention' in the working of the body; they are pictured as the times when the ancestors of our existing insects made their appearance. Figure 2 is a greatly simplified diagram of the evolutionary history of the present-day insects throughout the geological periods from the Devonian to the Recent. To the right appear the common names of the 'orders' that are recognized at the present time. The thick lines indicate the periods during which representatives of these orders have been found as fossils. The thin lines indicate their hypothetical origin. Some ten additional 'orders' of insects are known only as fossils; these are indicated by thick broken lines. And, of course, there must have been a vast number of insect types produced during the 'explosive' periods of evolution in Carboniferous and Permian times of which no trace has so far been discovered.

The study of this vast array of animals, comprising a greater number of species than all the rest of the animal and plant kingdoms put together, forms the science of entomology. On the one hand this embraces comparative morphology: the detailed study of the anatomy and development of the different sorts of insects. Comparative morphology provides the evidence for the evolutionary process that has been sketched above, and the basis for the broad classification and relationships between the various groups of insects. On the other hand, most entomologists are concerned with systematics and taxonomy. 'Systematics' is the continuous attempt to formulate a natural classification of insects into orders, families, and genera which will at one and the same time be convenient and orderly in use and will reflect what are believed to be evolutionary relationships between one sort of insect and another. 'Taxonomy' is the task of recognizing and describing the individual species and allocating them to genera in such a way that each may be named with certainty by subsequent collectors. An army of entomologists all over the world, in museums and universities or as amateurs working in their spare time, labour continually at these herculean tasks. Upon the accuracy and efficiency of their work all other entomologists depend.

But these matters are not directly the concern of the naturalist. He is concerned to know how the insect lives. He wants to know how the insects of today maintain themselves in a hostile world. How they compete and co-operate with one another, outwit their enemies, secure their prey, grow and multiply.

As a catalogue of the 'wonders of nature' the insects have no rivals. The writers of natural history books of a century or so ago were satisfied to describe these wonders and to admire them as examples of a divine providence. The passage of time has in no way diminished the wonders of insect life, nor have we many better clues to their source and origin than that summarized by an earlier generation as 'divine providence'.

Insects, like ourselves, live in a world that is dominated by physics and chemistry. They must abide by the laws of physics and chemistry or they could not live at all. The study of all the special arrangements and adaptations in the body which make this possible is the science of physiology. 'Physiology' aims at providing a physical and chemical description of all the activities of the insect. Its feeding, digestion and nutrition; the 'metabolism', or chemical transformations, which all the nutrient substances undergo in the body; respiration, by which oxygen is provided to feed the fires of metabolism, and carbon dioxide and water, the final products of this combustion, are eliminated; excretion, by means of which the other waste products of metabolism are got rid of; active bodily movements; the sensory perception of all the changes that go on in their surroundings; the organization of these sensations, and of the resulting muscular movements, by the nervous system which controls behaviour; growth and reproduction. All these physiological processes must eventually find a complete description in terms of physics and chemistry. That at least is the profound faith of the biologist.

It follows, I believe, that the thread which will best bind together and give meaning to all the wonders of insect life is physiology; and that is the purpose of this book. We shall not be concerned with the abstruse details of biochemistry or biophysics. But if we know in simple outline how the insect body works, what it was fashionable in the past to call 'divine providence' will become more intelligible —and more respected.

In the Appendix to this volume will be found a brief account of each of the twenty-eight existing orders of insects, included in the phylogenetic tree on p. 16. This survey is like the list of characters in the programme of a play. It may be studied before the play begins; though perhaps it will not convey very much on a first reading. But as the play proceeds we refer to the programme with increasing interest to learn just where the various characters tie in. That is the purpose of the 'Catalogue of Insects' (p. 313).

Chapter 2

THE INSECT AS A TERRESTRIAL ANIMAL

THE MOST primitive among the surviving types of insects, *Campodea* (Diplura), the minute Protura, and most of the springtails (Collembola) are to be found only in humid surroundings—in the mat at the base of growing vegetation, in the moist litter of forests, below fallen logs, or under stones. It was under conditions such as these that the terrestrial ancestors of the insects may be supposed to have existed.

But with the development of the diverse orders of insects as outlined in the Appendix (p. 313), they escaped from this restricted environment and have succeeded in colonizing every corner of the earth from the sub-polar regions to the equator, from the steamy rain forests to the parched deserts or high mountains. This emancipation was made possible by a few key chemical inventions and a few ingenious physiological adaptations.

'Life' has been defined as something which takes place in water. And although, as we shall see, some insects can survive in what appears to be a completely desiccated state, the normal manifestations of life—movement, feeding, chemical transformations or 'metabolism', growth and reproduction—can happen only in a body that contains 50 per cent or more of water.

The first great problem for every terrestrial animal is the

21

conservation of water. Water will be lost by evaporation from the surface. If the animal is small the size of its surface will be large in proportion to the total volume of water it contains. It will, therefore, tend to dry up very quickly—just as a raindrop will dry up more quickly than a bucket of water; but if the bucket of water is scattered in the form of fifty thousand raindrops its surface area is so much increased that it will dry up as quickly as a single drop.

The Outer Covering of Insects

Semi-terrestrial animals such as slugs protect the surface of their bodies with a moist layer of slime, or 'mucus'. Chemically speaking mucus is a mucoprotein, a compound of protein and sugar. One of the early inventions of the terrestrial ancestor of insects was to convert the carbohydrate, or sugar, of mucus into a tough fibrous polymer termed chitin. Chemically chitin is a polymer of acetylglucosamine; that is, it consists of long chains of the nitrogen-containing sugar glucosamine linked together—just as the cellulose of plants consists of long chains of the sugar glucose.

Chitin is a tough flexible fibrous material; it resembles the cellulose of plants that we see in pure form in blotting paper. Combined with protein it provides the basis for the surface covering of all the insects; it may be thought of as a tough dry kind of mucus.

The outermost cells of an animal form a sheet known as the epidermis. In the insects, and all the other Arthropods, the epidermis lays down an outer skin, or 'cuticle', and when we look at an insect the cuticle is all we see. Chitin forms the basis of the insect cuticle, but by itself it is not a suitable covering for a terrestrial animal. It is tough and flexible and is well suited to provide the hinges or joints where one segment bends upon another. But in most insects the segments of the body or of the limbs are firm and rigid. Their cuticle is quite stiff; it forms in fact an external skeleton to which the muscles are attached (figure 3).

What is the nature of this horny material with which the cuticle is stiffened? It is called 'sclerotin' and is produced in the following way. A large amount of protein is added to the chitin of the cuticle and then this protein is tanned very much as hides are tanned to produce leather. In fact, the insect may be said to tan its own skin! The chemical details of the process are not fully understood, but briefly it may be said that quinones of some kind react with the protein and

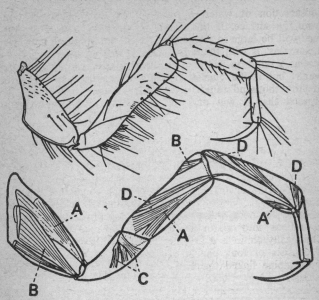

Figure 3.
A leg of the caddis fly larva *Triaenodes* and the same leg showing how the cuticle serves as a rigid skeleton for attachment of the muscles. (A. R. Tindall). A, 'flexor muscles' which bend the limb; B, 'extensor muscles' which unfold the limb; C, muscles which rotate the limb; D, 'claw flexor muscles' all of which are connected to the tendon that closes the claw.

link the protein chains together. They convert the protein into a cross-linked plastic which, like many artificial plastics, is hard and exceedingly resistant to chemicals.

The horny substance known as 'keratin' of which the scales of reptiles, the feathers of birds, and the hair and hoofs and horns of mammals are composed is a similar plastic in which the proteins are cross-linked through sulphur bridges; whereas in sclerotin the cross-links are provided by the benzene rings of the tanning substance (figure 4). Just as the invention of keratin was one of the things which made terrestrial life possible for the vertebrates and which provided the raw material for the flying equipment of pterodactyls, birds, and bats, and the covering of hair and feathers which mammals and birds use to keep themselves warm, so the invention of sclerotin has been an essential element in the evolution of terrestrial life in insects.

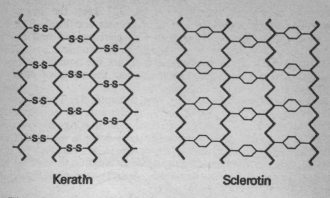

Keratin   **Sclerotin**

Figure 4.
Diagrams showing how the protein chains are believed to be linked through sulphur bonds in the keratin of birds and mammals, and through benzene rings in the sclerotin of insect cuticle.

Indeed, it is impossible to study the natural history of insects without discovering at every point how dependent they are upon this remarkable plastic, sclerotin. A boiled shirt is stiffened by the incorporation of starch along with the cellulose or cotton; the wood of trees is stiffened by the incorporation of lignin with the cellulose; in just the same way the hard parts of insects are stiffened by the incorporation of sclerotin with the chitin.

The resulting product forms a light but extremely strong skeletal substance. The jaws or mandibles of insects serve to illustrate how hard sclerotin can be made when it is necessary; wood-boring beetles can bite through sheets of lead, silver, copper, or zinc. This means that their mandibles are harder than these substances. The carapace of lobsters is hardened in a simpler way—by embedding lime in the form of calcite in the cuticle. But the parts of the lobster which it needs to have really hard, the tips of the mandibles and the claws, are coated with sclerotin. Fully hardened sclerotin is, in fact, harder than calcite.

Sclerotin is readily moulded into the most elaborate structures. The cells grow and form the required structures in soft protein with or without chitin. Then, by the appropriate chemical reactions, controlled by the appropriate enzymes, or catalysts, the structure is tanned and hardened to form sclerotin. In this way the great spines on the legs of cockroaches are formed, or the closely fitting coat of fine hairs or scales which, as we shall see (p. 32) keep the insect warm like the fur and feathers of mammals and birds. The delicate stylets of mosquitoes and other piercing and sucking insects, the intricate parts of which fit so wonderfully together, are built up in this way; and so are the equally elaborate mating organs of the two sexes, and the stings of bees and wasps.

Sclerotin is ideal material for wings (chapter 3). The effective wings are composed of thin membranes of sclerotin stiffened by rods, or 'veins'. The first pair of wings may be more or less thickened and leathery to form a protective covering for the delicate hind-wings, as in grasshoppers or cockroaches. This development reaches its limit in the beetles where the heavily sclerotized fore-wings serve only as sheaths, or 'elytra', to protect the hind-wings.

When the covering of sclerotin is very thick as in the dense black cuticle of the stag beetle (Lucanus) (figure 163) or in the black Tenebrionid beetles, which are such characteristic objects in hot dry deserts, the sclerotin alone may be efficient in keeping in the water of the body and preventing evaporation. Even if the surface of the sclerotin is ground away these beetles still do not lose water. But even in beetles sclerotin is necessarily absent from the cuticle of the joints, and it is absent from the upper surface of the abdomen, which is normally protected by the hardened elytra.

In such insects as caterpillars it is only the mandibles and a few other parts that are sclerotized. In this soft type of cuticle the colourless moist layer of chitin and protein is covered by no more than a very thin amber-coloured membrane called the 'epicuticle', which is much less than a micron (a thousandth of a millimetre) thick. The small soft white caterpillar of the clothes-moth (Tineola) is exceedingly resistant to drying—as it must be if it is to maintain itself in dry skins and furs or woollens. This waterproofing property resides in the epicuticle. The slightest injury to the epicuticle, and this property is lost. A caterpillar that would have been able to resist drying for many weeks will then die of desiccation in a few hours.

The waterproofing layer on the surface of the cuticle is extremely delicate and fragile. If a caterpillar is allowed to walk over a piece of blotting-paper which has been very lightly dusted with an abrasive, such as a fine silica or alumina dust, it will shrivel and die in a matter of hours. If the chrysalides of Lepidoptera are kept in a dry container many of them will survive and emerge. But if they become contaminated with fine dry dust from the earth, this will work into the intersegmental joints as they wriggle; the soft membranes are abraded and they soon dry up and die.

Abrasion of this sort can happen in Nature. Many soft-skinned insect larvae inhabit the soil—caterpillars of moths, larvae of beetles and flies. If these larvae are brought out and exposed in the dry air they soon dry up. By suitable tests it can be shown that that is because the surface of the cuticle has been scratched by the soil particles and become permeable to water. They normally survive in the soil only because the air in the soil spaces is more or less saturated with moisture. But if such larvae are kept away from the soil, and fed and allowed to moult so that they now have a new and unscratched cuticle, they are found to be as resistant to drying as other insects.

What makes the epicuticle so waterproof? There is still much to be learned about this but we do know that the barrier to the evaporation of water is a mixture of waxes that are spread as a very thin film over the surface. Indeed, the most effective part of the waterproofing wax is a mono-molecular layer—a single layer of the elongated wax molecules packed so closely together that the molecules of water cannot escape between them. A layer of wax freely exposed in this way would be excessively fragile. It is usually protected by another thin layer, a sort of thin varnish called the 'cement layer', which is poured out over the wax from tiny glands scattered all over the surface of the body.

Another problem which is incompletely solved is how the insect contrives to arrange this thin wax layer over its surface. We know that in the cockroach, wax is being continually exuded through the cuticle by the epidermal cells, dissolved in a volatile solvent. The solvent slowly evaporates leaving a waterproof grease. It is doubtful whether that happens in most insects, which waterproof their surface with very hard waxes. It has been shown by means of the electron microscope that these waxes escape through sub-microscopic pores in the surface of the cuticle. The same thing happens on a larger scale in the honey-bee. For in the bee there are small patches of the epidermis (on the lower surface of the abdomen) which have become specialized for the production of the waxy scales that are used to build the honey-comb (figure 120).

Whatever the refinements by which waterproofing is brought about, it is quite clear that the survival of the insect often depends upon its efficiency. When observing, for example, the swarms of flea beetles (*Phyllotreta*) sitting about on the seedling turnips in the hot sunshine of the early summer, I often reflect that if the impermeability of the cuticle were to be destroyed they would all die in a few hours. It is a common practice in North Africa, and has indeed been so since Roman times, to mix a little fine road dust with the stored grain to keep this free from weevils. And in Europe at the present day fine crystalline dusts of silica or alumina are sometimes used for this same purpose. There is some disagreement as to how these dusts work, but there is little doubt that a large part of their action results from the abrasion of the waterproofing waxes on the thin cuticle in the joints and elsewhere.

The Breathing of Insects

The waterproofing of the cuticle is an essential condition for the emancipated life of insects. But impermeability to water entails a very serious disability: the cuticle is impermeable also to oxygen. Another necessary condition for a free and active life is an abundant supply of oxygen which will sustain a 'high rate of metabolism' or, in other words, will permit the combustion of the large amounts of sugar and fat which provide the energy required for really active movement.

Many of the primitive Collembola, tied to moist surroundings, and with a cuticle permeable to water, can get enough oxygen for their relatively sedentary existence by the diffusion of gases through the cuticle. All other insects have a special respiratory system. This system was discovered in the silkworm by the Italian microscopist Marcello Malpighi in 1669. He found that along the sides of the body there is a series of holes ('spiracles') which lead in to air-filled tubes (figure 1). These are the 'tracheae', or breathing tubes, which link up with one another and branch repeatedly, becoming smaller and smaller until the finest branches, which are visible only with a high-powered microscope, either surround the living cells or actually penetrate inside them (plate 1).

The tracheal tubes are, in fact, ingrowths from the epidermis and are lined by cuticle continuous with the cuticle on the surface of the body. This cuticle is thrown into folds and stiffened with a thread, or filament, which runs a spiral course around the tube. This arrangement serves the same purpose as the folds and stiffening in flexible gas piping; it prevents the tube from collapsing when bent or compressed. The finest endings of the tracheal tubes have exceedingly thin and delicate walls. It is here that most of the oxygen diffuses through to reach the blood and the living cells.

When a freshly killed insect is opened up under water this tracheal breathing system presents a striking and beautiful appearance. Everywhere the body is traversed by silvery air-filled tubes and those organs whose need for oxygen is greatest, such as the muscles and the reproductive organs, may be almost hidden by them.

This system of invaginated tubes allows the insect to have a waterproof cuticle and yet to take in oxygen. But while the air enters through the spiracles, water vapour can escape; a further refinement is, therefore, necessary. Each spiracle is furnished with a valve which is held tightly shut by a tiny muscle. When the insect needs oxygen the muscle is relaxed and an elastic spring opens the valve. Thus the insect normally keeps its spiracles closed as much as possible and opens them only just frequently enough to let in the oxygen it needs and to allow the carbon dioxide to escape.

Entomologists were at one time puzzled as to how oxygen was conveyed from the spiracles along the tracheal tubes to the organs. But it has now been proved that this is brought about by diffusion. The diffusion of gases is a very rapid and active process; even a large caterpillar can get all the oxygen it needs simply by relaxing its spiracles and allowing the oxygen in the air to diffuse in.

But when an insect is very active it cannot get enough oxygen in this way; it pumps air in and out as we pump air in and out of the lungs. The abdomen is alternately expanded and compressed by muscular movements, and the changes in pressure in the tracheal system drives air out and draws it in. The ordinary tracheae are not readily flattened, but they can be compressed and expanded like an accordion. And in most actively running and flying insects, parts of the tracheae are dilated to form thin-walled bladders (air sacs) which expand and collapse as the insect breathes. A freshly killed cockchafer (*Melolontha*), or one of its allies, presents a remarkable appearance if it is dissected under water. The whole body appears to be filled with tiny pearls which are, in fact, little globular expansions, or 'air sacs', all along the tracheae (figure 5). Before a cockchafer takes flight it can be seen pumping vigorously with its abdomen. If bees or large flies, collecting nectar from flowers in the sunshine, are examined closely, it will be seen that the segments of the abdomen are elongating and telescoping together at a rapid rate; they are 'panting for breath'. Close study has shown that this process of ventilation is often exceedingly complicated: the spiracle valves open and close at different times in different parts of the body so that the air is directed as a stream in at one end and out at the other.

These very active insects are busy eating and drinking; they can afford to lose a certain amount of water as they move about. It is insects that are lying dormant for months on end, with no chance of getting more water, which must conserve with the greatest care all the water they contain. Overwintering pupae of Lepidoptera, for instance, keep their spiracles so firmly closed that, as the oxygen in the tracheal system is used up and the carbon dioxide goes into solution in the fluids of the body, a partial vacuum develops within the tracheal system. The spiracles may be opened only once a day and then air rushes in and very little water escapes. Some pupae remain dormant not for one season only but for several. The small eggar moth (*Eriogaster lanestris*) may

Figure 5.
The cockchafer *Melolontha* opened up from the side to show the breathing tubes or tracheae (Straus-Dürckheim 1828). The tracheae carry innumerable tiny bladders, or 'air sacs'.

lie over as a pupa for seven years before it finally completes its development and emerges. That serves to illustrate how efficient the machinery for the retention of water must be.

Water and Temperature

The products of the combustion, or oxidation, of foodstuffs are carbon dioxide and water, and this so-called 'water of metabolism' may be an important source of moisture for some insects. Many of the mammals that live in deserts, such as hamsters and jerboas, never drink at all; all the water in their bodies comes from the oxidation of grain and other foodstuffs. Of course, most foodstuffs, even when they appear to be dry, may contain quite an appreciable amount of moisture; flour beetles and flour moths cannot develop in grain or flour which is completely dry. But it has been shown by experiment that the flour moth *Ephestia kühniella* can obtain at least 95 per cent of all the water in its body solely from the oxidation of the starch in its food.

If water is to be retained in the body, not only must it not be lost by evaporation through the cuticle, it must not be lost through excretion. The same problem is seen among desert animals. The camel in the hot, dry deserts absorbs practically all the water from the food residue before it is discharged, so that the dung, or faeces, are exceedingly dry; and it excretes only a small amount of urine and that is highly concentrated. The most important single function of the urine is to get rid of waste nitrogen. Mammals get rid of most of their waste nitrogen in the form of urea; but that is a very soluble substance and a good deal of water is always lost with it. Birds and reptiles lose very little water in this way. They excrete their nitrogen in the form of uric acid which appears in the droppings of birds as a solid white deposit on the surface of the food residue.

Most insects do the same. Their excretory organs, the 'Malpighian tubules,' discharge uric acid and add this to the undigested residue of food in the gut (figure 6). And those insects which have special need to conserve their water supplies have arrangements in the last segments of the gut (the colon and rectum) which serve to reabsorb water from the mixed residue before it is got rid of. If a feeding caterpillar is dissected it will be found that the food in process of digestion is quite liquid; but after the urine has been added to the residue in the last segment of the gut, it passes through a succession of chambers in which water is progressively absorbed and the residue is finally discharged as a solid pellet. The drier the conditions under which the insect lives, the more efficient is the drying of the excrement. In the larva of the mealworm (*Tenebrio molitor*), a beetle that can exist in dry flour, the excrement is reduced to a bone-dry powder.

Drying up is not the only hazard that insects have had to face in entering upon the free life. They must also be prepared to cope with extremes of heat and cold. Not every insect, of course, is qualified to deal with every difficulty. Each species has become adapted to a more or less specialized way of life. It is because each has specialized on filling some particular niche that so many species of insects exist. Ways of dealing with the problem of heat and cold are among the specializations in question.

The body is a machine driven by chemical processes. Chemical processes take place most actively at high temperatures. But the organic materials of which the body is composed do not tolerate very high temperatures; proteins and lipids (fatty substances) become disorganized at temperatures only a little above those we can bear with the hand. Most animals operate best at a temperature around 40°C. Birds

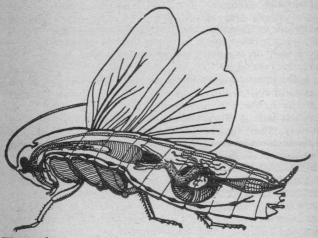

Figure 6.
A general view of the internal anatomy of the cockroach (Weber). The delicate tube that runs the whole length of the body just below the cuticle of the back is the 'heart'. The 'nervous system', with the 'brain' in the head and the chain of swellings forming the 'ganglia' behind, is shown in black. The mouth has two tubes opening into it; the small tube comes from the large 'salivary glands'; the large tube is the gullet which leads to the swollen 'crop' and at the end of this is the muscular 'gizzard'. The next section of the gut is the 'mid-gut' which carries blind tubes, or 'caeca', at its beginning; it ends where the excretory tubes, the numerous Malpighian tubes, open. Behind this point comes the coiled 'hind-gut' which ends at the 'anus'. The last stretch of the hind-gut is the 'rectum' where the oval 'rectal glands' can be seen. The reproductive system has been omitted.

and mammals have a temperature-regulating system which keeps the body at a temperature more or less constant for each species, which may range from 34–42°C (93–107°F). Insects do not possess such a system; they were formerly called 'cold-blooded' animals; now they are usually called 'poikilothermic', meaning that their temperature fluctuates with that of their surroundings. But this description hardly does justice to the ability which many insects have for regulating their temperature.

It is true that a sedentary or sluggish insect has a body temperature equal to that of its surroundings, or very little above. But the highly efficient muscles which operate the wings of insects cannot develop their full power until they have 'warmed up' to about 38–40°C—a temperature well above that of our own body. Hawk-moths (Sphingidae) and other large moths commonly sit with the wings quivering for some minutes before they take flight. If a thermocouple is inserted into the thorax to measure the temperature during this time, it is found that the temperature rises from that of the surroundings up to about 32–36°C before they take off.

Some insects do not use their own muscular activity to warm themselves up in this way but rely upon the radiant heat from the sun. Ringlet butterflies (*Erebia* species) of mountainous regions disappear from sight when the sun goes in; they are flying around again within a few minutes after the sun comes out. When the temperature in the thorax of a bumble-bee (*Bombus*) was measured in the shade it was 28.7°C. When exposed to the sun it rose in the course of five minutes to 41.6°C (some of this increase being due to increased activity) and it fell rapidly again when the sun was obscured by a passing cloud.

A bumble-bee has a fur coat and this can be quite important in keeping the thorax warm. If the hairs are clipped short a bumble-bee cools down very much more quickly. The scales of moths have the same effect; they enclose a thin sheet of air which serves to insulate the body. A privet hawk-moth (*Sphinx ligustri*) with its coat of scales intact, has a body temperature (under certain experimental conditions) about 17°C above the surrounding air; under the same conditions, but with the scales and hair rubbed off the thorax, the temperature fell to about 8°C above that of the air. It is characteristic of many alpine moths that they have a very woolly thorax; this may help to keep them warm. A dragonfly, on the other hand, has a smooth bare cuticle on the thorax; but it insulates its flight muscles in another way; it has air-filled expansions of the tracheal system (air sacs) spread out just *inside* the cuticle of the thorax.

The use of the radiant heat of the sun for regulating the body temperature has been reduced to a fine art by locusts and grasshoppers. In the early morning the temperature is too low; locusts are unable to fly. They turn themselves broadside on to the sun and lean slightly over so as to expose the greatest possible area of the body to the radiant warmth (figure 7). Later in the morning it becomes too hot and eventually, in the heat of the day, they will face the sun and raise the fore part of the body so as to reduce the exposed area to a minimum. Dr H. B. D. Kettlewell has recorded that many of the insects in the Brazilian forest, when they rest in the direct rays of the sun, orient themselves in this same way so that only a narrow edge is exposed to the sun and most of the body is in the shade.

But different insects can thrive at different temperatures. Many years ago Roy Chapman observed the insects as they began to move about on a sand dune in Minnesota in the

Figure 7.
Temperature control in locusts (Volkonsky). The insect to the left, in the early morning, is leaning over, broadside onto the sun. The insect to the right, in the middle of the day, faces the sun and raises the front of the body.

early morning as the temperature was rising after the cold night. The first to become active was the beetle *Geopinus* at 7°C; the grasshopper *Melanoplus* followed at 10°C; the hunting wasp *Sphex* did not appear until the temperature reached 17°C; the tiger beetle *Cicindela* at 18°C; the wasp *Chlorion* and the cricket *Gryllus* at 20°C; the hunting wasps *Bembex* at 26°C and *Microbembex* at 30°C.

There are other insects adapted to even greater extremes of temperature. In arctic streams the larvae of stone-flies (Plecoptera) and of the mosquito *Aedes punctor* remain active at 0°C; that is, down to the freezing point of water. Whereas in the hot springs of the Yellowstone Park there are larvae of midges (Chironomidae) that are active and growing normally at 49–51°C—hotter than can be borne by the hand.

If an insect such as a cockroach *Blatta* is observed over a wide range of temperature, it is found that as the temperature falls it becomes more and more sluggish until finally, at about 7°C, it enters a state of 'chill coma' in which it is incapable of any movement at all. When the temperature is lowered still further, to −5°C, it dies ('cold death'). At the other end of the scale, as the temperature is raised it becomes increasingly active until, at a temperature of about 40°C, it is again immobilized ('heat stupor') and on raising the temperature a degree or two higher 'heat death' occurs. The cause of death at high or low temperature is not known, but not only do these temperature limits vary very much in different species of insects, they even change in a single individual. The cockroach *Blatta* was said to enter chill coma at 7°C. But that is true only if it has been accustomed to a temperature of 30°C. If it is kept even for as short a time as one day at 15°C it can still move actively about at 2°C; and if it has been kept at 36°C it is incapable of movement below 9.5° C.

A few insects have acquired the ability to withstand far greater extremes of temperature by allowing the water in their bodies to evaporate. In this shrivelled and desiccated state they can remain dormant for very long periods. Dry collapsed eggs of the lucerne flea, *Sminthurus viridis* (one of the Collembola, figure 138), have survived for at least a year, and will then swell up and hatch within twelve days or so after moistening. There is a remarkable 'blood worm' or larva of a Chironomid midge, *Polypedilum,* that has been described by Dr H. E. Hinton. It inhabits rock-pools in West Africa, and when these dry up it retreats into the mud and is reduced to a little shrivelled husk. In this state the larvae can survive for years; on immersion in water they rapidly swell up and within half an hour they are again feeding and crawling about. In the dry state they have recovered completely after keeping in liquid air (−190°C) for three days, and after heating to 102°C (that is, above the temperature of boiling water) for one minute. They will even recover, for a short time at least, after exposure for five minutes at 200°C.

Such behaviour is highly unusual; most insects hold on to the water in their bodies very carefully and die when they become desiccated. Yet many of them are capable of withstanding the winter cold. An insect overwintering in the open in Continental North America or North Asia will be exposed to a temperature of −20° to −40°C or less.

Insects from the tropics would quickly die under such conditions. What are the means of survival?

There are a certain number of insects that can withstand freezing. The Japanese 'slug caterpillar' (*Cnidocampa*) hibernates in a hard waterproof cocoon and does not turn into a chrysalis until the spring. These overwintering caterpillars can be frozen at −15°C and kept in that state for eight or nine weeks without suffering any ill effects; they will even withstand freezing at −20°C. It appears that the blood of these caterpillars freezes but the living cells do not.

In the great majority of insects that are resistant to cold no freezing takes place. 'Cold hardiness' among them consists in the prevention of freezing. How is this done? It has been found in quite recent years that many insects hibernating in the open contain large amounts of glycerol in the blood. In the overwintering pupa of the giant silkmoth of North America, *Hyalophora cecropia,* this amounts to about 3 per cent. In the hibernating larva of *Bracon cephi,* a Hymenopterous parasite of the wheat-stem saw-fly (*Cephus cinctus*) in Western Canada, the blood contains 20 per cent of glycerol. It was an attractive idea that these insects might use glycerol as an 'antifreeze' as we use glycol in the radiator of a car. There is little doubt that the glycerol does help; but even 20 per cent glycerol will freeze at −4.8°C; and yet *Bracon cephi* survives unfrozen down to −4.7°C. There must be something else involved.

Water will freeze only if it contains minute particles ('nuclei') around which the ice can form. It is now believed that when an insect becomes 'cold hardy' in the winter (for the same insect when it is feeding and growing may be very susceptible to freezing) it has got rid of the contents of its gut and changed in some way the nature of its blood so that it no longer contains the necessary 'nuclei'. The large amount of glycerol present in the blood is thought to result from some adventitious change in metabolism that comes about during hibernation; it is not a genuine 'antifreeze'. But there may be more to it than that, for glycerol helps so much to protect vertebrate cells (spermatozoa, for example) when they are frozen.

The Size and Mobility of Insects

In this chapter we have laid particular stress on the many ways in which the insect has won freedom by regulating the internal state of its body—what is often called the 'internal environment'. It maintains a continuous supply of oxygen, a constant amount of water, a regulated temperature, and so forth. Writing of the physiology of man and animals in the middle of the last century, Claude Bernard pointed out that the constancy of the internal environment, the *milieu intérieur*, is the necessary condition for a free life. Insects have certainly not attained the degree of constancy that is enjoyed by man, but as we have seen they have come a good way towards it.

There is, however, another way of coping with the problems of an adverse world, and that is to find and select a favourable environment. In later chapters we shall be considering the movements of insects and their senses and behaviour. It is only necessary here to point out that the

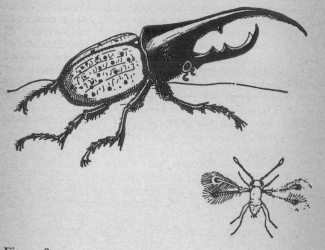

Figure 8.
The hercules beetle *Dynastes hercules*, one of the largest insects (160 mm long), and the fairy fly *Alaptus magnanimus*, one of the smallest insects (0.2 mm long).

mobility of insects is one of the reasons for their success; and coupled with mobility is size.

It is sometimes asked why living insects are so small? They range in length from 1/5 mm (less than 1/100 inch) in the little parasitic wasp (*Alaptus magnanimus*), one of the 'fairy flies' of the family Mymaridae, which develop in the eggs of other small insects, to 160 mm (6 inches) in the rhinoceros beetle (*Dynastes hercules*) (figure 8). The answer is that it is insects of the present size which have proved most successful in the present world. The giant dragonflies, with a wing span of more than 2 feet, died out in the Coal Measure Period; there are few insects today that approach the rhinoceros beetle in size.

Small insects require less food to reach maturity, just as it was the small-sized men who survived the conditions of semi-starvation in some camps for prisoners of war. Small insects can make use of small retreats to escape their enemies. Indeed their small size opens to them a whole world that is not accessible to larger animals. To mine between the two walls of a living leaf, to complete their growth within a single small seed, or to develop within the egg of another insect, is possible only for a very small animal.

Of course, there would be limits of size beyond which an insect with its body constructed as we know it could not function properly. In particular, the tracheal system of breathing, which is so largely dependent on the diffusion of gases for its effectual action, would need to be modified considerably in an insect the size of a dog. In the same way the skeleton of a man is so constructed that it could not support his weight if he were a hundred feet tall. On the other hand, there is no structural reason why men should not be nine feet tall; but the smaller size has proved more successful—and so it is with insects.

Chapter 3

THE MOVEMENT OF INSECTS ON LAND, IN WATER, AND IN THE AIR

INSECTS ARE highly organized creatures with a central nervous system receiving sensory nerves from every part of the surface of the body, and sending out motor nerves to an elaborate system of muscles (figure 92, p. 204). Effective movement requires all three components of this system: sense organs to inform the nervous system of what is happening in the surroundings, a central nervous system to co-ordinate this information, and muscles to carry out the movements that the situation demands.

Muscles can work efficiently only if they have a framework or skeleton on which to operate. The skeleton of insects is external; it is furnished by the sclerotized cuticle. The soft unsclerotized cuticle between the segments of the body or the segments of the limbs provide the joints; the muscles cross these joints and thus move one segment on another (figure 3). Sometimes the hard cuticle may extend some distance into the body to form a lever to which the muscles are attached; and sometimes these inward extensions are so large and so rigid that they provide what amounts to an internal skeleton. That is seen, for example, in the thorax of flying insects where the deep infoldings may actually join together and arch over the nerve cord to form a rigid support for the flight muscles.

39

In soft-bodied insects, such as caterpillars, the cuticle again serves as an external skeleton. But if a caterpillar is punctured the blood runs out, its body collapses and the cuticle becomes quite limp. The soft covering will serve as a skeleton only so long as it is kept firm and taut by the internal pressure of the blood. In fact the integument of the caterpillar is lined by criss-crossing bands of muscles (so-called 'turgor muscles') the purpose of which is not to carry out movements, but just to keep up a steady pressure on the blood so as to provide a firm basis for the operation of the other muscles.

The crawling of caterpillars is carried out mainly by the fleshy 'prolegs', or 'false legs', on the abdomen. These are worked by 'locomotor' muscles which are not concerned in

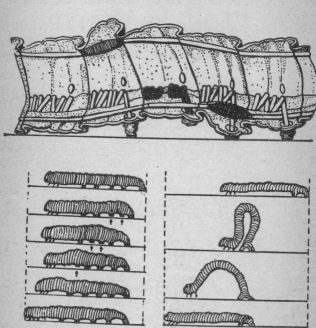

Figure 9.
The diagrams below show successive stages during the walking movements of caterpillars; to the left the movement of most caterpillars, to the right the movement of 'looper', or Geometrid, caterpillars (Weber). The upper figure is a schematic section through a caterpillar to show the sequence in the contraction in the muscles as the wave of movement passes forward along the body (Barth).

keeping up the general pressure of the blood. The process is illustrated in simplified form in figure 9 (below) from which the 'turgor muscles' have been omitted. The upper longitudinal muscles in one segment contract at the same time as the vertical muscles which lift the proleg in the segment behind, and as the lower longitudinal muscles in the segment behind that. This wave of movement sweeps forward and each pair of prolegs, starting with the last pair, is carried in turn one step forwards. When the caterpillar needs to extend a pair of prolegs again in order to gain a foothold in the new position, it relaxes the vertical retracting muscle and allows the leg to be inflated by the general pressure of the blood. This mechanism is modified in various ways for the looping progression of 'looper' or Geometrid (earth-measuring) caterpillars.

This practice of using blood pressure to move selected parts of the body is by no means confined to soft-bodied insects. The bugs (Hemiptera) unfold and extend their beak,

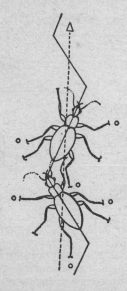

Figure 10.
A ground beetle *Carabus* walking in the direction of the broken line. The zigzag line shows in exaggerated style the course followed by the beetle. The circles indicate which feet are on the ground at the moment depicted (von Lengerken).

or 'rostrum', by this means. Flies and other insects ex-
trude their egg tube, or 'ovipositor', in the same way. And
we shall find that the same mechanism plays a most important part in the movements that take place during the
moulting of the old cuticle and the expansion of the wings.

The normal movement of insects is by walking or running
on the thoracic legs. There are six thoracic legs, and the co-
ordination of their movements so that the insect is carried
in the right direction at the desired speed is an exceedingly
complicated process. As a rough approximation it may be
said that the insect supports itself on a tripod consisting of
the first and third leg on one side and the middle leg of the
opposite side while the remaining three legs are moved forwards (figure 10). These in turn take over the weight of the
body and the other three legs are moved forwards. However,
examination of cinematograph films in slow motion proves
that this is only a rough description and the sequence is
often varied in detail, particularly in insects moving at high
speed. The complexity of the nervous control of walking is
proved by the fact that if one or more legs are lost, the

Figure 11.
Above, the foot of the honey-bee applied to a rough surface; it holds
by the claws. Below, applied to a smooth surface; it holds by means
of the adhesive pad (Cheshire).

sequence of movement is instantly changed to that which
will give the best results in the new circumstances.

If the insect is to walk effectively it must keep a firm grip
on the ground. For this it uses dual-purpose machinery. On
the last segment of the tarsus it commonly has a pair of
claws which are actuated by long and slender muscle tendons
that extend far up the leg (figure 3). When these muscles
contract, the sharp points of the claws catch in any ir-
regularities of the surface. Some insects can even hold to the

surface of glass by means of their claws, for glass soon becomes covered with a fine film of dirt, which is quite rough enough for the insect to cling to. But many insects can cling to perfectly clean glass, or to the smooth surface of leaves, or the smooth cuticle of other insects. For this purpose they have 'adhesive' pads. Sometimes a soft pad lies between the claws, as in the house-fly and the bee (figure 11) or there may be a series of pads below the segments of the tarsus (as in the cockroach and grasshopper) and occasionally a single pad at the lower end of the tibia.

There has been much argument as to how these organs work. The most convincing evidence has been obtained on the little pads that lie at the end of the tibia of the first two pairs of legs in the blood-sucking bug *Rhodnius* (figure 12). This pad is covered with fine tubular hairs which have their

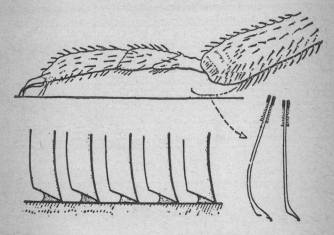

Figure 12.
Front leg of the bug *Rhodnius*, showing the adhesive pad at the lower end of the tibia applied to a smooth surface. Two hairs from the pad are shown highly magnified. The diagram below illustrates how the adhesive organ works, as described in the text (Gillett and Wigglesworth).

tip cut away obliquely so that only the hindmost part of each hair touches the surface. The tips of the hairs are moistened with an oily secretion from glands at their base. When this structure slides forward over the surface of smooth glass the tips of the hairs are lubricated and offer no resistance. (Engineers will recognize in this the principle of 'film lubrication' with the oil passing through a wedge-shaped space between the moving parts, as employed in the Mitchell Thrust Bearing that is used in hydroelectric turbines.) On the other hand if one attempts to slide the structure backwards the film of oil breaks down; the moving parts come into such close contact that adhesion or 'seizure' occurs; the two surfaces are held together by molecular forces of attraction.

With the aid of these pads *Rhodnius* can climb up a slope of thoroughly cleaned glass inclined at an angle of 89°. But structures held together by molecular adhesion in this way are very readily separated as soon as there is any force pulling them directly apart. That is clearly desirable from the point of view of the insect, so that it may have no difficulty in detaching its feet from the surface. Thus as soon as the inclination exceeds 90° the insect drops off. On the other hand there is no adhesion of the pads when

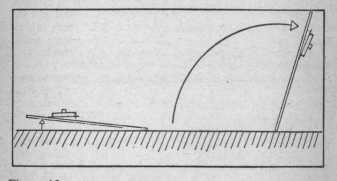

Figure 13.
A model to illustrate the action of the adhesive organ in *Rhodnius* as explained in the text (Gillett and Wigglesworth).

Rhodnius goes down a slope: the feet slip as soon as the inclination exceeds about 22°.

It is probable that this same mechanism, with suitable modifications, operates in many other insects. The large pads or 'pulvilli' which lie between the claws of house-flies, bluebottles and the like, are also covered with fine hairs with soft flattened tips which seem well suited to make molecular contact with really smooth surfaces. If a large flesh-fly (*Sarcophaga*) is obliged to cling to the lower surface of a clean sheet of glass it will be seen that it constantly draws its feet inwards towards one another. That is to be expected if it is supported by adhesion: the sliding movement is needed in order to bring the surfaces into such intimate contact that adhesion will occur.

The process can be illustrated by means of a simple model (figure 13). Take a thin glass disc about 3/4 inch across, such as is used as a cover glass for microscopic preparations, and secure to it a 10 gm weight. Attach a small fragment of thin glass to one edge of the glass disc so as to raise that side very slightly. Now place the model on a sheet of plate glass smeared with a film of oil. If the raised edge of the disc is leading the glass plate cannot be inclined more than 5° without the model sliding down: its movement is lubricated. But if it is turned the other way round and the glass plate is inclined very gradually, seizure takes place at the leading edge and it can actually be raised beyond the vertical without the model dropping off. The model, in fact, slides down the glass exceedingly slowly and this slow movement maintains the seizure between the surfaces in contact.

The ordinary property of friction between our feet and the ground which makes it possible for us to walk, does in fact depend upon the seizure between innumerable minute points of contact between the soles of our shoes and the ground. We appreciate this only when we come to walk on a smooth greasy surface on which seizure does not occur. The situation is not so very unlike that of the insects—with one important difference: the insects are so small that these forces of adhesion between surfaces are great enough to support the entire weight of the body.

It is easy to see why that is so. The volume of a sphere is given by the formula $4/3 \, \pi r^3$, where r is the radius of the sphere. Whereas the surface of a sphere is given by the formula $4\pi r^2$. As a sphere increases in size its volume (and therefore its weight) will increase as the cube of the radius, whereas its surface will increase only as the square of the radius. That is why, as an object gets smaller and smaller the surface becomes greater and greater in relation to its volume; and, therefore, the forces which exist in surfaces become relatively greater. The force of adhesion between surfaces in close contact is one example. But there are other examples of a similar kind which serve to show what an enormous part surface forces play in the lives of insects, forces which giants like ourselves commonly ignore.

Perhaps the most important among surface forces is 'surface tension'. Molecules sufficiently close together attract one another; and since the molecules in a liquid are far closer together than they are in a gas, those molecules that lie at the surface of a liquid will be strongly attracted to one another. As a result the surface of a liquid in contact with air is tending always to contract and reduce itself to the smallest area possible. In fact the surface often behaves as though it were covered by an invisible elastic film.

One other property of the surface of water must be mentioned if we are to appreciate the part played by surface forces in the every day life of insects. Some surfaces, such as perfectly clean glass, are easily wetted by water; they are said to be 'hydrophil'. Water will, therefore, run into a fine glass tube; and since the curved surface of the fluid is tending to contract, the water will be drawn far along the tube. When surface tension acts in this way in drawing liquid along a capillary, it is referred to as 'capillarity'. Other

Figure 14.
The springtail *Podura aquatica* standing on the surface of water. The claws are hydrophil and penetrate into the water; the leg above the claws is hydrophobe. The 'ventral tube' is hydrophil and by means of this the insect can anchor itself in the surface film.

surfaces, such as wax or glass smeared with grease, are not wetted by water; they are said to be 'hydrophobe' or 'hydrofuge'. A small drop of water placed on such a surface rounds itself up into a sphere as the result of its surface tension. Water will not run into a fine glass capillary that is lined with wax; the boundary between the air and the water is curved in the opposite direction and surface tension repels the water from the tube.

These powerful surface forces may sometimes involve insects in accidents. We often see insects that have landed on the surface of water trapped in the surface film. They seem to be struggling against invisible bonds that are holding them down. But far more important is the extent to which these forces have been exploited by insects in the course of evolution. Many insects have a waxy surface to the cuticle which effectively repels drops of rain. The lining of the tracheae is waxy so that water does not run into them by capillarity.

Insects which live close to water may produce a waxy secretion on their feet so that they can walk securely on the water surface. Some Collembola (*Podura aquatica* for example) form great colonies on the surface of water (figure 14); the feet rest in depressions of the surface film but the claws are hydrophil, they are drawn into the water and give the insect some purchase on it; the so-called 'ventral tube' (p. 316) which is also hydrophil anchors the insect to the surface. Perhaps the most familiar of the insects of water surfaces are the pond skaters, *Gerris* and its allies (figure 15). The second and third pairs of legs are held wide

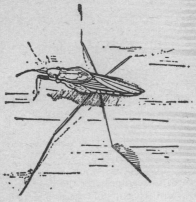

Figure 15.
The water-skater *Gerris* with its feet causing depressions in the surface of the water (Robert).

apart. The tips rest in depressions of the water surface which often show up as shadows on the bottom of shallow ponds. The insect rows itself along on the surface by the simultaneous backward movement of the legs pressing against the surface film. The whirligig beetles, *Gyrinus* (figure 17), adopt a half and half position. The water falls away from the smooth and shiny elytra when they come to the surface, but the lower parts remain immersed. They appear like points of burnished steel as they gyrate in swarms with just their backs protruding.

To accomplish these swimming movements both the structure of the limbs and the ways in which they are used have been modified. Most aquatic insects cling to the old-fashioned breast stroke. They swing both hind legs (and sometimes also the middle pair of legs) backwards at the same time. That is the method adopted by the diving beetles (*Dytiscus* and its allies), by the whirligig beetles and by many of the aquatic bugs (*Corixa, Naucoris,* etc). But the water-boatman (*Notonecta*) adopts a back stroke and with the legs uppermost it rows itself through the water with the hind pair (figure 16); and the great silver water-beetle (*Hydrous piceus*) and its allies employ an elementary type of 'crawl' in which the legs are moved alternately, much as in walking on land.

The legs themselves are modified to form efficient oars. This is usually done by the provision of a closely set row of stout hairs along the inner sides of the limb, which offer a good resistance to the water as they are swept backwards,

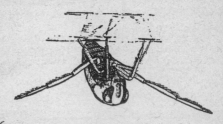

Figure 16.
The backswimmer or water-boatman *Notonecta* showing the resting position below the surface of the water.

but cut easily through the water as the leg is folded and carried forwards in readiness for the next stroke (figure 17). Perhaps the most elegant of these adaptations for swimming is that found in the whirligig beetles, which no longer rely on a fringe of hairs; the segments of the hind leg, including the tarsus, have all become flattened and broadly expanded. They can be folded up during the forward movement and then spread apart like a complicated fan for the backward stroke (figure 17). The efficiency of this arrangement is seen in the astonishing speed with which these beetles whirl around on the water surface.

There are plenty of other methods for moving in water that various insects have adopted. The aquatic 'fairy flies' (minute parasitic wasps of the family Mymaridae) swim through the water by flapping their tiny wings. The slender worm-like larvae of midges (Ceratopogonidae) swim like the eel by bending the whole body from side to side: the curves in the body press backwards against the water and the larva is propelled forwards. Mosquito larvae adopt the same procedure, but the chief propulsive force comes from the 'swimming brush', a closely set row of long hairs projecting downwards from the last segment of the abdomen (figure 26). The larvae of Anisopterous dragonflies have devised a method of jet propulsion. The rectum contains a series of overlapping 'gills' richly supplied by tracheae, and they normally breathe by pumping water in and out of the rectal chamber. The ordinary movement of these larvae consists in crawling rather slowly on the bottom of their ponds; but they have in

Figure 17.

To the left, the whirligig beetle *Gyrinus* showing the detail of the hind leg as modified for swimming (Bott). To the right, the hind leg of the water-beetle *Dytiscus* (see figure 23); above, as the leg is being swept backwards during swimming; below, as the leg is carried forwards and the hair fringes collapse.

reserve a quick get-away that is brought into action if they are suddenly touched. It consists in laying the legs close to the body and at the same instant violently contracting the rectum so as to expel a jet of water and drive themselves forwards for some inches at a high speed. An even more ingenious method is adopted by certain beetles of the Staphylinid genus *Stenus*. These are not truly aquatic insects, but they always live close to water; they may often be seen to walk onto the water surface and then without apparent effort to skim steadily along. The mechanism they employ is the same as that which drives along a camphor boat. They have glands at the tail end of the abdomen from which they discharge a secretion that lowers the surface tension of the water. The insect is, in fact, being drawn forwards by the normal surface tension of the water in front of it (figure 18).

It is particularly in the respiration of aquatic insects that we see how they have been able to take advantage of surface forces. Some aquatic insects breathe dissolved oxygen. Usually they have special areas of the body where a rich supply of tracheae is covered by thin permeable cuticle so that oxygen can diffuse from the water into the tracheal system. Such areas may extend all over the surface of the body, as in the larvae of Chironomid midges, or they may be in the form of filaments or leaflets containing numerous tracheoles, as in stone-fly and may-fly larvae (figure 19). In the larvae

Figure 18.
Diagram of the beetle *Stenus* skimming on the water surface. The arrows show the pull of the normal surface tension of the water; at the tail end of the insect the surface tension is reduced by the secretion poured out by the beetle.

of damsel-flies, or Zygopterous dragonflies, there are leaflets attached to the hind end of the abdomen and, as we have seen, in Anisopterous dragonfly larvae the gills are inside the rectum. But very many insects come to the surface to breathe; and it is in making contact with the atmosphere that the difficulties arise. This problem is solved by the appropriate use of hydrofuge structures. The openings of the spiracles are provided with glands which discharge a greasy or waxy secretion on to the surface of the cuticle. When this region of the cuticle is brought into contact with the surface, the water falls away and the spiracles and tracheae are at once exposed to the air. That is well seen in the larva of the *Anopheles* mosquito (figure 30).

In terrestrial insects the spiracles are arranged in a row on each side of the body. It would hardly be possible for an aquatic insect to open all such spiracles at the water surface. Various devices have been adopted. In the larvae of the water-beetles *Dytiscus* and *Hydrous,* and the larvae of Diptera such as mosquitoes, aquatic Tipulids (crane-flies) and Stratiomyids, the spiracles along the sides of the body are no longer used in respiration. Only a single pair of spiracles on the last or nearly the last segment of the abdomen are functional. This segment is commonly drawn out to form a respiratory tube, or siphon, with the spiracles opening at the end of it.

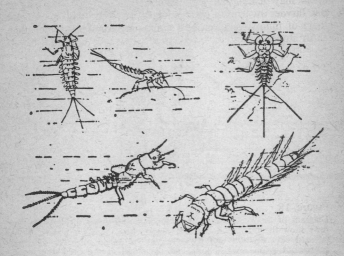

Figure 19.
Some aquatic insect larvae with gills on the abdomen. Top left: the may-fly larva *Clöeopsis*, an actively swimming insect from streams; below, *Ephemera* which is usually half buried in the mud; top right, the may-fly larva *Baetis* which clings to stones in torrents; below, the larva of the alder fly *Sialis* (Neuroptera).

A common arrangement to secure ready contact between the atmosphere and the air in the tracheae is a crown or fringe of 'semi-hydrofuge' hairs around the spiracles. This is beautifully displayed in some Stratiomyid larvae. A semi-hydrofuge hair will lie in the water surface, half wetted by water and half exposed to air, with surface tension operating along the boundary between the two. When a Stratiomyid larva is submerged, the hairs forming the crown are drawn together around a bubble of air at the spiracle opening. As soon as the larva touches the surface, the hairs are spread apart by surface tension, and it hangs suspended from the surface with the tracheae open to the air.

The extreme form of this method of respiration is seen in the rat-tailed maggot, the larva of the drone-fly (*Eristalis*). These larvae live in the mud at the bottom of shallow ponds and ditches. They have a highly extensible respiratory siphon that may be lengthened to 12 cm or more in a larva only 2

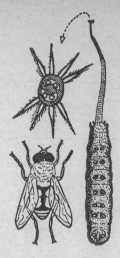

Figure 20.
The drone-fly *Eristalis* and its larva, the 'rat-tailed maggot', showing the breathing tube, or 'siphon', and the detail of the breathing holes ('spiracles') at its tip (Wesenberg-Lund).

cm long. While the larva lies concealed in the mud, the spiracles protected by their waxy secretion are exposed to the atmosphere (figures 20, 21).

It may require considerable force to detach the spiracles from the surface film. Mosquito larvae achieve this by giving a sudden flick with the swimming brush. The Tipulid or daddy-long-legs larva (*Limnophila*), which is provided with exceptionally long hairs around the spiracles, is obliged to curl its head round and pass this across the spiracles, thus pulling itself away from the surface (figure 22).

In adult aquatic insects the same principles apply; but instead of developing a respiratory tube, which enables a single pair of spiracles to open at the surface, they mostly carry an extensive store of air into which all the spiracles open; when they rise to the surface of the water it is for the purpose of renewing the air in this store (figure 23). The air store commonly takes the form of a silvery film held by a coating of hairs on the under-surface of the body, just as velvet held under water carries a film of air with it. In addition there may be a quantity of air enclosed between the wings and the upper surface of the abdomen (notably in water-beetles) and

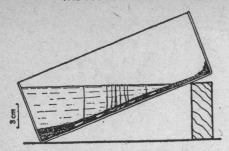

Figure 21.
Rat-tailed maggots in the mud at the bottom of an inclined aquarium, with their breathing siphons extended to the surface of the water. Most of them prefer a depth of three to four cm (Hase).

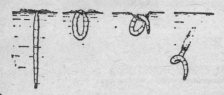

Figure 22.
The larva of the aquatic crane-fly *Limnophila* breathing at the water surface and detaching itself by curling the head and body across the spiracles (Lindner).

Figure 23.
The water-beetle *Dytiscus* replenishing its store of air at the water surface. The section below shows the large air store between the wing cases ('elytra') and the abdomen. The tracheae open into this air space (Weber).

Figure 24.
The water scorpion *Nepa* breathing at the surface of the water by means of its breathing siphon (Robert).

sometimes, continuous with this store, a bubble of air is attached to the tail end of the abdomen. In the adult water scorpion (*Nepa*), the end of the abdomen is drawn out to form a long respiratory tube which brings the air store into contact with the atmosphere while the insect remains submerged (figure 24).

The point where the air store makes contact with the surface is usually guarded by a fringe of semi-hydrofuge hairs which act in just the same way as in the aquatic larvae. Most commonly they are placed around the tail end of the abdomen, and the insect comes to the surface tail first. The silver water-beetle (*Hydrous*) is an exception. Here the insect rises to the surface head first, and the fringe of hairs which furnish the connection between atmosphere and air store is carried on the antenna. The same method is adopted by the related beetle, *Octhebius* (figure 25).

The air stores in these insects have an important hydrostatic function; they are so arranged that the insect rises to the surface with the desired point uppermost, and thus ensures that proper contact is made with the surface. The same thing applies to the air in the tracheal system of aquatic larvae. In larvae of such mosquitoes as *Culex* and *Aedes* the widest part of the trachea is that within the respiratory siphon. This is, therefore, the most buoyant part; and when the larva is motionless, it rises steadily like a diver so that the tip of the siphon alone breaks the surface (figure 26).

There is one mosquito larva in which this hydrostatic function of the tracheal system has become curiously specialized. That is the phantom larva, *Corethra* (or *Chaoborus*). Here the tracheal system has been virtually reduced to two pairs of bean-shaped sacs of air, one pair in the thorax, the other pair at the hind end of the abdomen (figure 26). These glassy transparent larvae float horizontally at a constant level. If they are in a closed container, and the pressure is increased by blowing in air with a cycle pump, the larva will sink after the manner of a Cartesian diver. But after a time they adapt themselves to the increased pressure and rise again in the water. There has been much argument as to how they contrive to do this. For long it was supposed that they pumped water in and out of the air sacs like a submarine. But it has now been proved that, by some means not fully understood, they are able to control the expansion or contraction of the tracheal cuticle forming the air sacs. When the air sacs expand the buoyancy is increased and the larva rises to a higher level in the water.

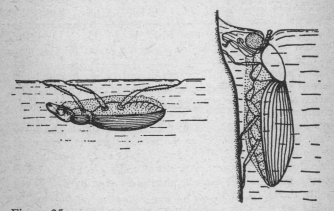

Figure 25.
The Hydrophilid beetle *Octhebius* with its air store. To the left it is walking below the surface film of the water (Hase). To the right, it is using its antenna to form a channel through the water surface so that it can renew its store of air (Beier and Pomeisl).

The air carried by aquatic insects, whether it is within the tracheal system or outside the body, has a hydrostatic or buoyancy function as well as serving as a store of oxygen. The stores on the surface of the body have a third function: they serve as gills which extract dissolved oxygen from the water. At first sight this is a little difficult to understand. As the oxygen in the air store is used up by the insect, an excess of nitrogen will be left behind and one would expect that some of this nitrogen would dissolve in the surrounding water to restore the balance. But it so happens that oxygen diffuses into and out of water more rapidly than nitrogen; therefore, when the oxygen in the air store is consumed, more oxygen leaves the surrounding water to replace it. Of course some nitrogen is lost at the same time, but as long as any nitrogen remains the process can go on and the insect can extract oxygen from the water. The air store is said to act as a 'physical gill'; and the insect may be said to rise to the surface as much to renew its store of nitrogen as to replace the oxygen.

The importance of this process can be illustrated by a simple experiment with the water-boatman, *Notonecta*. If this insect was put in water under nitrogen and not allowed access to the surface, it collapsed from asphyxia in five minutes. If it was put in water under pure oxygen, and again

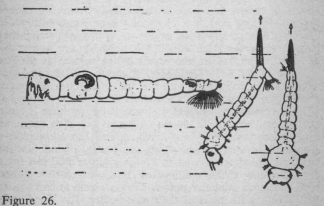

Figure 26.
To the left the phantom larva *Corethra* (*Chaoborus*) suspended in the water, its buoyancy controlled by the size of the two pairs of bean-shaped air sacs. To the right, mosquito larvae *Culex* rising vertically to the surface of the water through the greater buoyancy of the siphon at the tail end.

prevented from coming to the surface, it survived for thirty-five minutes. But if it was put in water under air (20 per cent oxygen, 80 per cent nitrogen), and treated in the same way, it was able to remain active for seven hours, extracting oxygen from the water by means of its physical gill.

When the air store is in the form of a bubble or is held by a simple pile of hairs it gradually dissolves, and the insect must come to the surface in order to renew it. If it were possible by any means to maintain a permanent air store then the insect would have a permanent physical gill and it could remain submerged indefinitely. Several insects have hit upon a way of doing this (figure 27). They have an air store of the usual type, carried by a pile of fine hydrofuge hairs; but the tips of the hairs are bent over at right angles so that they form a hydrophil surface, covering a thin film of air. This arrangement is found in the beetles *Haemonia* and *Elmis*. In these beetles the structure is relatively coarse when compared with the refinement found in the aquatic bug *Aphelocheirus* (Fam. Naucoridae). Here the hairs are so fine and closely set that there are some two million of them per square millimetre of surface. It is extremely difficult to displace this so-called 'plastron' of air, even by pressures of four or five atmospheres. The bugs live permanently submerged in streams and have been reported in the Danube up to a depth of 7 m (23 feet).

We were led into this discussion of the life and movements of insects in water from a consideration of surface forces. We have seen that many of the problems with which insects are faced and many of the strange powers which they possess arise from the relation between surface and mass: the relative increase in the extent of the surface as the size or mass of the body diminishes. A rather similar consideration arises in connection with the muscular power of insects. Here again, the power of a muscle is proportional to the *area* of its cross-section, whereas the mass it has to move is again proportional to *volume*. So that, whereas few men can jump much more than their own height, a flea can accomplish a high jump of 8 inches and a long jump of 13 inches. Size for size that would correspond to a high jump of 800 feet for a man. Because of this relation insects appear to be endowed with enormous muscular power. They are able to carry loads far exceeding the mass of their own bodies. The blood-sucking bug *Rhodnius* has no difficulty whatever in carrying a meal ten or twelve times its own weight. That would be equivalent to a drink of about 200 gallons for a man, which would weigh nearly a ton. But physiological studies of in-

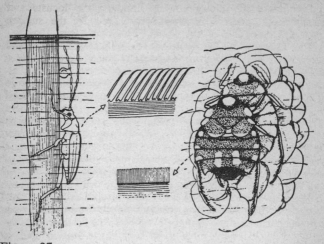

Figure 27.
'Plastron respiration' in aquatic insects. To the left, the beetle *Haemonia* renews the air in its plastron by taking up an air bubble from a plant by means of its antennae. The plastron hairs shown in detail are about thirteen microns long (Brocher). To the right, the bug *Aphelocheirus*. Here the plastron hairs are minute and hold a film of air only six microns thick (Thorpe and Crisp).

sect muscles have shown that they are closely similar in almost all respects with our own.

Many insects have adopted the practice of leaping. In Collembola, or 'springtails', a fork-shaped organ is attached to the hind end of the abdomen and is folded forwards and held below a catch, or 'retinaculum'. When the fork is forcibly extended it slips out of its catch and projects the insect for several inches. A similar mechanism occurs in click beetles (Elateridae) in which a point below the first segment of the thorax engages in a catch below the second segment. And in larvae of the 'cheese skipper' or cheese maggot (*Piophila*), the edge of the last segment of the abdomen is seized by the mouth hooks, and then suddenly released. All these insects adopt the same trick of building up a high muscular tension, which is suddenly released and the insect flicked a considerable distance. It may be that some of the insects which jump with the hind legs such as fleas, flea beetles (*Phyllotreta*, etc) or the jumping plant lice (Psyllidae) use the same mechanism; but it seems more likely that they, and certainly the most familiar jumpers, the locusts and grasshoppers, make a straightforward hop by the sudden combined extension of the tibiae of the hind legs.

The capacity for leaping has been invented again and again by insects both large and small. There were doubtless many jumping insects that have become extinct, and it is attractive to consider the possibility that it was in some large leaping insect that wings first made their appearance. Indeed the fossil evidence suggests that the first winged insects were large active creatures, and that the wings arose as expansions sideways of the upper part of the thorax. They were new structures, not modified limbs like the wings of birds and bats. They were presumably used after the manner of the fixed wings of aeroplanes to help sustain the body as it moved forward or glided through the air.

The first requirement of a fixed wing or aerofoil of this kind is a mechanism for controlling its inclination. It is now known that as insects flap their wings in flight their inclination is changed during each cycle of movement in such a way that the body is lifted and driven forwards. The development of a muscular mechanism for controlling this inclination was probably the first step in the production of a flapping wing. The appearance of muscles which could flap the wings came later; and provided that the control of inclination was already there, quite feeble flapping movements would improve the lifting powers of the wings. Along these lines it is possible to conceive how the flight machinery of insects could gradually have evolved. Small creatures such as spiders and mites, and even small hairy caterpillars, may be caught up in rising air currents and carried many miles by the wind (p. 279). Perhaps it was under these conditions that the early insects developed aerofoils and moveable wings.

It is generally believed that insect wings were evolved once only and that all the winged insects (Pterygota) come from one stem. The evidence rests on the fact that the thickened veins that serve to stiffen the wing membrane, and carry tracheae and nerves to all parts of the wing, are arranged upon a common plan which applies to all winged insects. Indeed the modifications of this plan of 'venation' provides one of the most valuable means of classifying insects. But while the venation has remained relatively consistent throughout the long evolution of the winged insects, the mechanisms of flight have undergone remarkable changes.

At first the wings were held permanently extended on each side of the body (as they still are in Anisopterous dragonflies) or held aloft above the thorax (as in may-flies). They were worked by muscles attached directly to the base of the wing: elevator and depressor muscles. That arrangement can still be seen in the dragonflies (figure 28). But in most existing insects two changes have come about: (*i*) muscles have been developed which will fold the wings backwards over the abdomen; (*ii*) the muscles which twist and incline the wing remain attached to the wings themselves, but the muscles that cause the wings to flap up and down are for the most part attached to the walls of the thorax. When they contract, they distort the shape of the thorax and thus act indirectly on the wings that are hinged to it (figure 28). One can imagine a finger and thumb placed in front of and behind the thorax, and a second finger and thumb placed obliquely above and below the thorax. It is the compression of the thoracic box in these two directions in turn which moves the wings.

Large insects flap their wings at a comparatively slow rate: butterflies at about 8–12 complete beats per second, locusts at 18–20 per second, dragonflies at 20–30 per second,

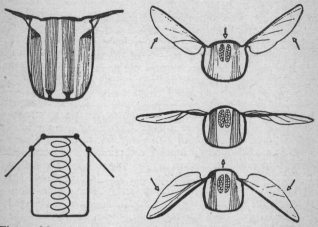

Figure 28.
Top left: diagrammatic cross section through the thorax of a dragonfly showing the 'direct' flight muscles which raise and lower the wings (Weber). To the right, the wings of a fly or bee are moved by 'indirect' flight muscles which change the shape of the thorax. As the wings move up and down they are twisted and their inclination is reversed (Snodgrass). Bottom left: the thorax behaves as though it contains a spring which resists both stretching and compression and thus stores the energy produced by the flight muscles (Weis-Fogh).

large moths at 50–70 per second. The rates are of the same order as those in humming birds (30–50 per second). At these speeds it is quite feasible for a nerve stimulus to be given to each opposing group of muscles in turn at this frequency, and thus to keep the wings moving. During this process the muscles are doing a relatively small amount of work in moving the wings through the air; most of their effort is expended in distorting the shape of the thorax. This could be a very wasteful procedure; but the walls of the thorax are elastic; most of the energy is, in fact, stored and used to help the opposing muscles during the next stroke (figure 28).

While this flapping movement is going on, other muscles are acting on the base of the wing and twisting it so as to control the inclination. Since the inclination of the wing is reversed during the upstroke and the downstroke, the effect is the same as that of a propeller that goes round and round. One gets a fairly accurate impression of the flight of an insect if one thinks of it as being drawn forwards by a couple of propellers which direct a stream of air downwards and backwards.

As flying insects became smaller it was necessary to increase the rate of the wing movements. Bees have a rate of 190 per second, the house-fly about 200 per second, the fruit-fly (*Drosophila*) 250, *Culex* and other mosquitoes up to 600, and the minute Ceratopogonid midge (*Forcipomyia*) has been shown to vibrate the wings at a rate of more than 1,000 beats per second. Those who have an absolute sense of musical pitch can tell the rate of vibration of the wings by listening to the tone they produce during flight. It is common practice in inspecting moving machinery to use a 'strobo-flash' lamp, which produces a brief flash of light some hundreds of times a second and at a controllable rate. If a gear is rotating at two hundred times a second, and it is examined with a lamp flashing at that rate, it appears to be standing still. The same procedure can be used for observing the flight of insects. If the speed of flashing is the same as the wing-beat the wings appear stationary, but if the speed is changed very slightly, the wings appear to be beating slowly, and the exact movement, and the changes in the inclination of the wing, can be followed during the wing strokes. The insect looks as though it were slowly 'rowing' itself through the air.

In no known animal can the nerves convey a succession of stimuli to the muscles causing them to contract and relax at these high speeds. For many years it was a puzzle how the insect was able to beat its wings so fast. The answer seems to lie in a further modification in the structure of the thorax. In the first place the articulation at the base of the wing has been elaborated so that it automatically makes the necessary changes in inclination as it moves up and down. There is, therefore, no need for muscles to change the inclination during the wing-stroke—which they would have to do at the same high speeds as the wing-beat itself. Then a so-called 'click mechanism' has been evolved. This is easily demonstrated in a newly killed blowfly. The wings are spread and raised above the thorax. If they are pressed downwards, the movement is resisted by the elasticity of the thorax; but as soon as a certain point is reached, this resistance suddenly vanishes, and the wings click into a new position below the thorax. Meanwhile the inclination of the wings can be seen to change in readiness for the upstroke.

When these movements take place in the living fly the muscles that are contracting are suddenly released as soon as the click point is reached, and this causes them instantly to relax. At the same time the opposing muscles are suddenly stretched, and this causes them instantly to contract. The result is a remarkable oscillating system which can operate at almost any speed, depending entirely on the elastic structure of the thorax. The nerves are needed only to start the machine working and to keep the muscles in such a state that they will keep on contracting in response to the sudden stretching.

While this more or less spontaneous process is going on, the direct muscles, that run to the base of the wing, can accentuate the changes in inclination of one or both wings, and so control the direction of flight, enabling the insect to dart sideways or even to fly backwards or to hover stationary in the air. The whole mechanism of flight in the most highly specialized flying insects is singularly reminiscent of that in a flying machine. There is a standard flight mechanism which is set in motion and then modified by secondary controls as circumstances demand. We shall consider some of these controls when we come to deal with the sense organs of insects.

Chapter **4**

THE DIETARY OF INSECTS

Food and Feeding Methods

IT WAS suggested in chapter 2 that the ancestral insects may have lived chiefly in the moist litter of the forest floor. If the bristletails (Diplura and Thysanura) and certain of the springtails (Collembola, p. 316) are pictured as continuing today the mode of life of the ancestral insects, we should regard these as being originally 'saprophytic' animals, feeding in the dead and decaying remains of plants, and particularly on the fungi and bacteria that are responsible for that decay. There are, indeed, plenty of higher insects which still subsist on this same diet during their larval life; but since those early days the diet of the insects as a whole has evolved along with the fauna and flora of the earth.

The majority obtain their food from living plants by feeding on the roots, burrowing in the stems or woody trunks, or feeding upon the foliage. The foliage of plants maintains more insects than any other class of diet; Orthoptera, the larvae of almost all Lepidoptera, large sections of Hymenoptera and Coleopteria, besides many of the lesser orders, are leaf eaters. Virtually the whole of the Hemiptera, larvae and adults alike, tap the cells or vessels of plants and live on their sap.

In the early Mesozoic period the first flowering plants made their appearance, and in parallel with their evolution there was a prodigious blossoming of the insects. It is no exaggeration to say that insects and flowers have evolved together (see chapter 16). Lepidoptera, Hymenoptera, Diptera, Coleoptera took to feeding upon flowers. Flowering plants came to rely more and more upon insects for the transfer of their pollen, and they developed nectaries as an additional attraction for those insects whose function it is (from the standpoint of the plant) to provide cross-pollination. Appropriate modifications for extracting nectar from flowers were developed by the insects.

During the Mesozoic era warm-blooded animals, mammals, and birds, began to replace the reptiles of the Permian and, by the dawn of the Tertiary, became predominant among the large fauna of the earth. The warm fermenting excrement of mammals, and their decaying bodies, furnished an excellent nutrient medium for many insect larvae, notably Diptera and Coleoptera, the adults of which found their nourishment in flowers. Some Hemiptera and Diptera have taken to piercing the skin of birds and mammals and feeding on their blood; and some small orders, the Anoplura, or sucking lice, and the Siphonaptera, or fleas, have become so specialized for this purpose that their relationship to other groups of insects is now uncertain.

Some insects also prey upon smaller insects or other living organisms, and many are highly specialized for this predaceous mode of life. Others are parasites feeding on or within the living bodies of larger insects or larger animals. Merely to list and illustrate the diversity of foods and feeding habits among insects would fill a very long chapter. For the purpose of a brief summary such as this it will perhaps be more instructive to look at some of the general principles which mark these dietary habits.

The first problem is that of securing the food and getting it into the mouth. As the dietary habits have changed so has the cutlery used in feeding. The standard arrangement of the mouth-parts is well seen in the cockroach or in the grasshopper (figure 29). A little flap hinged to the front of the head is the upper lip, or 'labrum'. Below or behind this come the 'mandibles', exceedingly powerful jaws closing in from the sides like pincers. Behind these come a second pair of less powerful pincers, the 'maxillae'. They are used more for steadying and manipulating the food than for crushing it; they have attached to them on each side a little segmented sense organ or 'palp' like a diminutive antenna. Behind the maxillae comes the 'labium'. This has been derived, in the course of evolution, from a second pair of maxillae, but the structures on the two sides have become joined together so as to form a sort of lower lip. This, too, carries a very small sensory 'palp' on each side. Finally, in the floor of the mouth is a tongue-like 'hypopharynx', from which the salivary glands discharge their juice.

This arrangement is remarkably consistent throughout the insects. It was evolved by the early omnivorous and plant-eating species and has remained substantially unchanged in all those insects which chew their food, whatever may be its nature; and that applies to both larvae and adults. Even in the caterpillars of Lepidoptera or the similar larvae of saw-flies (Hymenoptera-Symphyta) (figure 161) which in most respects are so unlike other insects, it is easy to recognize the usual components of the mouth-parts. Although the larvae of beetles have the most diverse forms, the mouth-parts are not much changed.

But where specialized feeding habits have arisen, the mouth-parts are so transformed as to be scarcely recognizable. A full description of these changes would carry us too far into comparative morphology. It will, however,

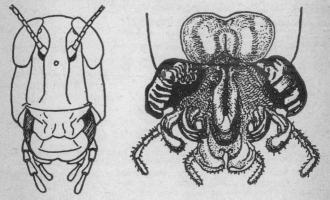

Figure 29.
Mouth-parts of the grasshopper (Metcalf and Flint). In the front view of the head (on the left) the mouth-parts are hidden by the upper lip ('labrum') except the surface of the mandibles (shaded) and the sense organs ('palps') below. On the right, the labrum has been folded upwards and the mouth-parts separated to expose the mouth. In the middle is the tongue-like 'hypopharynx' on which the duct of the salivary glands opens. The uppermost pair of mouth-parts are the powerful mandibles; next come the 'maxillae' each composed of a blade with sharp points, a soft hood, and a palp with five segments. The floor of the mouth is formed by the lower lip, or 'labium', with a palp of three segments on each side.

be worth while considering a few examples; for they illustrate in the most striking fashion the way in which the organs of an insect may remain substantially unchanged for millions of years and yet, under the influence of natural selection, may be led to undergo the most remarkable modifications in adaptation to a new use. There are examples also of parallel evolution in which the same ends have been reached independently in different insects along similar though not identical lines.

Sometimes the basic structures are little changed but new structures are added which serve some new use. The larvae of mosquitoes have chewing mandibles and associated maxillae which are easily recognizable (figure 30); but they have new structures composed of tufts of long hairs on the front

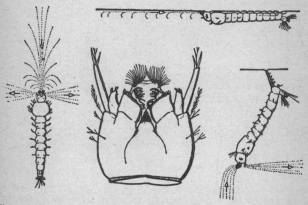

Figure 30.
Methods of feeding in mosquito larvae (Christophers and Puri). In the middle is the head of a larva seen from below. The feeding brushes arise from the labrum above. The mandibles with stout curved spines are partially hidden by the maxillae; both these mouth-parts have rows of hairs which filter out the food particles from the water. The lower lip forming a dark conical spine helps to mould these particles into a 'bolus' for swallowing.
    To the left, an *Anopheles* larva feeding at the water surface showing the currents set up by the feeding brushes (viewed from above). To the right, the same viewed from the side. Lower right, the currents set up by a feeding *Culex* larva.

of the head which can be folded in or spread open by muscles and swept through the water. These are the 'feeding brushes' which set up a current that carries suspended particles into the mouth. The larva of the *Anopheles* mosquito, for example, rises to the surface, anchors itself to the surface film by means of a series of hydrofuge rosettes along the top of the abdomen, rotates its head 180°, and proceeds to sweep with its feeding brushes in such a way that the layer of water immediately below the surface film, which is rich in minute algae and bacteria, streams towards the mouth and is there passed through rows of closely set bristles along the edges of the mandibles and maxillae. In this way fine particles, not only bacteria but even colloidal particles are filtered out, much as the baleen whales filter small pteropods, crustaceans, and other plankton from the sea. They are then collected into a mass, or bolus, and swallowed.

Figure 31.
The honey-bee sucking up liquid and, to the left, a front view of the head with the mouth-parts separated. Just below the head are the small mandibles used chiefly for moulding the wax of the honey-comb. The long flexible tongue, or 'glossa' (an extension of the labium), is deeply grooved below. In the normal feeding position, as shown in the cross-section, it is enclosed by the maxillae above and the labial palps below to form the sucking tube.

Likewise in the honey-bee, the general structure of the mouth-parts follows the usual pattern, save that the mandibles are no longer sharp pincers as they are in the predaceous ants or wasps, but are small and blunt and well suited for moulding the wax for the honey-comb. But a new structure has appeared—the tongue, or 'glossa', a sucking organ formed as a long, flexible extension from the end of the labium, with which the nectar is collected in the field and honey is manipulated in the hive. The sides of the tongue are curved downwards and inwards, until they almost meet below to form a tube which is enclosed by the maxillae and labial palps (figure 31).

The coiled tongue of butterflies and moths is a totally different structure. The mandibles of almost all Lepidoptera have disappeared; the tongue is formed by the highly modified maxillae. These are greatly elongated and channelled

Figure 32.
The proboscis of the cabbage white butterfly *Pieris* (Eastham and Eassa). The figures above show various stages in the uncoiling of the proboscis. Note the knee-like bend half-way along. Lower left is a diagram showing the arrangement of the oblique muscles which uncoil the proboscis. To the right is a cross-section of the proboscis showing the two maxillae linked together to form the sucking-tube. The broken line shows the altered form of the cross-section when the muscles contract and the proboscis is uncoiled. Bottom right, diagram showing how the uncoiling of a spring is brought about by transverse bending (broken line).

along their inner surfaces and then held together by means of hooks and interlocking spines (as it were a 'zip fastener') so as to form a tube. In the head this tube is connected with the mouth, and fluids are sucked in by the pumping muscles of the pharynx.

This proboscis, or 'tongue', in the butterfly is an exceedingly complicated structure (figure 32). Each maxilla, that is, each half of the sucking tube, has an elastic rod of cuticle in its upper wall and it is this stiffening which keeps the tongue coiled like a watch spring. In this coiled state the elastic upper surface of the tongue is more or less flat. But all the way along the tongue are tiny oblique muscles; when these contract they have the effect of bending the upper surface transversely, and it is this bending which causes the tongue to uncoil and extend.

The mechanism is like that of a steel measuring tape, but reversed. The natural state of the steel tape is curved from side to side, and therefore it stands out straight; it is coiled and flattened by the spring in the case. The natural state of the butterfly tongue is coiled; it is extended by muscles which bring about the transverse bending of the upper surface. About one-third of the way along the proboscis there is a region with special muscles which oppose the curving of the upper surface. In this region the tongue does not uncoil but forms a 'knee joint', which makes it possible for the butterfly to insert its tongue into a flower at any angle (figure 32 above and figure 128).

Certain Noctuid moths, such as *Anomis*, have developed powerful spines around the tip of the proboscis, by means of which they can lacerate the surface of fruit; they cause considerable damage in orchards, particularly in the tropics.

The production of a sucking tube by bringing together two grooved blades, as in the tongue of butterflies, is a common practice among sucking insects of all kinds. The larvae of ant-lions and other Neuroptera have a pair of formidable curved mandibles through which they suck the juices from their prey (figure 33). Each mandible is grooved on the inside, and applied to each is a grooved maxilla. The larvae of the water-beetles *Dytiscus*, *Cybister*, etc, suck out the contents of other insects in the same way; but here the mandibles themselves are traversed by a fine, almost closed in, groove which forms the sucking tube (figure 34).

This is not the place to give a full account of all the different ways in which piercing and sucking mouth-parts have been evolved, by modification of the standard components, in those insects which feed on the sap of plants or the blood of animals: the bugs, the blood-sucking lice, the blood-sucking flies, and the fleas. We may take the Hemiptera, the common bed-bug (*Cimex*), for example, to illustrate the type of mechanism that has been produced.

The visible proboscis of the Hemiptera, which is normally kept folded back below the head, is an elongated lower lip, or labium. This is deeply grooved on its upper surface and simply forms a sheath for the business part, the bundle of fine stylets (the modified mandibles and maxillae) that pierce the skin. The labial sheath remains at the surface of the skin

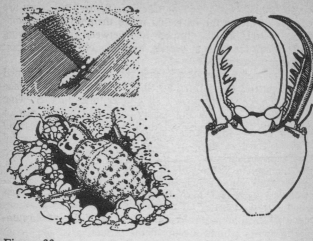

Figure 33.
The larva of the ant-lion *Myrmeleon*. To the left, above, diagram of the larva in its pit in the sand (Doflein). Below, detail of the larva. To the right, the head from below, showing how the maxilla is applied to a deep groove in the mandible to form the sucking-tube (Weber).

and buckles as the stylets penetrate. Figure 35 (lower left) shows a transverse section through the beak of the bed-bug, from which it can be seen how slender is the bundle of piercing stylets in comparison with the visible proboscis; and the proboscis itself is only 1/10 mm in cross-section. It can be seen also in this same figure that each of the modified maxillae has two grooves, a large and a small, on its inner surface, thus forming two tubes: a larger one in front, up which the blood is sucked, and a smaller one behind, through which the saliva is injected into the wound. The blood tube is so fine that there is only just room for two blood corpuscles to slide along it side by side. The muscles of the pharynx, by which the blood is pumped up, are the most powerful in the body. If a bed-bug is observed with a hand lens while in the act of feeding, they can be seen pumping at a rapid rate. Meanwhile the saliva is forced down into the wound by a pump which bears a striking resemblance to an aural syringe complete with plunger and valves.

The operation of these excessively slender stylets raises some interesting problems. How are such delicate threads able to pierce the tough outer skin? In plant-sucking insects

such as Aphids (figure 36) or Coccids (figure 154), how are
they able to pierce the bark and make their way, sometimes
curving to right or left, through and between the underlying
cells to reach the phloem vessels, and thus obtain the sap on
which these insects feed?

The first point to realize is that the stylets are moistened
with saliva; this binds them together by virtue of its surface
tension. They can, however, slide over one another. One
stylet, say the left mandible, firmly supported by the rest of
the stylet bundle to which it is bound (like the flexible steel
core in a Bowden cable) is driven forwards by the powerful
muscles at its base. The tip is sharply pointed; it penetrates
the skin, and its withdrawal is hindered by the backwardly
directed teeth at its tip (figure 37). The maxillae, forming the
sucking tube, may now follow, and then the right mandible is
pushed ahead and the operation repeated. The precise sequence of movements probably varies in different circum-

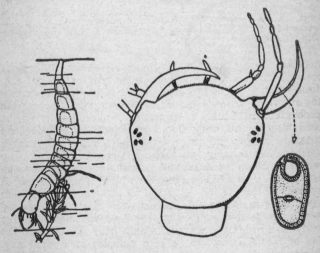

Figure 34.
Larva of the water-beetle *Dytiscus* with the spiracles opened at the
water surface. To the right, the head of the larva with the mouth-
parts. The curved mandibles have a deep groove (shown in cross-
section), almost closed except at the tip of the mandible, which
forms a sucking-tube leading to the mouth.

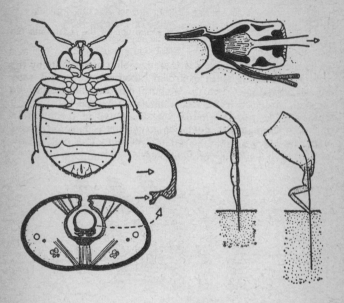

Figure 35.

View of the bed-bug *Cimex* from below showing the proboscis (labium) folded back below the head (Terzi). Lower left, tranverse section through the proboscis showing the stylet bundle in the deep groove of the labium. Each maxilla has two grooves, a large one above which forms the sucking-tube, a small one below which forms the duct for the saliva. The mandibles are applied each to another groove below the maxilla. The figures to the right show diagrammatically two stages in the penetration of the stylet bundle into the skin as the labium is folded (Kemper). Top right shows a section through the 'salivary pump'. The plunger is being withdrawn; the valve from the salivary duct (below) is open; the valve leading to the mouth-parts (top left) is closed (Weber).

Figure 36.
An aphid feeding. Three stages in the insertion of the stylets into the plant (Snodgrass).

stances, but always there are these stabbing movements by the individual stylets, succeeding one another at a rapid rate. Sometimes one mandible, say the left mandible, may be pressed far ahead, and it then curves to the right and forms a guide for the maxillae which likewise curve to the right. In this way the blood-sucking bug may probe in all directions until it pierces a blood-vessel, or the plant bug may search around until it strikes a phloem tube.

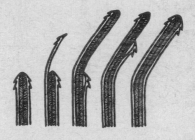

Figure 37.
Diagram of the way in which the slender bundle of stylets of a bug pierces an animal or plant. The two maxillae are shaded, the toothed mandibles in outline (Weber; Miles).

Biologists recognize a law, called 'Dollo's Law', which states that if an existing organ is lost in the course of evolution it cannot be regained. If an animal that has suffered such a loss should later come to want the lost structure, it can only meet this need by modifying an existing organ in a new way.

This process is strikingly illustrated in the mouth-parts of Diptera. The horse-flies *Tabanus*, *Haematopota*, and *Chrysops* inflict a sharp painful bite. They have flattened sword-like mandibles with a toothed edge; these work from side to side like scissors to cut through the skin (figure 38). They also have maxillae in the form of rods with sharp points and back-

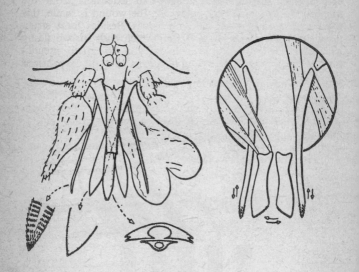

Figure 38.

To the left, the mouth-parts of the horse-fly *Tabanus bromius* (Wigglesworth). The antennae have been cut away; on the left the large 'maxillary palp'; then the needle-like 'maxilla' with backwardly directed teeth at the tip; in the middle of the sucking-tube formed by the 'labrum' above (which has been broken short) and the 'hypopharynx', which carries the salivary duct to its tip, below; beneath the sucking-tube are the scissor-like blades of the 'mandibles' with saw-like teeth along the margin; the fleshy 'labium' on which the other mouth-parts rest is displaced to the right; it shows the converging tubes of the 'pseudotracheal membrane'. The diagram to the right shows the arrangement of the muscles which bring about the saw-like action of the mandibles and the needle-like action of the maxillae.

wardly directed teeth; these are drawn rapidly up and down in a vibratory movement like a pneumatic drill as they are driven in. Between these cutting implements is the sucking tube formed by a long extension of the upper lip (the labrum epipharynx) above and a tongue-like extension from the mouth (the hypopharynx) below. As the wound is made, this tube is plunged into the bleeding tissues. Besides these structures the horse-flies have a labium which ends in two fleshy expansions (the labella) which carry a so-called 'pseudo-tracheal membrane'. This simply means that the expansions

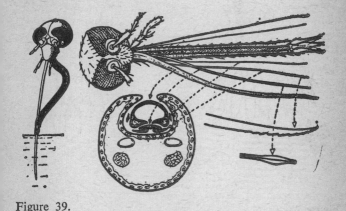

Figure 39.
The diagram to the left shows the stylet bundle of a mosquito piercing the skin, while the sheath (labium) buckles and the stylets come out of the groove (Weber). The main figure shows the mouthparts of the yellow fever mosquito *Aedes aegypti* with the stylets removed from the groove and spread apart, and in cross-section in their normal position (Wigglesworth). The largest stylet is the 'labrum', grooved below to form the sucking-tube when the groove is closed by the 'hypopharynx' carrying the salivary duct. The 'mandibles' are the most slender stylets applied to the sides of the labrum. The chief cutting stylets with barbed tips are the 'maxillae'.

have tubes running through them which resemble the ringed tracheae. These tubes are, in fact, split open along one side, so that when the 'pseudo-tracheal membrane' is spread out on a moist surface, the liquid can enter the tubes through this cleft (see house-fly, figure 40). These split tubes converge to the point where the sucking tube ends.

The net result of this complicated arrangement is that these flies can feed in two ways. They can either cut into the flesh and suck the escaping blood directly into the sucking tube. Or they can spread out their labella with the

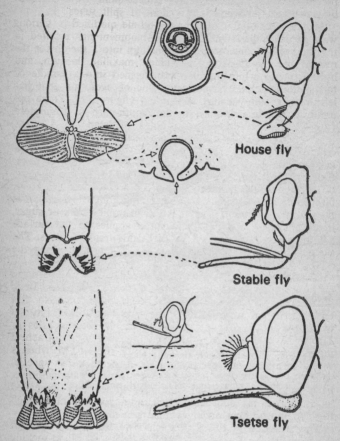

House fly

Stable fly

Tsetse fly

Figure 40.

The evolution of the mouth-parts in the 'higher flies' (after various authors) as described in the text. The three figures on the left show the modification undergone by the 'labella'. In the house-fly (*Musca*) liquid is collected through the split tubes of the 'pseudo-tracheal membrane', which converge upon the opening that leads to the sucking-tube. Near this opening are minute teeth, the 'prestomal teeth'. In the stable-fly (*Stomoxys*) the powerful prestomal teeth are shown in the everted position for cutting through the skin. In the tsetse-fly (*Glossina*) the slender tip of the proboscis is highly magnified and again shows the prestomal teeth and the 'rasps' everted.

pseudo-tracheal membrane and collect fluid from surfaces by means of the converging system of split tubes.

Mouth-parts of this kind have become modified in various ways in other flies. One line of development has resulted in the progressive conversion of the labium into a sheath for the rest of the mouth-parts (mandibles, maxillae, labrum, and hypopharynx) which become transformed into a bundle of fine piercing stylets. That is the line of evolution that has led to the mouth-parts of mosquitoes (figure 39). These operate on the same principle as the mouth-parts of Hemiptera (though there are differences in points of detail).

Another line of development has resulted in the loss of the cutting and piercing mouth-parts (the mandibles and maxillae) and the perfection of the pseudo-tracheal membrane on the labella. That is the line which has led to the mouth-parts of higher flies, the house-fly *Musca* (figure 40) and the blow-flies *Calliphora, Lucilia,* etc. The folding 'tongue' of the fly is the labium, and when it extends this to imbibe milk or sugar, it spreads apart the two labella and applies to the surface a wonderfully elaborate system of pseudo-tracheal tubes. The sucking tube, formed as before, lies in a groove along the surface of the labium.

But some tropical species of *Musca* have acquired a taste for blood. They stand around while *Tabanus* and other horse-flies are feeding on animals, and jostle them aside so that they themselves may suck up the blood exuding from the wounds made by the biting flies. Some of these species of *Musca* have tooth-like projections on the 'pseudo-tracheal membrane', with which they can scratch the surface when a wound is drying, and get at the juices beneath. Some species, which used to be put in a separate genus *Philaematomyia,* have gone a stage further and have these teeth (so-called 'prestomal' teeth) sufficiently well developed to cut through the undamaged skin and get blood for themselves.

The evolution of this new mechanism for cutting through the skin can be followed through a series of blood-sucking flies. The best known is the stable-fly *Stomoxys,* which looks very like a house-fly, though it holds the wings a little more widely apart, and its piercing mouth-parts project forwards like a little rod below the head (figure 40). This little rod is the labium itself, now stiff and narrow and armed at the tip with stout teeth. The tip is like the invaginated tip of a glove finger. The teeth line this invagination and, as the tip is everted and retracted at a rapid rate, the teeth cut through the skin and the labium itself is driven into the flesh. It is not surprising that when *Stomoxys* chooses an ankle for this operation, as it commonly does, it produces a sharp stinging pain.

The ultimate refinement in biting mouth-parts along these lines is in the tsetse-fly *Glossina* (figure 40). The principle is the same, but the teeth are reduced in size and increased in number so as to form a sort of microscopic rasp. The base of the labium which contains the muscles that operate the cutting mechanism is bulbous and swollen, but the tip is ex-

Figure 41.
Head of the dragonfly larva *Aeschna* showing the so-called 'mask'—the folding labium with claw-like pincers used for capturing prey (Weber).

ceedingly slender. The whole structure is so delicate that the bite of a tsetse-fly may be quite unnoticed—unless it happens to strike a nerve ending, and then it feels like a red-hot needle. The tsetse-fly has a long conspicuous 'proboscis' projecting forward from the head. This object consists of the maxillary palps, which remain although the maxillae have been lost; they are long and stout and grooved on the inside and held together to provide a protective sheath for the delicate labium!

It will be noticed that many of these insects have lost their pincerlike mandibles. Such pincers are a useful tool, particularly for predatory insects, and some which have lost their mandibles altogether, or have adapted them for other purposes, have evolved new pincers from a different source. The usual practice is to modify the front legs. In the predaceous bugs such as *Naucoris, Laticerus,* or the water scorpion *Nepa*, each fore-leg is like a clasp knife with the tibia lying in a groove along the femur (figures 24, 152). They are well suited for holding the prey while the beak is plunged into it.

The legs, indeed, are often modified to help in capturing the prey. One has only to think of the spiny legs of dragon-

flies (p. 319, figure 140), the raptorial legs of the praying
Mantids (figure 142), and the similar legs of Mantispidae (p.
336). But other structures can be used to form pincers. The
so-called 'mask' of dragonfly larvae is the folded labium,
which is shot forwards and the prey held in an effective pair
of pincers developed at its tip (figure 41). Perhaps the most
remarkable substitute for mandibles is to be seen in the predaceous fly *Melandria* (Fam. Dolichopodidae), which has developed hook-like pincers on its labium that bear a striking
superficial resemblance to true mandibles (figure 42).

Figure 42.
Head of the fly *Melandria* (Dolichopodidae) showing the 'false mandibles' that have been developed on the labium (Séguy).

The maggots or larvae of the higher flies have a characteristic method of feeding. The usual components of the mouth-
parts have disappeared and have been replaced by new structures, commonly called the 'mouth-hooks', which are controlled by powerful muscles attached to an elaborate internal
skeleton (figure 43). The horse bot *Gastrophilus* holds firmly
to the lining of the stomach of the horse by the insertion of
these hooks. The ordinary maggots of house-flies and blowflies, living in decaying refuse or in the carcasses of animals,
use them for scratching and tearing and burrowing in the
food. But there are certain maggots which use the mouth-
hooks, with very little modification, for sucking the blood of
birds and mammals.

The procedure is the same as that employed in past times
in the method of blood-letting known as 'wet cupping'. The
sharp hooks first cut through the skin down to the blood-
vessels. They are then withdrawn; the front segment of the

body is brought up against the skin to form an air-tight seal, and the larva then proceeds to suck. Obviously, this method

Figure 43.
The 'mouth-hooks' of a fly maggot and the 'pharyngeal skeleton' which supports the muscles that operate the hooks (Metcalf and Flint).

can only work when the skin is smooth and hairless. It has been adopted by *Protocalliphora* and other maggots which feed on nestling birds. It is used by certain flies which develop in the burrows of sparsely haired mammals such as the wild pig and and aard-vark in Africa, and by the Congo floor maggot *Auchmeromyia* which lives in the floor of human habitations and sucks the blood of men sleeping on the ground.

Digestion and Nutrition

After the food has been taken in, it is exposed to the digestive juices from the salivary glands and from the secretions of the gut itself. The carbohydrates, fats, and proteins which the food contains are broken down to smaller molecules by a whole range of digestive ferments, or enzymes, and the products absorbed into the blood. In some insects which take in coarse food, such as grasshoppers and cockroaches, there is an internal gizzard furnished with more teeth by which the food is ground and made more accessible to the digestive enzymes. The grinding or milling structure is often followed by a filter of closely set hairs which permit only liquids and quite fine particles to pass on to the next segments of the gut.

The lining of the gut is delicate and readily injured by hard particles of food. In most other animals the cells protect themselves by secreting a covering of slime, or mucus. We saw that the chief component of the protective cuticle of the insect is chitin, which can be regarded as a tough solid sort of mucus. Insects do not secrete mucus in the intestine. The first part of the gut (the fore-gut) is formed in development by an ingrowth from the surface; it is lined by a chitinous cuticle like that which covers the surface of the body. The last part also (the hind-gut) is similarly lined with cuticle. The intervening section where the greater part of digestion and absorption takes place has no cuticle, but it is generally protected by a thin detachable membrane of chitin that is called the 'peritrophic membrane'.

Many insects have no equipment for grinding up their food; and some adopt the procedure of disgorging the digestive juices, allowing them to act outside the body, and then reingesting the nutritious fluid that results. Predaceous and carnivorous ground beetles (Carabidae) feed in this way; and so do the larvae of the tiger beetles (Cicindelidae). These larvae make vertical burrows in sandy soil and lie in wait at the top of the burrow, scanning the horizon and ready to seize with their formidable jaws any insect that ventures within reach (figure 83). The large tiger-beetle larvae of Northern Nigeria are known locally as 'furau', and the same name is given to foot sores—in the belief that these fearsome-looking insects are the cause of the disease. But in trials on the human skin no damage of this sort could be produced by the bites of these larvae.

External digestion plays some part in the feeding of plant-sucking bugs. Although they are taking in chiefly the plant sap, which is to some extent a predigested food, they also eject enzymes into the plant cells, which will dissolve the stored grains of starch and act upon the 'hemicellulose' and so render the cell walls more permeable. But it is in certain predaceous insects that the method reaches its greatest degree of refinement.

The sickle-shaped mandibles of water-beetle larvae, *Dytiscus* and its allies, have exceedingly sharp points (figure 34). As soon as the prey has been impaled on them, powerful digestive juices are ejected from the stomach and driven down the grooved mandibles into the body of the victim. Within a matter of minutes the organs dissolve and become dispersed into a uniform soup which can be seen streaming into the points of the mandibles when the larva begins to suck. The method seems particularly suitable for an aquatic larva feeding upon insects; for there is no dilution by the surrounding water and no wastage; nothing remains but an empty skin.

The same technique, however, is used by some terrestrial

insects, notably the larvae of Neuroptera: the ant-lion *Myrmeleon* (figure 33), the brown lacewings *Nemerobius*, and the green lacewing *Chrysopa* (figure 156). The larva of *Chrysopa* attaches the cuticular husks of the victims to a loose coating of silk threads which covers the abdomen.

Some insects are more economical than others in their feeding habits. Blood-sucking insects which live as parasites continuously on the body of their host, such as the sucking lice (Anoplura) and many of the fleas (Siphonaptera), with an inexhaustible supply of blood always on tap, tend to be wasteful feeders whose excrement contains much undigested blood. Indeed, for certain fleas, notably the rat flea *Ceratophyllus*, in which both larvae and adults live in the dust and debris in the nest of the host, the residue of blood in the excrement of the adults is an essential element in the food of the larvae.

This practice is in marked contrast with the habit of such insects as the bed-bug *Cimex* or the mosquitoes, in which successive meals of blood may be separated by long intervals. They digest the blood completely, and the excrement consists mainly of uric acid plus haematin, the black indigestible residue from haemoglobin.

Leaf-eating insects also are often wasteful feeders. Caterpillars chip off with their mandibles little fragments of the leaf margin. In so doing they break open many of the plant cells and the contents of these are dissolved out and digested. But many of the cells that escape damage by the mandibles pass through the intestine and appear in the excrement with their contents untouched. Many plant-sucking insects, notably the Aphids and Coccids, are exceedingly wasteful in their feeding habits. The sap is passed quickly through the gut and the components that the insect needs are presumably absorbed; but much passes out again as a liquid excrement containing plenty of amino acids, sugars, and other nutritious substances. In dry weather this material forms the sticky residue on the leaves of plants that is called 'honey dew', which is sometimes collected by bees to make a rather disagreeable kind of honey. Honey dew provides a medium for the growth of fungi, notably the 'sooty fungus' (*Dematium pullulans*) which can be so disfiguring to ornamental trees and shrubs in a dry summer. The corresponding residue in the excrement of the Coccid *Trabutina mannipara*, that feeds on the tamarisk in the deserts of the Middle East, falls to the ground in the form of glistening scales. This material is used as food by nomadic tribes, and was indeed the 'manna' that helped to supplement the diet of the wandering Israelites in the Sinai desert.

A large part of the body of the plant is made up of the tough supporting substances cellulose and lignin. The term 'cellulose' covers a mixture of different substances, certain of which, the 'hemi-celluloses', are digested by many plant-eating insects; but most insects are unable to digest true cellulose, and this passes through the gut unchanged. No insects are known that can digest lignin, the material with which cellulose is impregnated to form wood. An insect like the caterpillar of the goat moth *Cossus* is obliged to pass enormous quantities of chewed wood through its intestine in order to get enough of the nutritious contents of the plant cells to provide for its growth. It usually takes three years to mature, but if it is given a diet of beetroot it can become full grown within one year.

There are, however, some insects, notably among the wood-boring beetles, which can digest cellulose. For example, the larvae of long-horned beetles (Cerambycidae) contain an enzyme that readily breaks down true cellulose.

When plants die, their woody skeleton of cellulose and lignin gradually disintegrates. The agents responsible are cellulose-fermenting bacteria, which are abundant in the soil, and fungi of many kinds. Insects, in fact, are largely dependent on these micro-organisms for converting the residues of plants into a state in which they can be assimilated. Many wood-boring beetles attack for preference damp wood that has already been subject to fungal decay. Though they appear to be feeding on wood they are, in fact, to a large extent feeding on fungi. Larvae of Lamellicorn beetles, such as the stag beetle *Lucanus,* many of which feed on decaying wood, have the hind-gut dilated to form a vast pouch, readily visible through the white skin of these grubs (figure 44). This is termed the 'fermentation chamber' and is filled with wood particles, and cellulose bacteria in process of breaking these particles down.

Some insects go further than this and provide the fungi that will infect the wood on which their larvae will feed. The egg-laying females of bark beetles (Scolytidae) regularly infect the burrows, in which they lay their eggs, with moulds ('ambrosia fungi'). In some species the female has brushes on the front of the head which convey the infective conidia. The larvae feed largely on the resulting growths of fungi in the burrows. When the giant wood wasps of the genus *Sirex* lay their eggs, they also transmit a fungus which infects the wood and penetrates the surface layers so that they become suitable as food for the burrowing larva.

Perhaps the best known example of this co-operative, or

'symbiotic', relation between insects and micro-organisms in the digestion of cellulose is that found in the termites. These also have a 'fermentation chamber' in the hind-gut which is populated by an amazing fauna of protozoa feeding upon cellulose. A drop of fluid expressed from the rectum of a

Figure 44.
Larva of a Lamellicorn beetle.

wood-eating termite is teeming with the most fantastic protozoa, which live nowhere else. So long as these 'symbionts' are present the termite can live indefinitely on the pure cellulose of blotting paper; without them termits die of starvation. In America there is a wood-eating cockroach called *Crytocercus* which has developed the same relationship.

Another curious diet which micro-organisms help to digest is beeswax. The larva of the wax moth *Galleria* lives exclusively on the honey-comb of the hive bee. Of course, this is contaminated with other substances, honey, pollen, etc; but the wax itself forms an important part of the food of *Galleria*. It carries in its alimentary canal a special bacterium which is able to break down wax to simpler substances. Keratin, on the other hand, the substance of wool, hair, feathers, horn, etc, which is quite indigestible for mammals, is readily digested by such insects as the clothes moths *Tineola*, etc, and the carpet beetle *Anthrenus*, which feed on such things. And this digestion is effected by the insect itself; it does not rely on bacteria. The secret is the production of a strong reducing enzyme which breaks the sulphur bonds (p. 24) and thus exposes the protein chains to the action of the ordinary digestive enzymes.

Roughly it may be said that food is required for two purposes: to provide energy for the movements and workings of the body, and to provide material for growth and reproduction.

For the muscular activity of most animals, sugar seems to be the preferred fuel; and the same is true of many insects.

The honey-bee is absolutely dependent on sugar if it is to fly. It has a rather large amount of glucose in its blood; but its chief reserve of fuel is the nectar carried in its crop or 'honey stomach'. This will keep it going for about a quarter of an hour, which gives the bee a flight range of about four miles. It cannot fly on fat or proteins.

The fruit-fly *Drosophila* carries large stores of glycogen (animal starch) and smaller stores of fat. If *Drosophila* has its thorax fixed with wax to the head of a very fine entomological pin, it can be induced by a slight jar or an occasional puff of air, to beat its wings in 'stationary flight'. It may continue doing this for about five hours, but at the end of this time it is completely exhausted; it can spread its wings, but can no longer flap them. In this state all the glycogen has disappeared but the stores of fat are unchanged. The flight muscles of *Drosophila* can use only carbohydrate. If the exhausted fly is given a tiny drop of syrup to drink it is in full flight again within thirty seconds. Acetate, alcohol, etc, cannot restore the capacity for flight in this way. For other activities *Drosophila* can make use of fat. If it is given nothing but water and allowed to run around, it dies in about forty-eight hours, and by then all the reserves of glycogen and fat have been consumed.

But glycogen is not an economical fuel for long distance flights; because, along with every gramme of glycogen that is carried, there must be about 2.3 gm of water to keep it in suspension, whereas fat can be stored in the form of droplets without any water at all. In fact, allowing for the water that is always carried with the glycogen, and the higher calorific value of fat, it has been estimated that weight for weight fat is eight times more efficient than glycogen as a source of energy.

It is not surprising, therefore, that insects which make long migratory flights use fat as their main fuel. Every year vast numbers of leaf hoppers (*Empoasca*) fly northwards from Florida and other Southern States and colonize States to the north. The distance they have flown can be judged from the level of their fat reserves. The monarch butterfly *Danaus plexippus* builds up large stores of fat before it sets off on its long migratory flights. And although migratory locusts, *Schistocerca, Locusta,* etc, may utilize carbohydrate at the start of their flights, they soon go over to burning fat alone.

Perhaps the most surprising discovery is that butterflies and moths which take no food but nectar are unable to use sugar as a fuel for their flight muscles. They must first convert it into fat before it can be burned. Even sugar injected into the blood cannot be used directly for flight.

Flapping flight, with the alternate starting, stopping, and reversing of the wing stroke (p. 60) consumes more energy than any other activity known in animals, and that is particularly true of small insects with their very high rates of wing beat. A locust in flight, burning fat, consumes about 0.8 per cent of its body weight in an hour. Insects burning carbohydrate consume much more: the fruit-fly Drosophila 7 to 10 per cent, the blowfly 27 to 35 per cent. The corresponding figure for a helicopter burning petrol is 4–5 per cent, and for a jet transport plane 12 per cent. Even a locust, which beats its wings comparatively slowly, consumes energy in its flight muscles at ten to twenty times the rate of a man working at maximum speed. The efficiency of the muscles in man and insect is about the same; that is, between 14 and 20 per cent of the chemical energy consumed appears as work done.

The use of food for growth and reproduction is a much more complex affair. The classic needs for a complex animal are fats, carbohydrates, protein, salts, water, and various odd substances, commonly called 'vitamins', which the animal cannot make for itself, and which are needed in small quantities only. The nutritional requirements of growing insects vary very much from one species to another, but in general all these standard needs must be met. In an insect feeding on a good mixed diet this presents no difficulty. The trouble arises when insects live in special circumstances, or feed on a restricted diet that is lacking in some essential component.

One curious example is seen in the aquatic larvae of mosquitoes or Chironomids. These mostly live in fresh water and are continually losing small amounts of salts, notably sodium and potassium chloride, in the urine. If they are kept in water that is completely without any salt at all and is constantly changed they cannot grow. But they are able to collect salts from the water, even water containing less than 0.006 per cent of chloride, and to concentrate them in the blood up to something like 0.3 per cent. The organs used for this purpose are the 'anal papillae', a group of four little conical or sausage-shaped organs projecting behind the anus. If mosquito larvae are reared in water with only the minutest trace of salt in it, the anal papillae work overtime and become hypertrophied. This hypertrophy occurs naturally in mosquito larvae that live in the rain-water collected in the axils of plants and in Chironomid larvae from alpine lakes.

One example of a restricted diet is the blood of mammals. This is an excellent nutritious food in most respects, but it is deficient in vitamins, particularly vitamins of the B group. It had long been known that certain blood-sucking insects contain peculiar micro-organisms (yeasts or bacteria) which are invariably present within certain special cells. The group of special cells was called a 'mycetome' and the micro-organisms were regarded as 'symbionts', which were transmitted in the insect from one generation to the next, and were believed to perform some service of benefit to their host.

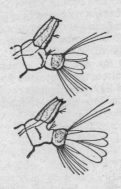

Figure 45.
The tail end of the mosquito larva *Aedes aegypti* showing the respiratory siphon (above) the last segment of the abdomen (below), with the long hairs forming the 'swimming brush', and the delicate 'anal papillae'. The upper larva has been reared in tap water containing traces of salt. The lower larva has been reared in salt-free distilled water and has the anal papillae greatly enlarged (Wigglesworth).

Then it was noted that symbionts are present in those insects which take no food but blood through their entire life, such as the sucking lice Anoplura, the bed-bug *Cimex*, the blood-sucking bugs *Rhodnius*, *Triatoma*, etc, the tsetse-fly *Glossina*, and the parasitic flies of the group Pupipara; while they are absent from such insects as the fleas, mosquitoes, blood-sucking midges, the higher flies (*Stomoxys*, etc) which feed on blood only in the adult state, and have a mixed diet rich in micro-organisms during their larval or growing period. That led to the suggestion that the symbiotic micro-organisms might be providing their hosts with a private source of vitamins.

This suggestion has been fully confirmed by experiments.

In the bug *Rhodnius*, the micro-organisms, called *Actinomyces rhodnii*, are not enclosed in a mycetome but live quite free inside the alimentary canal. By sterilizing the surface of the eggs before they hatch and rearing the larvae under clean conditions one can obtain *Rhodnius* without their symbionts. These will grow for a little while and then stop. Growth is renewed and completed if they are reinfected or if they are fed on blood to which B vitamins have been added.

It may be that symbiotic micro-organisms assist their hosts in other ways besides providing vitamins; but this seems to be their main value. The human louse *Pediculus* from which the mycetome has been removed surgically will not grow unless given vitamins in addition to blood; the beetles *Lasioderma* and *Sitodrepa* which have symbionts will develop quite well in highly refined white flour, whereas *Tribolium* and *Ptinus,* which do not carry symbionts, must have a whole range of vitamins added to the flour before they will grow properly. Cockroaches whose symbionts have been killed out by treatment with antibiotics must have extra vitamins in their diet.

Chapter 5

THE EGGS OF INSECTS

MANY OF the problems that confront the insect must be faced by the insect egg. The egg is well supplied, in the form of yolk, with all the nourishment it requires. But water is no less necessary, and so is oxygen. Special arrangements of many sorts exist to meet these needs.

Eggs that are exposed to the full rigours of the weather, such as the eggs of most butterflies and moths, usually have a robust shell, or 'chorion', made of a tough protein called 'chorionin'. This shell, like the shell of the hen's egg, is provided by the mother when the egg is laid. As a covering it is firm and rigid, but it is not waterproof. If these tiny objects are not to dry up it is essential that they should be extremely waterproof; and this is assured by the egg itself: at about the time of laying it deposits a thin sheet of waterproofing wax on the *inside* of the shell.

In some insects, such as locusts and water-beetles, the eggshell as laid down by the mother is thin and delicate. Indeed, in locusts it often breaks up and peels away. The embryo, at a very early stage of its development, therefore, covers itself with a tough cuticle (the 'serosal cuticle') which resembles the cuticle of the active insect in being composed of chitin—unlike the chorion formed by the mother, which contains no chitin.

It was observed by Réaumur in the eighteenth century that the eggs of many insects, notably ants and saw-flies, swell greatly by the imbibition of water after they are laid, and for this reason they must be deposited in places that are sufficiently moist. The egg of the water-beetle *Dytiscus,* which is inserted into the leaves and stems of aquatic plants, almost doubles its diameter by the absorption of water, and so do the eggs of crickets, chafer beetles, and many more. Locusts such as the desert locust *Schistocerca gregaria* may range widely over very dry country; but the eggs are laid in sandy soil after rain, and their weight is more than doubled by the uptake of water. The swelling of these eggs, however, is no haphazard affair. The water is taken in through a special region at one end of the egg, called the 'hydropyle'; the amount absorbed is carefully controlled, and the process is stopped when the supply is adequate.

The water obtained in this way is necessary for development. Like the dried larva of the Chironomid *Polypedilum* (p. 34) dried eggs remain dormant. Eggs of the South African locust *Locustana pardalina* have been kept in this desiccated state for three and a half years; on moistening they absorb water and complete their development within a couple of weeks. The eggs of the lucerne flea *Sminthurus viridis* have survived in their dry shrivelled state for 271 days; they swell up and hatch within twelve days after wetting. On the lower surface of cabbage leaves there are nearly always to be found the eggs of the cabbage white-fly *Aleurodes.* When the female lays these eggs she keeps her head in one place and rotates around it, laying the eggs as a circle of squat upright pegs. The lower end of each egg is actually inserted into the leaf and is modified to absorb moisture (figure 46). If the plant is well supplied with water, development in the egg goes forward normally. But if the leaf wilts from drought, development in the eggs is temporarily arrested.

Apart from this state of 'dormancy' from lack of moisture, some eggs remain dormant under perfectly favourable conditions, and even fail to absorb water though it is available. This obstinate type of arrested growth is commonly called 'diapause'. It seems to have arisen as an adaptation for surviving the winter or the hot, dry summer. A similar arrest of growth is seen in the later stages of development and we shall have more to say about it in that connection (p. 115).

A different type of arrest is seen in the eggs of mosquitoes of the genus *Aedes.* Many of these mosquitoes scatter their eggs broadcast in the dry summer; or, as in the case of the yellow fever mosquito *Aedes aegypti*, they lay them in small collections of water in tree holes or on the leaves of plants which are liable to become dry for many months. Development in these eggs goes forward until the larva is fully formed, and then it remains dormant until conditions are favourable for hatching. The broadcast eggs of *Aedes* in Northern Europe or Northern Canada, are carried by the winter rains or the melting snows into temporary pools where hatching takes place in the warm days of spring. But sometimes it seems that the presence of micro-organisms which reduce the amount of oxygen in the water are necessary to give the right stimulus for hatching.

The next prime need of the egg, after water, is oxygen. Some eggs, such as those of locusts, seem to be able to get enough oxygen by diffusion through the general surface of the shell; but most have special respiratory mechanisms. The problem is the same as that faced by terrestrial insects in general: how to take in oxygen without losing water. The solution was pointed out by Leuckart (1857) and is

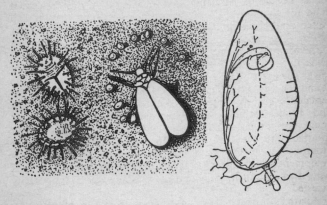

Figure 46.
Female of the glasshouse white-fly *Trialeurodes vaporarium* with ring of eggs inserted into a tomato leaf; also a larva and an empty larval skin showing the split from which the adult has emerged (Bovien and Thomsen). To the right, a single egg with developing embryo inside, showing the water-absorbing process inserted into the leaf (Weber).

in principle the same as that adopted by the active stages of insects: most of the surface of the egg is impermeable to oxygen; there are only limited spots, comparable with the spiracles, through which oxygen can get in.

The classic example is the egg of the water scorpions *Nepa* and *Ranatra*. This egg is inserted into the stems of aquatic plants, but at the exposed end it has a pair of long horns which Leuckart showed to be respiratory structures (plate 2). They do not lead to air-containing tubes like tracheae, but into what appears to be a spongy material with minute cavities containing air. This system takes many forms. In the bugs, such as *Rhodnius* or *Cimex,* there is a ring of fine ducts filled with this spongy air-filled protein; these connect with an air-containing layer which lines the entire shell. In Lepidoptera, such as the silkworm, the shell likewise has an air-filled spongy lining which is connected to the exterior through fine, tapering canals.

It is not uncommon for a whole batch of eggs to be laid at one time and cemented together in a pod, or 'ootheca'. Locusts insert their eggs into the soil and glue them loosely together in this way. The water-beetle *Hydrous* encloses her eggs in a silken cocoon with an upright chimney which leads to the outside air (figure 47). The ootheca of some

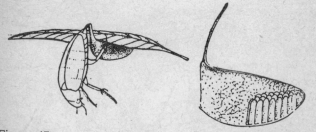

Figure 47.
Female of the water-beetle *Hydrous piceus* spinning her egg cocoon (Miger, 1809). To the right, detail of the eggs in the cocoon and the 'chimney' for supplying atmospheric air (Wesenberg-Lund).

Mantids is an elaborate affair with some resemblance to a miniature fir cone. Cockroaches fasten their eggs together in a very neat packet of the same kind by pouring out over them a self-tanning cement (p. 22). These packets may be dropped in their haunts by the egg-laying female or, in some species of cockroach, she may carry the packet protruding from the end of the abdomen until the young are just about ready to hatch.

The mechanism for getting oxygen into the egg of the cockroach is very remarkable (figure 48). Each egg has a knob of spongy air-filled substance which leads to an air-filled layer of the usual type inside the egg-shell. But how does the egg breathe when it has been thickly covered by the tanned cement? As each egg in turn is discharged into the brood chamber it is carefully placed in position by the side of the preceding egg, and then the cement is poured over them. But while this is happening a tiny structure with two horns is held above the respiratory knob. These horns are so arranged that when the cement has hardened they leave a couple of open canals connecting the knob on the egg to the outside air. This happens with each egg in turn, so that in the end, all along the crest of the ootheca are a series of little air-containing cavities each with two air-filled ducts leading to the outside. All are identical in form since they have all been moulded by the same die.

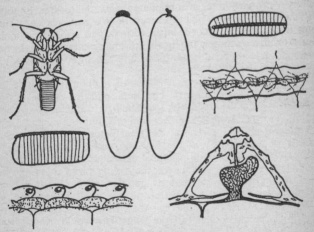

Figure 48.
Top left, female of the German cockroach *Blattella germanica* carrying the egg capsule, seen from beneath. Immediately below is the capsule seen in side view, and, top right, seen from above (Robert). In the middle is a single egg with the sausage-shaped air-containing organ in side view and seen end on. On the right side in the middle is an enlarged view of the crest of the egg capsule seen from above. The row of air-containing chambers can be seen above the sausage-shaped organs on the eggs. At bottom left is a side view of these same structures showing the air duct leading to the egg; and bottom right a transverse section of the crest showing how the air-filled egg-shell is connected to the exterior (Wigglesworth and Beament).

The ootheca of the cockroach is hardened not only by tanning but by filling the cement with crystals of oxalic acid. Many stick insects (Phasmida) have exceedingly hard eggs resembling seeds, in which the chorion is impregnated with lime. They, too, have elaborate respiratory mechanisms.

A subject about which almost nothing is known is the nature of the cement which insects produce to stick their eggs firmly down. Whatever the nature of this substance, it is usually quite colourless, hardens very rapidly, and is exceedingly tenacious. That is well evidenced by the eggs of lice which are cemented on to the shaft of the hair (figure 150). They are normally attached to the hair close to the skin. So strong is the adhesive that as the hair grows the eggs remain attached and become conspicuous as 'nits'; but that is usually long after the young lice have hatched.

We shall not concern ourselves here with the processes of embryonic development that go forward within the egg, the ways in which these are regulated and the origin of the anomalies which occasionally result in two embryos developing in a single egg or in a larva with two heads or two tails. But we must consider the problems that confront the larva when its development is complete and the time has come to escape from the egg-shell.

As the embryo develops it is bathed in fluid, the amniotic fluid. When its organs are complete and its cuticle fully formed it can be seen, if the shell is sufficiently transparent, to start swallowing the amniotic fluid. The pumping movements of the pharynx are clearly visible in dragonfly larvae, in caterpillars, in the bed-bug and louse, and many other insects. The body is thus enlarged until it fills the shell, and often the surface of the young larva dries and a film of air appears between its cuticle and the shell. Then by muscular exertion it may rip open the shell and escape.

But the coverings of the egg may be too tough for that. The thick 'serosal cuticle' of the locust egg would never yield to such pressure. It is first digested and dissolved by enzymes (chitinase and proteinase) that are discharged into the amniotic fluid. These enzymes come from a most unexpected source. On the first segment of the abdomen in the insect embryo there is often a pair of outgrowths known as 'pleuropodia', which are commonly believed to represent the vestiges of ancestral abdominal limbs. In the locust they have become glandular organs and they are the source of the enzymes. If the egg is tied round the middle with a ligature placed just behind the pleuropodia, then the serosal cuticle is dissolved in the front half of the egg alone; if the ligature is placed just in front of the pleuropodia, then only the back half has the serosal cuticle digested. When the digestion process is complete in the normal egg, only a very thin epicuticular layer remains and this is easily broken through.

Not all insects dissolve their egg-shells in this way. In many there are preformed arrangements for hatching. Phasmids have a circular cap at one end of the egg which is readily pushed off from the inside. Caps of this kind are very general in the Hemiptera and in the lice (Mallophaga and Anoplura). Eggs of the higher flies, *Musca, Lucilia, Calliphora*, etc, have a groove between the two folds in the egg-shell along one surface of the egg. This serves not only as the point of entry of oxygen into the air-filled layer of the chorion, it also provides a line of weakness in the shell in readiness for hatching. The roof of the groove is raised as a strap-like lid when the larva makes its way out. The young larva of the cockroach has no difficulty in breaking out of the egg itself, which is very fragile. The ootheca, which is the main obstacle, yields to the combined pressure of the emerging larvae and opens like a lady's handbag. A split appears along the preformed line of weakness where the two sides were pressed together, and the larvae come tumbling out through the cleft.

Many insect larvae are furnished with special tools for opening the egg. The mouth-hooks are used by Muscid larvae to force up the lid of their egg-shell. Caterpillars use their mandibles to bite through the shell. Others have 'hatching spines' or 'egg teeth' which are no longer present in the later stages. Mosquito larvae have a stout spine arising from the floor of a pit on the upper surface of the head (figure 50) which serves to concentrate the pressure exerted by the larva at one point and so to split the shell. The larva of the flea has a similar spine with a sharp point. It creeps round the inside of the egg, pressing this point against the shell, until it cuts through and a long slit is made as by a tin opener acting from the inside (figure 49).

In these last two insects the hatching spines are a part of the cuticle of the first-stage larva and they persist until the next moult. But very many insects undergo a preliminary moult while they are still inside the egg. By the time it is ready to hatch the first-stage larva is enclosed in an outer loose cuticle, the 'embryonic cuticle', which is shed during the act of escaping from the egg, or very shortly afterwards. The hatching spines are often carried by this embryonic cuticle and are, therefore, left behind when this splits and is discarded with the egg-shell. That is what hap-

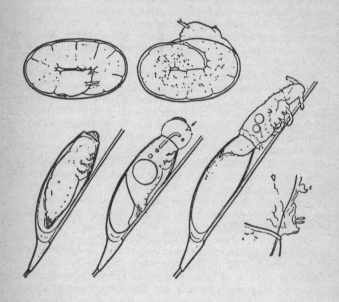

Figure 49.
Top left, the larva of the flea bathed in fluid inside the egg. In the
figure to the right it has swallowed the fluid and the tracheal system
has filled with air; it has crept round inside the shell and cut a slit
with the hatching spine on the head.

The series below shows the hatching of the mouse louse *Polyplax*.
To the left, bathed in fluid in an egg cemented to a hair. In the
middle, it has swallowed the fluid and the shell contains air; it is
now swallowing air and has pushed off the cap of the egg and is
bulging through the opening. The 'embryonic cuticle' is just beginning
to split (arrow). To the right, the louse has escaped from the embryonic cuticle which remains as a frill round the mouth of the egg;
the tracheal system is filled with air. The detail (bottom right)
shows the two 'hatching spines' on the embryonic cuticle (Sikes and
Wigglesworth).

pens in locusts, in Mantids, in Hemiptera, in the lice, and many more.

Another of the accompaniments of hatching is readily observed in the louse and bed-bug. After these have swallowed all the amniotic fluid they begin to swallow air (figure 49). At first they do this rather slowly and the tiny bubbles of air taken in dissolve and disappear as fast as they are swallowed. But near the time of hatching the swallowing of air becomes very active and the gut is distended with bubbles. At one time it was suggested that in the louse the air is forced out through the anus, and accumulates under pressure at the back of the egg until the cap is pushed off and the insect driven out! That does not, in fact, happen. The air serves merely to increase the bulk of the young larva; then rapid and powerful waves of muscular contraction in the abdomen drive the body fluids forwards into the head and thorax, the egg teeth press against and displace the cap, and the head and thorax bulge through the opening. At this

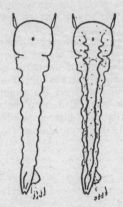

Figure 50.
Newly hatched mosquito larva *Aedes aegypti* with the hatching spine like that of the flea larva on the head. To the left, three minutes after the spiracles on the respiratory siphon have made contact with the air; air just beginning to enter the main tracheal tubes. To the right, twelve minutes later; the entire tracheal system is now filled with air (Wigglesworth).

moment the embryonic cuticle splits, and with the aid of more wave-like contractions of the abdomen the larva glides gently out. The swallowing of air may then continue for a time; the new cuticle is distended and held in this state until it has hardened.

At some stage in this process the liquid which fills the tracheal system throughout the period of its development is absorbed into the tissues and the system fills with air. This may not happen until after hatching is complete. It does not occur in the louse or bed-bug until the embryonic cuticle is shed. It does not take place in mosquito larvae until they have left the egg, risen to the surface of the water, and exposed their spiracles to the atmosphere (figure 50). But in many insects (such as caterpillars, or the mealworm *Tenebrio*) air appears in the tracheal system while the young larva is still bathed in the amniotic fluid. And some aquatic larvae, Chironomid larvae for example, hatch into water and fill their tracheal system with air while still submerged.

This phenomenon has excited some controversy in the past because the surface tension of water around minute bubbles of gas creates such a very large pressure that an enormous suction is needed to cause the liberation of gas from solution. But the situation is very different if the water is in contact with a greasy or waxy surface. Here the 'work of adhesion' of water to the surface is very small; it is necessary to lower the pressure by only a very small amount in order to liberate gas in contact with such a surface. It is the fact that the lining of the tracheae comes to behave like a waxy surface at the time of moulting, which makes it so easy for gas bubbles to be liberated from solution there—just as gas bubbles are liberated on the slightly greasy walls of a water jug that has been filled from the cold tap, but not in a glass container that is quite grease-free. The reason why the tracheal lining behaves like a waxy surface is a more difficult problem.

Chapter 6

THE GROWTH
AND METAMORPHOSIS
OF INSECTS

AS SOON as the arthropods developed a hard cuticle it became necessary for them to moult in order to grow. The softer types of integument, such as the general cuticle of a caterpillar, can be provided with a loosely fitting and highly folded superficial layer or 'epicuticle'. This allows room for growth; the folds in the surface are smoothed out; more chitin and protein are added progressively to the inner layers of the cuticle, and within the limits provided by the inextensible epicuticle the body can continue to grow. The most impressive example of this process is in the queen termite (figure 51). As the reproductive organs grow the abdomen becomes distended; the epicuticle gradually unfolds and the abdomen may increase in length from half an inch to four inches or more, with a total increase in surface area of perhaps fifty-fold.

But rigid sclerotized structures, such as the head capsule that has to support the mandibles, the firm skeleton of the thorax or the legs, cannot stretch any more once they have hardened (p. 22). In the queen termite, the original sclerotized plates which once covered the segments of the abdomen, persist unchanged in size and appear like small brown islands in the vast extent of soft white cuticle.

The process of 'moulting' in the broad sense is made up of a very complex series of activities. It is set in motion by

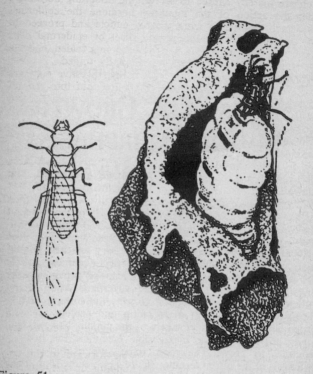

Figure 51.
On the left, young unmated female termite. The wings on the right side have been shed along the preformed breaking line and only the stumps remain. On the right, mature female, or queen, as seen when the royal cell is cut open. Abdomen distended with eggs; the sclerotized plates appearing as islands along the back (Holmgren).

a secretion from special cells in the brain (figure 54). This secretion acts upon glands of internal secretion that lie in the head or thorax ('ventral glands' or 'thoracic glands') which are thereby caused to secrete the 'moulting hormone'. Under the action of the moulting hormone the epidermal cells detach themselves from the old cuticle and proceed to grow and multiply. Of course, the sheet of epidermal cells can increase in surface area only by becoming folded, and the new cuticle that they lay down is similarly folded.

When this new cuticle is nearly ready, digestive enzymes that dissolve chitin and protein are poured out into the so-called 'moulting fluid' which fills the space between the old and the new cuticles. These enzymes dissolve all the soft inner layers of the old cuticle; and then the moulting fluid, with these products of digestion, is absorbed through the new cuticle, and the space between the two becomes almost dry. When most of the cuticle is soft, as in caterpillars, well over 90 per cent of the old cuticle is digested, and nothing but an exceedingly thin skin is finally cast off.

Sclerotin (p. 22) cannot be digested in this way. How then does the insect break through the hard sclerotized head or thorax? It provides what are usually called 'moulting sutures', or lines of weakness. These appear as fine white lines in the brown cuticle of the head or along the mid-line of the thorax. In the active insect these regions of the cuticle are just as strong as the rest, but they appear white because along these lines the cuticle is not sclerotized. When, therefore, the old detached cuticle is dissolved by the moulting fluid they become lines of weakness indeed; only the delicate epicuticle bridges the gap; and at the slightest pressure the cuticle splits at this point.

While these changes have been going forward in the cuticle, the growing insect has been building up the muscles in the abdomen. These muscles run longitudinally from one segment to the next and are well placed to increase the pressure of the blood. When the moment for 'moulting' (in the narrow sense of casting off the old cuticle) arrives, the muscles contract and force the body fluids into the thorax. The pressure may be still further increased by the swallowing of air. Under this internal pressure the cuticle splits along the lines of weakness, and the insect gently withdraws itself from the remnants of the old skin. It is not only the cuticle of the body surface that is cast, but the lining of the hind-gut and the fore-gut and of the tracheae. The firm rings, or spirals, of the tracheae are likewise dissolved by the moulting fluid, and nothing but an excessively delicate membrane is drawn out through the spiracles.

During and immediately after the escape from the old cuticle, the swallowing of air may be very vigorous and the body is tensely distended. A cockroach trodden on at this time may pop like a burst balloon. The pressure produced by the muscle contractions in the abdomen distends the limbs, the head and the wings to their proper form (figure 52). In the emerging flesh-fly *Sarcophaga* the internal pressure may be raised to 95 mm of mercury. Butterflies and moths, when they emerge from the pupa, have the normal colour pattern on their diminutive wings. No further changes take place until a convenient perch has been found, which will allow the wings to enlarge without obstruction. Then the expansion begins; without apparent effort the wings become extended and the scales, which were erect, come to lie like smooth roof tiles. The absence of effort is, of course, illusory: the muscles are hard at work, pumping in air and compressing the body fluids. If the tips of the wings are pricked, blood drips from them.

The whole procedure is like that followed at hatching from the egg (p. 94). That is particularly true of the emergence of flies from their egg-like 'puparium'. They have a cleft on the front of the face along which the cuticle is folded deeply into the head. When the blood pressure is increased by muscular contraction in the abdomen this cuticular fold is everted and the head is blown up like a balloon; then it is withdrawn again by muscles (figure 53). Flies use this so-called 'ptilinum', which is alternately expanded and withdrawn, not only to crack open the end of their puparium, but also for burrowing upwards through several inches of friable soil.

The expansion of the wings is simply an extreme example of the smoothing out of folds in the cuticle under internal pressure that takes place everywhere. The hardening of the cuticle (in most parts of the body) is deferred until expansion is complete. Then a 'chemical messenger', or hormone, is set free into the blood, perhaps from the brain or other ganglia, and is carried to all parts of the body. This hormone sets in motion the final steps in the moulting process, the hardening and darkening of the cuticle, which then take place simultaneously throughout the body. In some insects the pressure muscles of the abdomen are retained; but in most they are dismantled as soon as moulting is complete; and the protein they contain is dispersed and used for other purposes, such as the development of eggs or for thickening the cuticle.

Darkening is generally complete within an hour or so after moulting; but hardening continues for some days or even weeks. This may be due to a progressive change in the 'sclerotin' of the cuticle; but much of the hardening results from the addition of more and more chitin and protein to the inner layers. This may continue in the adult stag beetle, for example, for at least three weeks after moulting, until the final thickness of the cuticle may be more than three times what it was when moulting took place.

Among the Thysanura, such as the silver-fish *Lepisma* or the fire-brat *Thermobia*, the insect that hatches from the egg is closely similar in general form to the adult of the same species. The food and the whole way of life remain unchanged from hatching until death. When they attain a cer-

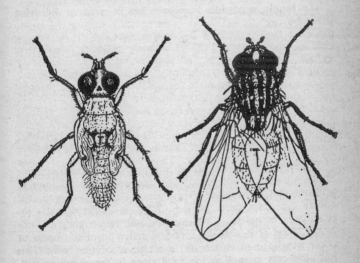

Figure 52.
The house-fly *Musca* newly escaped from the puparium, with pale soft thorax and abdomen and crumpled wings; and the same insect half an hour later with thorax and abdomen blown up, hardened, and darkened, and with the wings expanded (Thomsen).

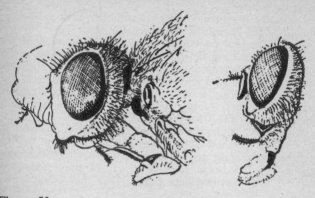

Figure 53.
The house-fly in process of escaping from the puparium. The head and proboscis are blown up and the 'ptilinum' is forced out from the face like a balloon. The head to the right shows the normal appearance when the pressure is reduced and the ptilinum withdrawn (Thomsen).

tain size these insects become sexually mature. The female will lay a batch of eggs and then moult again. Continuing in this way, alternately moulting and laying eggs, she will moult up to fifty times after the adult state has been reached and will increase some three times in size.

In all other insects, however, as soon as the adult state is reached, the glands of internal secretion that produce the 'moulting hormone', the 'thoracic glands', or 'ventral glands', break down and disappear. That is one of the characteristic accompaniments of maturity. The Thysanura are unique in keeping their ventral glands so that moulting can continue.

Little is known about how the activity of the thoracic or ventral glands is controlled. But it is known that it is set off by another hormone secreted by cells (so-called 'neurosecretory cells') in the brain (figure 54). Still less is known about the control of the neurosecretory cells; but the important point is that in the brain lies the ultimate centre which decides whether growth and moulting are to take place or not. In the blood-sucking bugs it is the stretching of the abdomen by a large meal of blood which gives the nervous stimulus to the brain that sets the whole chain of hormone secretion going.

In the winged insects, the Pterygota, a new feature ap-

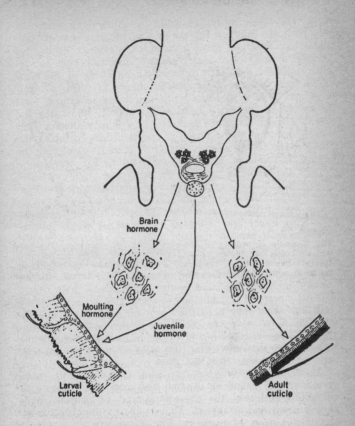

Figure 54.

The glands of internal secretion and the hormones controlling growth
and metamorphosis, illustrated in the blood-sucking bug *Rhodnius*.
The brain at the back of the head contains 'neurosecretory cells' the
'axons' from which end in the 'corpus cardiacum' where the *'brain
hormone'* is set free into the blood. This acts on the 'thoracic gland'
and causes this to secrete the *'moulting hormone'*. When the moulting
hormone alone acts on the 'epidermal cells' (on the right) these cells
during moulting produce an adult type of cuticle. But when the
moulting hormone acts in the presence of the *'juvenile hormone'*, secreted by the 'corpus allatum' lying just behind the corpus cardiacum,
the epidermal cells (on the left) produce a larval type of cuticle
(Wigglesworth).

pears. The young stages resemble the Apterygota—more or less. They are wingless, but they do not become sexually mature. They feed and grow and undergo a series of moults. There is a progressive enlargement of the wing pads at successive moults, but little other change. Then, at the final moult, they undergo a spectacular change in form, a 'metamorphosis'. The sexual and reproductive organs assume their mature form, fully developed wings appear, and often the structure and pattern of the cuticle is strikingly altered. That is what happens in the group of insect orders, including the cockroaches (Dictyoptera), the Orthoptera (figure 55), the Hemiptera (plate 3), etc, which make up the Exopterygota.

Once the sexual organs and the wings are developed these insects do not moult again. There is only one curious exception, that of the Ephemeroptera or may-flies (p. 319) in which the aquatic larva, or 'nymph', gives rise to a winged and flying insect that is called a 'subimago', which quickly moults again to produce the true adult.

In the higher groups of winged insects, the Endopterygota, a further new device has been adopted. We may take the beetles (Coleoptera) as an example. Their larvae, for instance the larvae of ground beetles (Carabidae), often bear a striking superficial resemblance to apterygote insects. As they feed and moult they keep this form unchanged and no vestiges of wings are to be seen outside the body. The wings are indeed developing, but in the form of 'buds' beneath the cuticle. The epidermis forms little pockets that grow inwards, and the wings arise from the floor of these pockets. By this device the epidermis of the growing wings does not have to join in the labour of cuticle formation that takes place at each recurring moult: wing development can go forward without interruption. At the moult before the last the wing buds are everted, and now for the first time they appear on the surface and cover themselves with cuticle.

This stage, when the wings first make their appearance, is the 'pupa'. In the beetles the pupa has not only rudimentary wings, but legs and antennae and mouth-parts, which are not capable of movement but stand out from the surface and later serve as sheaths for the mobile structures of the adult that develop inside them. In most Lepidoptera the pupa has much the same appearance when it is first revealed by the casting of the larval skin. But almost at once the wings and mouth-parts, legs and antennae all fit together like the pieces of a jig-saw puzzle. Then a cement substance is poured out over the surface and all the parts become firmly glued together, so that in the fully formed chrysalis of the butterfly or moth the various parts are visible only in outline in the surface.

In the pupal stage the insect does not feed; it is like a second egg stage during which embryonic development is renewed. It is often protected by enclosure in a cell within the earth, or in a silken cocoon built in readiness by the full-grown larva. The 'puparium' of the house-fly or blowfly already mentioned (p. 102) represents another method of protection for the pupa. The true pupa of the fly is a most fragile white object enclosed within the hard brown or black puparium, which is, in fact, the skin of the last stage larva (figure 56). The soft white maggot of the blowfly, when it is fully grown, rounds itself up into an egg-like form. It then proceeds to harden and tan its cuticle to furnish a protective shell of sclerotin for the fragile pupa that is to form inside.

Within the pupa a most complex development proceeds, and the adult insect that emerges at the next moult, when the process is complete, is strikingly different from the stages that went before. The insect has undergone a 'complete metamorphosis'. These remarkable transformations raise questions which have exercised the minds of naturalists from the earliest times. How are the changes in form regulated? How did they arise in the course of evolution? What is the significance and what the origin of the pupal stage?

The first of these questions is the easiest to answer, at least in a rather superficial fashion. Immediately behind the brain is a tiny gland of internal secretion called the 'corpus allatum' (figure 54). Throughout the young stages this gland secretes a hormone usually called the 'juvenile hormone'; so

Figure 55.
Three stages in the growth and metamorphosis of a grasshopper. To the left newly hatched from the egg (about 3 mm long). In the middle an intermediate stage (about 1.2 cm long). To the right the winged adult (about 3 cm long) (Boas).

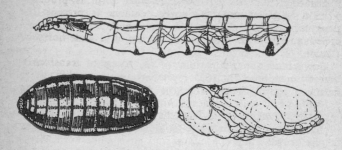

Figure 56.
Stages in the metamorphosis of the house-fly *Musca*. Above, the larva. To the left, the hardened larval skin (the 'puparium') enclosing the pupa. To the right, the delicate pupa exposed after peeling away the puparial shell (Thomsen).

long as this substance is circulating in the blood, the epidermal cells lay down a cuticle of larval type when the insect moults. It seems to be the brain which decides whether or not the corpus allatum shall secrete the juvenile hormone. Very little is known about the nature of this control; but we do know that throughout the larval stages in a locust, a cockroach, or a bug, the juvenile hormone is present. When the last larval stage (in Orthoptera and Hemiptera usually the fifth moulting stage) is reached, the juvenile hormone is absent, and when the insect moults again it transforms into an adult.

These conclusions have been reached by means of simple experiments. Removal of the corpus allatum from the head of young insects leads to precocious metamorphosis and the appearance of diminutive adults. On the other hand, if the corpus allatum is taken out of a young insect and implanted into the abdomen of an insect in the last larval stage, so that this is now supplied with juvenile hormone, then instead of undergoing metamorphosis when it moults, it turns into a giant larva (plate 3).

The same principles apply to the endopterygote insects, but with a difference. If the corpus allatum is removed from a young caterpillar this proceeds to moult into a tiny pupa, which in turn gives rise to a very small moth (plate 4). On the other hand, if the corpus allatum is taken out from a caterpillar in the last larval stage it turns into a monstrous creature with characters intermediate between those of a

pupa and an adult moth. From these and other experiments
it has been inferred that the caterpillar form is produced
when a large amount of juvenile hormone is present; the
pupa form when only a trace of juvenile hormone is secreted; and the adult form in the absence of juvenile hormone
(figure 57).

The second question, how did this process of transformation arise in the course of evolution?—is more difficult to
answer. The most likely supposition is that there has been an
independent evolution of the different 'stages' of insects.
The form of an animal is the outcome of a series of growth
processes that are under the control of the hereditary 'genes'
in the chromosomes of the cell nuclei. The genes provide
the 'blue print' which forecasts the form and pattern of the
animal. In insects, for example in the silkworm, it is well
known that some genes are responsible mostly for the characters of the larva, and other genes are responsible mainly
for the characters of the adult. Very great variations can
take place in the form of the caterpillar without any visible
difference in the resulting moth. Similarly, there are species
of Lepidoptera such as the dagger moths *Acronycta psi* and
A. tridens which are almost indistinguishable as adults but
quite unlike as larvae; and many more with virtually identical larvae and very different adults.

As soon as two partially independent sets of genes become separated in this way it is easy to see how the larva
and the adult could proceed to evolve and change independently of one another. And when the larva and the adult
come to live in different surroundings, and to feed on different foods, they will become more and more unlike one
another—until a spectacular 'metamorphosis' is needed to
convert the one into the other.

It is perhaps not altogether surprising that, when widely
unrelated insect larvae have come to live under similar conditions, they should assume a similar general form. The leaf-
eating larvae of saw-flies (Hymenoptera-Apocrita) are strikingly like the caterpillars of Lepidoptera (figure 161); and
the larvae of some beetles (Chrysomelidae), or the Tipulid
Cylindrotoma splendens, which likewise feed exposed on
leaves, also show some similarities. The legless grubs of social Hymenoptera, which live a protected life with abundant
food at hand, resemble the grubs of weevils (Curculionidae)
living in a cell within the fruit or stem or root of their
food plant.

Conversely, the aquatic larvae of mosquitoes, the leaf-
eating larvae of the Tipulid *Cylindrotoma,* and the headless

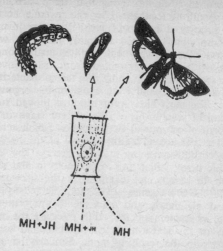

Figure 57.
Diagram to illustrate the control of metamorphosis in Lepidoptera, etc., by means of hormones. When the epidermal cells are exposed to moulting hormone (MH) plus a large amount of juvenile hormone (JH) the larval form is produced on moulting. When moulting hormone plus a trace of juvenile hormone is present, the pupal form appears. When moulting hormone alone is acting, the adult moth develops (Wigglesworth).

maggots of house-flies and blowflies, illustrate the highly diverse larval forms that may appear within a single order of insects as adaptations to special environments. The larvae of ground-beetles (Carabidae), chafer- and dung-beetles (Scarabaeidae), water-beetles (Dytiscidae, etc), weevils (Curculionidae), and the leaf-eating Chrysomelidae show a similar diversity within the Coleoptera.

We may, therefore, regard metamorphosis as having arisen as the result of the divergent evolution of the young and growing stages of the insect on the one hand, and the adult reproductive stage on the other. Perhaps the origin of the pupa is to be sought along the same lines, the independent evolution of an intermediate stage, the form of which is controlled by yet other genes, and which serves to bridge the widening gap between the structure of the larva and the structure of the adult. It is not difficult to imagine how a protected transitional stage between larva and adult could have had selective value in the course of evolution.

How has it come about that these striking changes in form should be controlled by the juvenile hormone? It has been discovered in recent years that the juvenile hormone (or some closely related chemical substance which has just the same effect) is very widely distributed among animals and plants. It has been extracted from many invertebrate animals, from protozoa and from some bacteria and yeasts, from soya beans, and from many of the organs of man and other mammals. This substance has proved to be farnesol, a chemical which forms the halfway stage in the synthesis of certain lipid or fat-like substances (cholesterol and carotenoids) by plants and animals.

It would seem that we have here an example of a well-known phenomenon that is known as 'hormone capture'. A widely distributed chemical substance, sometimes perhaps a mere by-product of metabolism without any physiological significance, is selected for use as a signal substance, or hormone. A gland, in this case the corpus allatum, comes to specialize in its production, and when it reaches the various organs of the body, notably the epidermal cells which lay down the cuticle, it calls forth particular activities.

Such a hormone may be likened to a key which opens a particular door. What is inside that door bears no relation to the nature of the key. Exactly how it brings about its effect we do not know; but that effect is to bring into action those sets of genes that are responsible for the production of larval characters. Normally this happens in all parts of the body, so that the entire insect is larval, or pupal, or adult. But the genes which contain the blue print for the characters of the body are present in the nuclei of every cell. In experiments, therefore, it is possible to expose just one part of the insect to the juvenile hormone and so to cause formation of that part in larval cuticle while the rest of the insect becomes adult (plate 5).

Under normal circumstances an insect is either a larva, a pupa, or an adult; but occasionally the proper regulation goes astray. If the larva of the mealworm Tenebrio, for example, has been kept at too low a temperature, the hormone balance for some reason is upset and monsters intermediate between larva and pupa, or between pupa and adult, may appear—a phenomenon called 'prothetely' or 'metathetely'. Silkworm larvae with conspicuous antennae, that were described at the beginning of the last century, were of this kind. They can be produced at will by suitable experiments with hormones (plate 4c, d).

In some sorts of insects, however, the juvenile hormone seems always to be unduly persistent. The common stick insect (*Dixippus morosus*) is an example of this. The female begins to reproduce and lay eggs without having developed any wings, and when many features of the body are still more or less larval. This persistent youthfulness is known as 'neoteny'. It is present in a small degree even in the cockroach; for if the corpus allatum is removed from a full-grown larva of the cockroach this turns into a 'super-adult', an insect more adult than normal. From this we must infer that the normal adult cockroach is very slightly juvenile.

What is perhaps an example of the same phenomenon is seen in locusts. The destructive migratory locusts exist in two quite distinct forms, known as 'phases', which are so different in both shape and colour that they were at one time believed to belong to separate species. The one form is a restless, conspicuously coloured and gregarious insect, that builds up into the great swarms of locust plagues. The other form is solitary, relatively sluggish and coloured green like its background of vegetation (plate 13a). In many respects the solitary locust seems to be a slightly juvenile form, and there is evidence that an excessive activity of the corpus allatum in producing juvenile hormone may be responsible for its appearance.

Insects, like other animals, are 'polymorphic'; they exist in more than one form. The most familiar example is sex; an insect is either male or female, and these two forms may be so unlike that they have often been thought to belong to different species. The appearance of male or female is decided by a different balance in the genes controlling the body form: a predominance of the male-forming genes or of the female-forming genes. When the form of the body is controlled by genes in this way it is often exceedingly constant and fixed; but the action of some genes can be influenced

Figure 58.
On the left, head of normal male of the solitary bee *Andrena solidaginis* seen from the front. In the middle, head of normal female. On the right, head of female parasitized by *Stylops*, showing male coloration (Salt).

and over-ridden by the conditions of life. Even sex can be affected in this way in some insects. For example, in certain solitary bees and wasps occasional individuals appear which should have been males but have developed the colour pattern of females, or *vice versa*. That has come about because they have been parasitized by *Stylops,* belonging to the curious order Strepsiptera (figure 164). It seems that when the body is weakened by the loss of nourishment the genes which ought to bring about the development of one sex are superseded by the latent genes of the opposite sex (figure 58).

Other genes exert their characteristic influence only if the temperature is unduly low, or if there is a lack of vitamins in the diet. The minute parasitic wasp *Trichogramma semblidis* has one form if it develops in the eggs of Lepidoptera, quite a different form if it develops in the eggs of the alder fly, *Sialis* (figure 59). It does not seem too much of an assumption to suppose that when the form of the body is consistently influenced by some external factor of temperature or diet, or some internal factor such as a hormone, these influences are controlling the activity of a group of genes.

Besides the 'phases' of locusts there are other polymorphisms which seem to be controlled by the juvenile hormone. That is true of the winged and wingless forms in aphids, or greenfly; the former develop under crowded conditions; the latter when the mother aphid is living in isolation; and an excess of juvenile hormone will lead to the formation of the wingless form—which has many other features to distinguish it from the winged variety besides the absence of

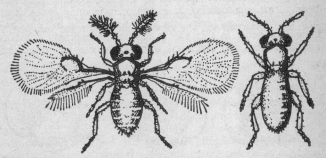

Figure 59.
Males of the egg parasite *Trichogramma semblidis* (0.5 mm long). To the left, winged form with bushy antennae reared in eggs of Lepidoptera. To the right, wingless form with changed antennae and legs, reared in eggs of *Sialis* (Salt).

wings (figure 68). Termites show a remarkable degree of polymorphism; and the soldier caste, with their huge sclerotized heads and powerful mandibles, seem to be the result of an excess of juvenile hormone (figure 144).

Sometimes the influence that controls the change in form comes from outside the body. The queen honey-bee differs from the worker bee in a great many structural details, but she is produced from precisely the same type of fertilized egg. If an egg or a recently hatched larva is moved from a worker cell to a large queen cell, where it will be given large amounts of the special salivary secretion called 'royal jelly', it will develop into a queen. If it is not transferred until it is two to three days old it may develop characters intermediate between a worker and a queen. Abundant food, combined probably with some special substance or substances present in royal jelly, leads to the full development of queen characters.

During its normal life history, as we have seen, the insect may show still more remarkable changes in form. The larva, the pupa, and the adult can be regarded as different forms in a polymorphic animal, which succeed one another during the life of a single individual. The appearance of these forms is controlled by the presence or absence of the juvenile hormone, in the same way as external factors control the form of different individuals in a polymorphic species—perhaps by influencing the activity of particular genes.

There are some insects in which the changes in form during the life cycle are even more numerous and more extreme. Take, for example, the meloid beetle *Sitaris,* the biology of which was vividly described by Fabre a century ago. The eggs are laid in the late summer near the nests of the solitary bee *Anthophora*. The newly hatched larvae are active hard-skinned creatures with a body form resembling *Campodea* (p. 315); they are called 'triungulins'. These hibernate until the spring, and then a few of them succeed in attaching themselves to the hairy body of the male bees, which are on the wing well before the females. In due course they transfer themselves to the female and so get carried to the nests in the ground, each of which contains a supply of honey and a single egg. While the bee is laying her egg on the honey, a triungulin slips off her body, alights on the egg, and is sealed up in the cell. It first devours the contents of the egg and changes to a fleshy grub that feeds upon the store of honey. It then changes to a form resembling a pupa, and usually spends the winter in this state. But in the spring it moults once more, reverting to the fleshy grub-like form, which soon changes to a true pupa and gives rise to the adult beetle. This remarkable succession of changes is called 'hypermetamorphosis'. It will be interesting to discover just what part the juvenile hormone plays in bringing it about.

Arrested Growth

If an insect larva has no food it obviously will not grow. Many larvae when starved simply use up their reserves and die. But there are others in which the moulting cycle continues without any increase in size; indeed the insect may grow gradually smaller. Perhaps the most remarkable example that has been recorded was that of larvae of the beetle *Trogoderma*, which at the outset measured 8 mm in length. They were kept without food, but regular moulting took place until, at the end of five years, they had been reduced to the size of larvae newly hatched from the egg, about 1 mm in length and about 1/600 of their original weight. Or the food available may be adequate for maintaining life but not for growth. The larva of the North American wood-boring beetle *Eburia quadrigeminata* has remained alive in dry wood for at least forty years.

An alternative method for achieving long survival without food is for the insect to enter a state of dormancy, in which all growth changes cease and metabolism falls to a very low ebb, only just sufficient to keep the body alive, so that any reserves of food that are available may last for an extremely long time. This dormant state, or 'diapause', may supervene at any stage in the life history of an insect: in the egg, in the young or in the full-grown larva, in the pupa, and even in the adult—where the arrest of growth means the cessation of reproduction (p. 131). It is not uncommon for diapause to persist for more than one season, and for a pupa to lie over two or three years before it completes its development and emerges. The small eggar moth *Eriogaster lanestris* is a familiar example of this. But the record is probably held by *Sitodiplosis mosellana,* one of the wheat blossom gall midges (Cecidomyidae), which passes the winter as a full-grown larva in a cocoon in the soil. In this midge dormancy has persisted for as long as eighteen years, and yet in the end the larva has been able to pupate and emerge.

Diapause is a means for surviving adverse seasons. It is particularly frequent in temperate latitudes where the cold winter is unsuitable for insect growth. But it may also occur in parts of the tropics where there is a dry season that must be survived. Several questions present themselves. What is the nature of the change that comes over the insect so that all growth ceases? How does it know when to make this change? And how is diapause brought to an end and growth resumed?

If the larva of the bug *Rhodnius* is decapitated soon after a large meal of blood, it is deprived of its brain which is the source of the hormone that sets growth and moulting under way. Such a larva enters a state of arrested growth and may survive for more than a year. Most examples of natural diapause that have been studied seem to be of the same nature: arrested growth occurs because the necessary hormones are not being secreted.

The life of many insects in northern latitudes is so arranged that they get through one cycle during the year and then invariably enter diapause (as egg, larva, or pupa) and pass the winter in this state. But there are others, such as the common white butterflies (*Pieris*) which have two or, in a warm summer, three generations in the year. It is only in the autumn that the pupae fail to develop and remain dormant until the spring. This decision may be taken in September; how do they know that the winter is coming?

Reflecting on this problem early in the last century Kirby and Spence wrote in their *Introduction to Entomology* (1815), 'To refer the hibernation of insects to the mere direct influence of cold, is to suppose one of the most important acts of their existence given up to the blind guidance of feelings which in the variable climates of Europe would be leading them into perpetual and fatal errors . . . It is not, we may rest assured, to such a deceptious guide that the Creator has entrusted the safety of so important a part of his creatures.'

Of course they were right. Some insects do respond to a fall in temperature by going into diapause; some are affected by the less nutritious foliage on the trees as autumn approaches; but it has been found in recent years that most detect the late season of the year by the length of day. So long as the day length exceeds about thirteen hours, development in the large cabbage white butterfly (*Pieris brassicae*) proceeds without interruption; but as soon as the hours of light to which the caterpillars are exposed fall below about twelve hours, the pupae enter diapause and do not develop until the following spring. By increasing the day length up to sixteen hours by artificial light, we have kept *P. brassicae* breeding without interruption for more than ten years. Of course, the light must be above a certain brightness if it is to be effective. The reaction of these insects is so arranged that they do not respond to the light of the full moon.

The length of day at a given season of the year varies in different latitudes, and there are corresponding variations in the control of diapause. It has been found in Russia, for example, that the moth *Acronycta* requires a day length of nearly twenty hours to keep it from entering diapause in Leningrad (60°N), eighteen hours at Vitebsk (55°N), seventeen hours at Byelgorod (51°N), and fourteen and a half hours at Sukhumi on the Black Sea coast. These are, in fact, local races of the species, each of which adopts a different day length as the signal for entering diapause. A few insects, notably certain dragonfly larvae, and the larva of the carpet beetle *Anthrenus,* respond to the *shortening* of the successive days in autumn rather than the actual day length.

These insects may all be described as 'long-day insects'; they require a long period of daylight to prevent diapause. A curious exception is the silkworm, which can be described as a 'short-day insect'. Here diapause and over-wintering occur in the egg, and it is the egg itself, of the preceding generation, which is the sensitive stage. If these eggs are laid in the spring (short-day period) there will be time for a second generation before winter comes; but if they are laid in the high summer (long-day period) there will be time for one generation only. Therefore, a long day (exceeding sixteen hours) is taken as the signal that the following generation of eggs (the eggs laid by the moth developing from an egg that was exposed to the long day) must go into diapause.

There is a great deal about this phenomenon that is not understood. The light seems not to be perceived by the eyes. It probably penetrates to the brain and acts there; and it seems likely that it acts upon some light-sensitive chemical causing the gradual accumulation of some product which is then progressively removed during the hours of darkness. The resulting products presumably influence the neurosecretory system in the brain which is the source of the growth-stimulating hormones. But the details of this story have yet to be worked out.

The next problem for the insect is bringing diapause to an end. In some insects, such as the larvae of the emperor dragonfly (*Anax imperator*), diapause is soon over, but development is not renewed because the winter temperature is too low for growth. As soon as it gets warm in the spring, growth starts again. Some few insects remain sensitive to day-length throughout diapause, and an increased period of daylight may serve as a signal to bring them out of diapause again. That applies to the larva of the moth *Dendrolimus*, which may go into diapause several times in the course of its development. But most overwintering insects require a more or less prolonged period of chilling before they will renew their growth. It was discovered in the middle of the last century that silkworm eggs would never hatch if they were kept warm in the winter; they must have a period of two to three months at a temperature around 5°C.

This effect of chilling in the 'breaking' of diapause is best understood if one imagines that there is some particular process that must be completed before growth can be renewed, and that this process works best over a low range of temperature. This is illustrated diagrammatically in figure 60. The curve A represents the speed of development at different temperatures. In the example shown the optimum temperature is 37°C; above and below this temperature development is delayed, and above 40°C and below 25°C no development occurs. The curve B, on the other hand, represents the speed of the diapause process (sometimes called 'diapause development') at different temperatures. In this example the optimum temperature is 7°C; below 0°C and above 20°C the process of 'diapause development' is never completed. Kept at either of these temperatures the insect remains permanently in diapause. In some cases the two curves A and B overlap slightly (broken lines) so that if the insect is

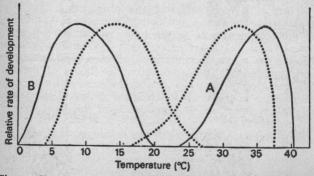

Figure 60.
Diagram to illustrate the effect of temperature on the ending of diapause as explained in the text.

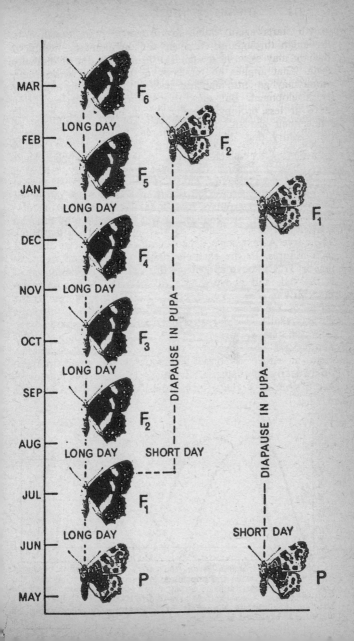

kept at some intermediate temperature, development eventually takes place, although greatly delayed. In other cases the overlap may be so great that careful experiments are necessary in order to show that there is any diapause at all.

When there is more than one brood of an insect, there are sometimes differences in structure and in pattern between the spring brood and the summer brood. One of the most famous examples is the nymphalid butterfly *Araschnia*, in which the pale spring form *A. levana* was originally believed to be a separate species, distinct from *A. prorsa*, a dark coloured insect which appears in the late summer. These are, in fact, seasonal forms of a single species: *levana* is produced from diapause pupae, resulting from the short days of the previous autumn, *prorsa* from non-diapause pupae. By exposing the caterpillars to a long day or to a short day, either form can be produced at will at any time of the year (figure 61).

Figure 61.
In the butterfly *Araschnia levana* the dark form (*prorsa*) is produced without diapause when the caterpillars are exposed to a long day; the pale form (*levana*) appears after a prolonged diapause when the caterpillars have been exposed to a short day (H. J. Müller).

Chapter 7

MATING AND REPRODUCTION

THE ACTIVITIES which lead up to reproduction are the most important in the life cycle of the insect. Indeed, it is possible to argue that the entire life of the insect is aimed at this one objective. As in all higher classes of animals, reproduction among insects is of the sexual variety. An egg cell or 'ovum' produced by the female combines with and is thus 'fertilized' by a 'spermatozoon' from the male. These cells, the ovum and spermatozoon, are the products of the sex glands, the 'ovary' in the female and the 'testis' in the male. In their final ripened state the ovum and the spermatozoon, as in other animals and plants, contain within the nucleus only half the normal complement of chromosomes. During fertilization the two nuclei unite to form a single nucleus which now has the full set of chromosomes, half having come from the mother and half from the father. It is this fertilized egg cell which, by repeated division and subsequent specialization among the daughter cells, grows into a new insect; an insect that combines within itself hereditary traits carried in equal numbers by the chromosomes from the two parents.

There is endless variety in the process of nourishment of the ripening egg in the body of the female, in the ways in which the sexes are caused to meet, in the physical means by which spermatozoon and ovum are brought together, and in the liberation of the fertilized egg to embark upon its free and independent life. It is these variants that form the subject of this chapter.

As to the anatomy of the reproductive system (figure 62) it will be sufficient to point out that the female glands or ovaries consist of a series of tubes ('ovarioles'); at the upper end of each ovariole the egg cells are set free; they move slowly down, one at a time, and during their passage they are provided with a store of yolk and, finally, a shell (p. 89). The ripe eggs escape at the lower end of the egg tubes into a single tube or 'common oviduct' which reaches the exterior as the 'vagina'. The male glands or testes also consist of tubes down which packets of male cells move, dividing as they go, to give rise to enormous numbers of slender motile spermatozoa, which are likewise discharged into the single tube that leads to the external male organ, or 'penis'.

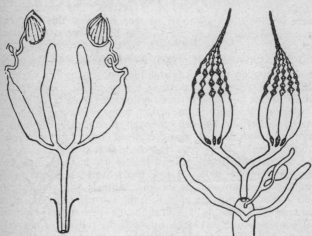

Figure 62.
Anatomy of the reproductive system—typical examples (Snodgrass). In the male (left) each 'testis' discharges the sperm into a thin coiled duct. The sperm are stored in an enlarged part of this duct. Before being discharged during copulation they receive the secretion from a pair of 'accessory glands'. In the female (right) each 'ovary' is made up of a bundle of 'ovarioles' which set free the eggs into a single tube on each side; these tubes join to form a single 'common oviduct' which leads to the 'vagina'. At the upper end of the vagina is the sperm sac which stores the sperm received during copulation; and at the lower end a pair of accessory glands which coat the egg with cement.

The aquatic ancestors of insects, like other aquatic animals, probably discharged their sexual cells into the surrounding water where fertilization took place; and one of the first changes that would be needed for life on land would be the discovery of some new way in which the spermatozoa could reach the egg without drying up. In the most primitive existing insects, Thysanura and Collembola, the males deposit at random tiny droplets or packets of sperm on little stalks (figure 63). When these packets come into contact with the sexual opening of the female, they break open and the spermatozoa enter the vagina. Such packets of sperm are termed 'spermatophores'; they are produced by the males of most insects, but instead of being scattered at random they are introduced into the sexual opening of the female, whence the spermatozoa pass directly into the female reproductive system.

Many of these spermatophores are highly elaborate structures. They are composed of protein and are secreted by glands connected with the male system. The secretion is poured out around the mass of sperm so that this becomes enclosed in a small bag with a long neck. One of the most remarkable of spermatophores is found in the crickets; this is a pear-shaped structure with an elaborate wall made up

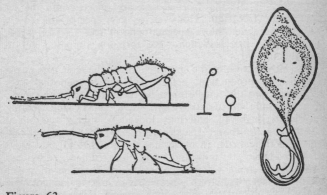

Figure 63.
To the left, above, a male springtail *Orchesella villosa* has just deposited a spermatophore; and below, the female collecting the sperm deposited by the male. The figure also shows for comparison the spermatophore of *Orchesella* and the squat spermatophore of the bristle-tail *Campodea* (Schaller). To the right, diagram of spermatophore of the cricket *Liogryllus campestris* showing the spermatozoa in its centre, surrounded by the 'pressure body' (shown in white) which forces out the sperm (Regen).

of several layers (figure 63). The innermost layer is called the 'pressure body', because as soon as the spermatophore has been inserted into the female opening and comes into contact with the fluids that the female system contains, the 'pressure body' begins to swell and fill the cavity of the spermatophore forcing out the spermatozoa.

Very often the spermatophore is only partially inserted into the female, and as soon as it is emptied it falls away or is taken out by the female and eaten. Indeed special precautions have sometimes to be taken to make sure that the female does not eat the spermatophore before its purpose has been served and the sperm discharged. In the tree cricket *Oecanthus* the male has a pair of glands in the thorax which pour out a secretion on which the female feeds greedily during mating. When that is finished, after about a quarter of an hour, she turns to the spermatophore and removes it; but by that time the spermatophore has already been emptied. The scorpion fly *Panorpa* supplies the female with droplets of secretion from the salivary glands, and some predaceous empid flies will provide the female with a captive fly on which she may feed. In butterflies and moths the spermatophores are deposited right inside the female, and are never got rid of; and in some insects, such as two-winged flies and fleas and many bugs, there is no spermatophore at all: the spermatozoa are injected into the female in the free state. However, as new species are closely studied, more and more spermatophores are, in fact, being discovered in insects which were formerly supposed not to have them.

The introduction of the sperm is one of the later acts in the process of reproduction; before that can happen the sexes must meet and the female must be ready to accept the male. In the mating of insects vision, smell, touch, and hearing may all be involved, and may indeed be highly specialized for this one purpose. Usually it is the male who actively seeks out the female. In butterflies the colour and movement of the female is important: in the fritillary butterflies *Argynnis* the male will pursue imitation butterflies of paper which has been coloured a brownish orange to simulate the female; and the attraction is much greater if the paper wings are made to flap. The grayling butterfly *Satyrus semele* is attracted to the female by the characters of her flight movements, which can be simulated by a piece of paper. But the female has a scent gland towards the hind-end of the abdomen, which can be everted to produce an additional attraction. Indeed most female Lepidoptera have such scent-forming patches, and females awaiting fecundation will take up a characteristic attitude, the so-named 'calling' position, with the scent-producing membranes exposed.

The male on his side may be specially modified for the recognition and location of these scents. That is most evident in the Saturniid, Bombycid, and Lasiocampid moths, in most of which the female is sluggish and sedentary, in some, such as the domestic silkworm *Bombyx mori*, incapable of flight, and in others, such as the vapourer moths *Orgyia*, almost completely wingless. These insects are dependent for mating upon the ability of the actively flying male to find the stationary female. In all of them the male has enormously developed 'plumose' antennae whose sole function seems to be the detection of the female scent (plate 6). This they will do from very great distances. When marked males of the Chinese Saturniid moth *Arctias selene* were released 11 km from caged females 26 per cent of them were able to find their way to the cage; from a distance of 4.1 km, 46 per cent arrived. In the Saturniid *Callosamia promethea* the male is not concerned with the colour pattern of the female, no matter how abnormal this is made by painting; he will pay no attention to females enclosed in a glass container or with the abdomen removed; but he is strongly attracted by the isolated abdomen or even to places where the female has been resting (figure 64). Males of the vapourer moth *Orgyia* will try to copulate with pieces of blotting paper on which droplets of secretion from the everted gland of the female have been imbibed.

The scent extracted from the tip of the abdomen of the gypsy moth *Lymantria* is regularly used for trapping the males of this insect in North America—not with the object of reducing the numbers of the pest, but in order to detect whether it has spread into a particular district. A great deal of effort has been put into the study of these sex attractants, notably in the silkworm moth. The active substance was extracted from the tail-end of the abdomen of 500,000 moths and finally obtained in a pure state. Chemically it is a simple alcohol with two double bonds in the chain, with the empirical formula $C_{16}H_{30}O$. In order to detect the presence of this substance during the chemical procedures for its isolation, a test was used which consisted in dissolving it in petroleum ether, dipping a glass rod in this solution and bringing it near the antenna of a male silkmoth. If the test was positive the male immediately began violently to vibrate his wings. The smallest amount of material which would give a positive test when dissolved in one cubic centimetre of petroleum ether was defined as a unit of attractive scent. When the pure substance was obtained, one such unit was contained in 10^{-10} microgram of the material; that is, one ten thousand million millionth part of a gram. In the drop of solution on the glass rod there must be comparatively few molecules of the active substance. One interesting feature about this reaction is that the male seems to respond only to this one scent, and if all kinds of other strong odours are present in addition, these do not disturb him in the least; he pays no attention to them.

Figure 64.
The giant silkmoth of North America, *Hyalophora cecropia*. The isolated abdomen of the female has developed and moulted and is laying eggs. The male, with bushy antennae is attracted to the isolated abdomen (Williams).

But it is not only the female which produces sexual scents. In many male Lepidoptera scents are liberated by special glands which have an aphrodisiac function, and excite the female to accept the courting male. These structures often consist of tufts of scales on the abdomen, legs, or wings, which can be suddenly exposed and spread out so as to disperse a scent produced by glands at their base. These scales often have elaborate and beautiful forms calculated to hold the scent and disperse it rapidly when required (figure 65). We may take as an example the grayling butterfly *Eumenis* (*Satyrus*) *semele*. As in all Satyrine butterflies, the male scent scales, or 'androconia', lie in an elongated patch that runs obliquely across the fore-wing and is commonly called the 'brand'. The scales themselves are elongated structures which end in a tiny tassel like the flower head of some grass. There is an elaborate courtship between the two sexes of the grayling butterfly and in the final stages of this the knobs of the antennae of the female come to lie be-

Figure 65.
Bottom left, fore-wing of the male speckled wood butterfly *Pararge aegeria* showing the dark 'brand' of scent scales. Below is a section through this region of the wing showing the detail of the feathered scent scales ('androconia') and two of the scales, in side view and front view, more highly enlarged (Wigglesworth). Top right, a courting pair of grayling butterflies *Satyrus semele;* the male (right) is batting the antennae of the female so that they come into contact with his scent scales (Tinbergen).

tween the wings of the male and are batted by the patches of scent scales (figure 65). This provides the final excitation to the female and copulation then begins.

The details of the use of male scent organs in the mating of most butterflies is largely unknown. In many the structural arrangements are far more elaborate than in the grayling. For example, in some Danaine butterflies the pencil of hairs that is used for dispersing the scent is withdrawn into the last segments of the abdomen, but the gland that produces the scent lies in a pocket in the middle of the hind-wing, into which the pencil of hairs is inserted in order to pick up the scent.

The part played by vision in mating is often no more than that of causing a male insect to turn aside towards some moving object of the size and colour appropriate to the female; and then, on nearer approach, if it is indeed a female of the same species, he confirms his diagnosis by scent and other means. But sometimes vision plays an over-riding part. The males of certain insects, such as Chironomid midges, caddis flies (Trichoptera), stone-flies (Plecoptera), and may-flies (Ephemeroptera) dance in compact swarms and the female is attracted to them by vision. Certain of the minute midges (Ceratopogonidae) do not suck the blood of mammals but feed upon small insects such as mosquitoes or Chironomid midges. The female will enter a swarm of Chironomids, seize one and probe it at some constant spot, and digesting all the tissues will suck it clean. During mating the female follows the same procedure. She enters a swarm of male midges of her own species, seizes a male, pierces his head with her mouth-parts, and while mating takes place sucks out the whole contents of his body.

The most remarkable examples of the use of vision in mating are to be found among the fire-flies and glow-worms. In the common glow-worm *Lampyris noctiluca*, for example, the female is wingless but emits her 'amorous fire' as a strong luminous glow from the abdomen. The male is winged and has large globular eyes well suited for locating the luminous female (figure 72); he himself gives out only a feeble glow. The North American fire-fly *Photinus pyralis* emits flashes of light in both sexes. If there is an answering flash about two seconds after his flash, the male will turn accurately in that direction and proceed towards the lure. But if there are answering flashes close to him, which occur at about the time when he would be expected to flash again, he responds by flashing synchronously with them. This appears to be the basis of the spectacular pulsating swarms of fire-flies in the East. These great gatherings are made up solely of males; the wingless females remain in the adjacent jungle. The phenomenon recalls the chirping in unison of certain crickets and grasshoppers. But what the meaning of the community singing of the cricket or the community flashing of the male fire-flies may be we do not yet know.

Sounds also may provide the basis for the meeting of the sexes. Male mosquitoes, for example the yellow fever mosquito *Aedes aegypti*, are attracted to the note given off by the vibrating wings of the female. The flying male will turn aside and attempt to mate with a tuning fork which produces a note of approximately the same pitch. In crickets it is

I. (a) Bed-bug *Cimex* with the tracheal tubes injected with black material. Note the rich tracheal supply to the sucking muscles, or 'pharynx', in the head; (b) wing pad of a young cockroach *Periplaneta* showing tracheal tubes injected; (c) electron-microscope picture of the ending of a tracheole of the blood-sucking bug *Rhodnius* magnified about 20,000 times.

a

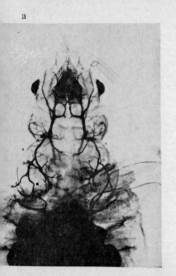

b

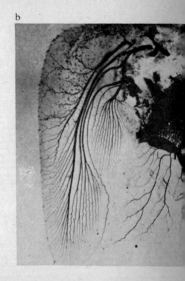

c

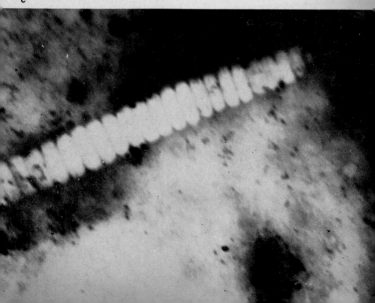

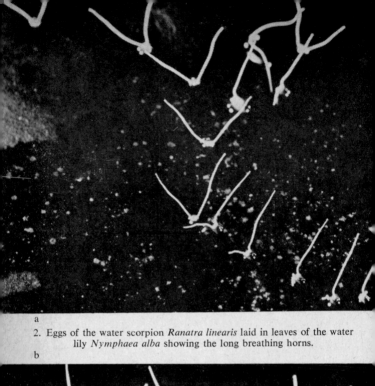

a

2. Eggs of the water scorpion *Ranatra linearis* laid in leaves of the water
   lily *Nymphaea alba* showing the long breathing horns.

b

a

b

c

3. (a) 5th-stage larva of the blood-sucking bug *Rhodnius prolixus;* (b) adult *Rhodnius;* (c) giant, or 6th-stage, larva produced by implanting the corpus allatum of a 4th-stage larva into the abdomen of the 5th stage.

4. (a) Cocoons of the silk-worm: from larva in which the corpora allata were re-moved in the 3rd stage; from larva similarly treated in the 4th stage; and from normal larva pupating after the 5th stage; (b) silkmoths derived from the cocoons shown in (a).

a

b

(c) Front view of a normal mature silkworm larva (5th stage); (d) front view of a 6th-stage silkworm larva produced by hormone experiments. It has developed pupal antennae (prothetely).

c   d

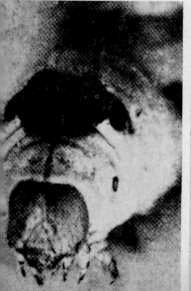
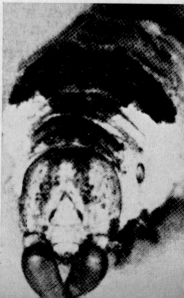

a

5. (a) Adult *Rhodnius* with a larval wing on the right side following the local application of juvenile hormone in the 5th-stage larva.

b

(b) Upper surface of the abdomen of an adult *Rhodnius* with one larval segment.

c

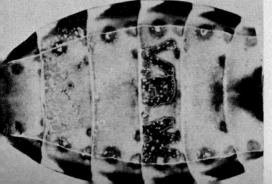

(c) The same with initials marked out in larval cuticle on one segment.

a

b

6. (*above*) (a) Male silkmoth *Hyalophora calleta;* (b) male *Antheraea pernyi* showing the 'plumose' antennae.

a

b

7. (a) Larva of the New Zealand glow-worm *Bolitophila luminosa* showing the hanging 'fishing lines' with sticky beads; (b) adult *Bolitophila* with the tip of the abdomen glowing; (c) threads from the roof of a cave, illuminated by the glow-worm.

c

8. (a) The toad *Hyla versicolor* just after spitting out a bombardier beetle *Brachinus*; (b) *Brachinus ballistarius* discharging at an attacking ant.

9. Soldiers of *Nasutitermes* ejecting threads of sticky secretion at a fruit-fly *Drosophila* which has entered their nest.

a

b

b¹

c

c¹

10. Mimicry in *Papilio dardanus*; (a) is the typical black and yellow form; (b) is the form *planemoides* which mimics the distasteful butterfly *Amauris albimaculata* (b¹); (c) is the form *cenea* which mimics the distasteful model *Bematistes poggei* (c¹).

a

b

11. Caterpillar of the peppered moth *Biston betularius* on a birch twig. The lower picture shows the fringe of finger-like protuberances where the body is in contact with the twig, which serves to eliminate the shadow.

a

b

12. Above, the caterpillar of the eyed hawk-moth *Smerinthus ocellatus* in the normal position of rest: countershading eliminates the shadows on the insect. Below, the same inverted: the shadows are conspicuous.

the male which sings and the female that is attracted to his song. The chirping of crickets and katydids is produced by rubbing together two modified areas of the fore-wings; males without these organs no longer attract the female, whereas the female *Gryllus* will come to a chirping male from a distance of more than 30 feet, and if the sound is transmitted through a telephone she will still respond (p. 219).

The males of the long-horned grasshopper *Ephippiger* likewise attract females by their mating 'stridulation'; but they also use another method. When there is a female in the neighbourhood, they will show brief periods of vibration or violent trembling, lasting barely a second at a time, about twenty vibrations per second. These are transmitted by the plant on which they rest, and the female responds in a similar way.

The meeting of the sexes, courtship, and mating culminate in the supply to the female of the sperm necessary for fertilization. Some insects will mate repeatedly, but others mate only once, and the spermatozoa received are stored by the female in a special pouch for the duration of her life. The queen bee, on her nuptial flight, flies upwards followed by the drones which, attracted by the odour of the 'queen substance' (p. 256) that is carried down wind, may come to the mating place from some ten kilometres around and, according to popular belief, she finally mates high in the air with the strongest flier among her suitors. In fact it has recently been proved that she mates with an average of five or six drones on a single flight, and she may be driven out by the workers to mate again on several succeeding days. The sperm received at that one mating period keep her supplied throughout her several years of life. The spermatozoa are allowed to make their way, a few at a time, into the ripe egg just before it is laid. By now the shell is fully formed, but it is pierced by a few minute holes (the little gateways, or 'micropyles') and it is by means of them that the spermatozoa get into the egg. How they manage to find their way is almost unknown, but it is commonly arranged that as the egg passes down the vagina the micropyle comes to lie just opposite the opening of the sperm pouch.

The number of eggs produced by a single female varies enormously in different species. Under the most favourable conditions the female of the small fruit-fly *Drosophila* will lay up to three thousand eggs, the large cabbage white butterfly *Pieris brassicae* about six hundred; the garden chafer-beetle *Phyllopertha horticola* lays an average of fourteen eggs only. Mature queens of Termitidae, on the other hand, will lay several thousand eggs per day (at least over short periods) and since they may live for fifteen to fifty years, and the colonies at any one time may contain over a million individuals, all derived from a single royal pair, it is evident that the egg-laying capacity of these termite queens must amount to several millions at least.

It clearly needs a good supply of nutriment, both of protein and of energy-yielding materials such as fat and sugars, to build up a quota of eggs, each rich in yolk containing all that is necessary to furnish a complete insect larva. The total quantity of eggs laid by a queen bee, amounting to several hundred thousand, by a queen termite, or by a blowfly or *Drosophila,* will far exceed the weight of the mother. Obviously the female will be dependent on a rich and abundant supply of food to provide this great quantity of material. On the other hand, butterflies and moths either do not feed at all in the adult state or they take in only nectar and water. All the reserves of protein which they need must be stored during the larval stage and carried forward through the pupa for the adult. Many need sugar or water or both in order to produce their full quota of eggs; but there are others, such as the silkworm and most Lymantriid and Saturniid moths, which take neither food nor drink in the adult stage. The eggs are fully developed while the moth is still in the pupa. They are ready for laying in a large batch by the time the adult moth emerges. Likewise in the garden chafer-beetle noted above, the average of fourteen eggs represents the quantity of reserves accumulated by the larva. Later on the adult beetles feed on leaves, etc, but this food is not converted into eggs, but only into energy for moving around.

When the ripe and fertilized eggs are ready, the female is seized by a new mood. She becomes subject to a new plan or pattern of behaviour. Sometimes this may be no more than an urge to fly around in the dusk broadcasting the eggs into the damp herbage, as is done by the swift moths (Hepialidae) or some of the Tipulid, or crane-flies. Or the egg-laying female may become strongly drawn to some odour that is characteristic of the surroundings which their larvae will require; so that blowflies, which earlier were visiting flowers and feeding on nectar, are now allured by the smell of carrion; and the females of the Chalcid wasps parasitic on the larvae of blowflies, are likewise attracted to the smell of carrion where their hosts are likely to be found. Butterflies may be attracted to the foliage on which their caterpillars feed by the essential oils or other odorous substances by which they can be recognized. Females of the horse bot *Gastrophilus* will seek out horses and attach their eggs to the shafts of the hairs, where these can be licked by the intended host. The *Rhynchites* beetle of birch will cut the leaf and roll it into a tight funnel before laying its egg in the centre (figure 66); the bark beetles will prepare the beginnings of tunnels in the bark of trees before laying their eggs; the dung-rolling scarab beetles prepare a ball of dung, and the Sphegid wasps a live but paralysed insect for their larvae to feed upon (figure 111)—and so on in increasing complexity and endless variety. We see once more the convergence and concentration of the whole life of the insect upon this final act in the reproductive process. It is here that the most elaborate forms of insect behaviour are to be found.

Some insects pass the winter in the adult state, and then the whole process of reproduction is arrested; the insect enters a condition of adult diapause. The eggs are usually held at an early stage of development, and once again the arrest seems to be caused by the lack of a hormone—in this instance a lack of the juvenile hormone, which is again secreted by the 'corpus allatum' of the adult insect. Some butterflies, such as Vanessids, will emerge and mate in the autumn but the eggs do not ripen until the spring. The potato beetle *Leptinotarsa* in Europe likewise passes the winter as an adult in diapause, and various beetles such as *Dytiscus* and *Carabus* have a breeding season at some characteristic time of year, which may be renewed at about the same date for two or three years. In some cases at least, notably in *Leptinotarsa,* this cycle, like diapause in the larva, is controlled by the length of day (p. 116).

This reproductive process as we have considered it so far, which ends in the formation of an egg protected by a shell, and its deposition in some appropriate site, where it is left to develop and to hatch in due course, is the standard pattern in most insects. But there are all sorts of variants that have been adopted by certain insects. It is not uncommon for the eggs of the blowfly *Calliphora* or the house-fly *Musca* to be held back and to begin their development in the vagina. Among the parasitic Tachinid flies this often becomes the normal process. The vagina may be enlarged and coiled to form a sort of uterus and, as the eggs move down, development proceeds; at the lower end the eggs contain fully formed larvae which escape from the shell as the egg is being laid.

Among the grey flesh-flies, the Sarcophagidae, there are fewer eggs and they hatch inside the uterus. *Sarcophaga* is said to drop its larvae through the wire mesh of meat covers on to the meat below. The sheep bot *Oestrus ovis* also hatches within the uterus; the female will hover around the face of the sheep and inject these larvae into the nostrils, where they complete their growth in the cavities of the face. In other Diptera, of which perhaps the best known is a large black-fly that is commonly seen resting on palings and tree trunks in the late summer, and is named *Mesembrina meridiana*, only one large egg at a time passes into the uterus; this egg may be half a centimetre long; it hatches as it is being laid. And there is a strange fly called *Termitoxenia* which lives in

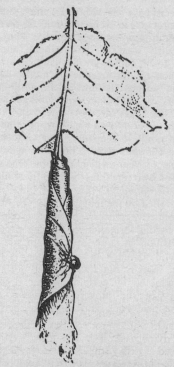

Figure 66.
The Rhynchites beetle of birch *Deporaus betulae* cutting and rolling a beech leaf to contain its egg.

the nests of termites, in which the egg is still larger; it hatches immediately after laying and the larva rounds itself up to form the 'puparium' (p. 107) a few minutes later.

In none of these flies does the embryo or the larva receive any nourishment from the mother during its stay in the uterus; it is dependent entirely on the yolk provided in the egg. But in the tsetse-fly *Glossina* and the parasitic flies of the group called Pupipara (the sheep ked and its allies), the larva which hatches in the uterus from an egg of normal size is nourished until it is fully grown by special 'milk' glands, which ramify throughout the abdomen, and open on a small nipple close to the mouth of the larva. These larvae are matured singly, moulting their cuticle at intervals as they grow, and breathing through a pair of black nobs (modified spiracles) which are pushed out through the opening of the vagina. They are fully grown when they are deposited, and almost at once they round up to form the puparium. A female tsetse-fly will live about six months, and during this time she will give birth to not more than twelve larvae. It is interesting to reflect that the tsetse-fly, which still makes large tracts of Africa uninhabitable for man, breeds and multiplies very much more slowly than the rabbit.

Viviparity, this process of giving birth to living larvae, turns up among many kinds of insects. It happens in quite a number of cockroaches in which the egg sac, or ootheca, is a soft structure that is retained inside the uterus until the eggs hatch. In one of the commonest small may-flies *Cloëon dipterum* the eggs have an exceedingly delicate shell; after mating, these eggs are not immediately deposited, but remain in the lower parts of the egg tubes for nearly two weeks, and then the female seeks the water and deposits the newly hatched larvae or nymphs. But the most familiar examples are found among the greenfly, or Aphids, and the scale insects, or Coccids. Here the coverings of the egg are exceedingly delicate, and the walls of the egg tubes serve as a sort of 'placenta' providing nutrient materials which diffuse into the egg. The embryos develop rapidly, and these insects may give birth to a dozen or so young in the course of twenty-four hours, so that the mother is quickly surrounded by a little flock of young Aphids (figure 67).

The Aphids which produce their offspring in this way are not only 'viviparous', they are also 'parthenogenetic'—their eggs proceed to develop without fertilization. These parthenogenetic generations succeed one another throughout the summer months; indeed, so rapid is the process of reproduction in greenfly that, while the embryos are de-

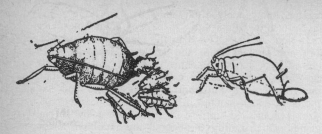

Figure 67.
Viviparous aphid female giving birth to living young (left) (Buckton); and egg-laying (oviparous) female (right) (Snodgrass).

veloping in the egg tubes of the mother, they already have embryos developing in them. The female greenfly can be properly spoken of not merely as an 'expectant mother' but as an 'expectant grandmother'.

The viviparous parthenogenetic type of reproduction in Aphids changes in the autumn to the normal sexual and egg-laying type (figure 68). The change is brought about by the shortening length of day. Aphids usually overwinter in the egg stage, and on hatching in the spring they resume the parthenogenetic type of reproduction, and no males appear again until the autumn.

Parthenogenesis, or virgin birth, occurs in many other insects besides Aphids. Unfertilized eggs of locusts and grasshoppers nearly all start developing, but very few hatch and fewer still grow up. However, if the successful individuals are kept and the process repeated, it is possible to select a strain of locusts which will reproduce regularly without the male. Cockroaches and many Lepidoptera will occasionally develop from unfertilized eggs, and in the common stick insect *Dixippus morosus,* parthenogenesis has become the normal mode of reproduction. Males are extremely rare and when they appear are usually not capable of normal mating.

Perhaps the most remarkable example of parthenogenesis is the most familiar, that of the honey-bee. We saw that the queen bee obtains her entire store of sperm during a single period of mating. She has a muscular pump attached to the sperm pouch so that she can control at will the escape of spermatozoa. In this way she can control the fertilization of the eggs. The unfertilized egg contains only half the normal complement of chromosomes; but in most parthenogenetic

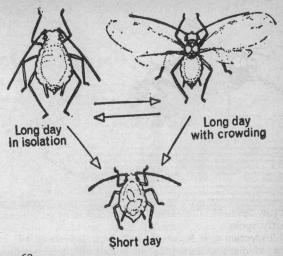

Figure 68.
Polymorphism in Aphids. Above, parthenogenetic females producing live young during the summer; to the left, wingless form appearing in isolated individuals; to the right, winged form developing in crowded colonies. Below, egg-laying (bisexual) females appearing during the short days of autumn.

insects normal development takes place only if the normal (diploid) or paired set of chromosomes is restored in one way or another as development proceeds. The bee, with other Hymenoptera is one exception. The unfertilized egg develops normally with the single (or haploid) set of chromosomes; such eggs give rise to males or drones; the fertilized eggs give rise to females, which are bred up into workers or queens according to the current needs of the community (p. 258).

There are two other methods of dispensing with a separate male which are met with in a few insects. One is to replace the female by a hermaphrodite, which combines within it the sex glands of both sexes. This happens very rarely in insects, but there is one well known example in the cottony cushion scale, or fluted scale *Icerya purchasi*, the Californian race of which is both hermaphrodite and self-fertilizing; males are extremely rare and true females are unknown. In these hermaphrodites the anatomy is quite constant and is so arranged that the spermatozoa can actually fertilize the öocytes (the developing eggs) of the same insect.

Figure 69.
'Gynandromorph' of the gypsy moth *Lymantria dispar*, right half female, left half male with bushy antenna (Berlese).

This condition is quite distinct from the so-called 'intersexes' and 'gynandromorphs' in which there is patchy and inconstant distribution of male and female characters in different parts of the body. In these types even the sex glands may be partly male and partly female, but they can function only as one or the other. It is not uncommon to come across insects with one side male and the other female, or with the front half of the body male and the back half female (figure 69). This can happen in many different ways, but always some accident in development occurs, so that certain of the cells receive the chromosomes that will lead to the development of the opposite sex from the rest of the body; and as development proceeds all their daughter cells retain these same sex characters. If this happens at the very first division of the nucleus in the egg, exactly one half of the resulting insect will be male and the other half female. These mosaics of male and female are called gynandromorphs.

Intersexes are somewhat similar but they arise in a different way. There is no loss of chromosomes during development but the balance between male producing processes and female producing processes gets upset for various reasons, and in various parts of the body the cells switch over from the male type of development to the female type, or *vice versa*, so that a very confused structure emerges in the end. Sometimes the result is a patchy distribution of male and female structures which resembles a gynandromorph. Sometimes the switch over may be so complete that an insect which, according to its chromosomes, should be a male, will develop into a normally functioning female. The classic example of this appeared in the gypsy moth *Lymantria* when a race of 'weak' males was crossed with a race of 'strong' females. But these abnormalities do not really concern insect reproduction.

The other way of multiplying without the male is the asexual method of 'budding'. This is well known in many primitive animals. In ourselves we have the example of identical twins. These arise from a single fertilized egg which divides as usual into two daughter cells, but then these cells become separated from one another and each proceeds to grow into a complete individual. Certain insects have developed this capacity to a remarkable degree. It is best known in various parasitic Hymenoptera which lay their eggs in the larvae of other insects. Sometimes the multiplication is quite modest; after dividing a few times the embryo may split to form two embryos or eight embryos; but in some Chalcids they may progressively break up to give a chain of a hundred or so embryos. It has even been claimed that in certain species more than a thousand individuals can arise from a single egg.

In 1861 the German entomologist N. Wagner wrote a paper in which he claimed that in the larva of the midge

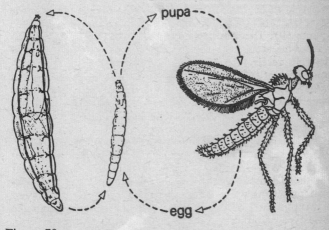

Figure 70.
The fungus gnat *Miastor metroloas* can show a developmental cycle of the usual sort: egg, larva, pupa, adult; or reproduction may occur by 'paedogenesis' in the larva, and pupae and adults may be absent for long periods (Pagenstecher).

Miastor, living under the decaying bark of fallen trees, the egg cells would start developing parthenogenetically, and that this often continued until the body of the larva was filled with a mass of daughter larvae, which then broke through the skin of their mother and left her to perish. He sent his paper to von Siebold, the editor of the *Zeitschrift für wissenschaftliche Zoologie,* and it was rejected because von Siebold could not believe this story. But before long the facts were confirmed by others, Wagner received a prize, and the strange phenomenon of paedogenesis, or reproduction in childhood, was added to the other curiosities of insect reproduction. It has since been observed in a number of different insects, including a beetle. *Miastor* and other midges which show paedogenesis still retain their normal method of sexual reproduction (figure 70). If they are kept under favourable conditions, with fresh moulds to feed upon, all the larvae are female and they continue to reproduce paedogenetically as larvae for many generations. But if they are overcrowded, or if the culture of moulds becomes old, both male and female larvae appear, and these grow up to pupae and winged adults of both sexes which mate and lay eggs in the normal way.

Chapter 8

LUMINOUS INSECTS

FLUORESCENT SUBSTANCES,
which give out light when they are exposed to the energy of
radiation by ultra-violet or visible rays, are extremely common in living cells; and free energy is constantly being produced by the oxidative reactions within the cell. Luminescence may well have been developed in the course of evolution by some slight change in the respiratory mechanism already existing within all living cells. As Robert Boyle showed
in 1667, the 'living light' is always extinguished if air is excluded. We have merely to suppose that some transformation
of the respiratory mechanism in the cell has been combined
with the development of substances with actively fluorescent
groups, excited to luminescence by the energy of cellular
oxidations.

It is among the insects that some of the most brilliant and
certainly the most complex types of light-producing organs
are to be found. Indeed all degrees of complexity exist within
the insects. Luminous caterpillars have often been observed,
but they all owe their light to bacteria with which they
chance to be infected. They are destined to die sooner or
later of a luminous disease. There are primitive Collembola
which emit a faint continuous glow throughout their lives.
Here the light seems to be a mere side-product of their
metabolism, without any obvious function.

The larvae of certain fungus gnats (Mycetophilidae) give out a steady glow during the hours of darkness. They build sticky branching webs after the manner of spiders. They hide in crevices during the day, but come out below their webs at night; and the purpose of the light seems to be to lure small insects to these traps. The New Zealand glow-worm (*Bolitophila luminosa*) belongs to this group (plate 7). The larvae form vast colonies in caves. The snare consists of a silken runway lying horizontally. From the sides of this are suspended vertical 'fishing lines', provided with a chain of sticky mucous beads, which are secreted one at a time as the silk line is held and lowered by the larva.

But it is among the beetles known as glow-worms and fire-flies that luminescence in its most striking forms is to be found. No other animals have luminous organs of such size, such brilliance, and such complexity. There is a vast scientific literature on the light of fire-flies, with contributions by the old naturalists Swammerdam and Spallanzani, by the chemists Davy and Faraday, and by such well-known figures as Darwin and Pasteur; but only in quite recent years have we come to understand the chemistry of the process of light production, and we still have much to learn about the physiology and the biological significance of the phenomenon.

Even within this group of beetles there are varying degrees of complexity. In size, the light-producing organs range from minute pin-head structures to masses occupying the greater part of the lower surface of the body. They vary in position from the head to the tip of the abdomen. There are often striking differences between the sexes, and the larvae and even the eggs of many of the fire-flies are luminous. The mature female may show a diffuse glow throughout the abdomen which is caused by the generation of light in the yolk of the unfertilized eggs.

The familiar glow-worm of Britain (*Lampyris*) emits a steady glow during the hours of darkness and extinguishes its light by day. The brilliant 'cucujo' beetle of the West Indies (*Pyrophorus*), the most brightly luminous animal known (figure 71), has two bright eye-like organs on the front of the thorax, giving out a greenish light, and a third organ, orange in colour, on the lower surface of the abdomen, which is visible only during flight. This is the insect which the early travellers in the New World described as being used by the West Indian natives in place of candles in their huts. Native girls, they said, used the insect for decoration in the hair, and tied them to their feet to light up forest paths at night. Like many of the fire-flies, *Pyrophorus* emits an inter-

mittent glow which lasts for seconds or minutes and then
fades. The Mediterranean fire-fly *Luciola,* and the North
American *Photinus,* give out their light in regular flashes,
one or two per second; sometimes for brief spells so that they
may appear in flight like a shooting star whose light turns
on and off, sometimes as a single flash. The most elaborate
flashing of this kind is seen in the fire-flies of Burma and
Siam. These may collect in thousands on the leaves of every
tree for a distance of several hundred yards, and then proceed
to flash in unison. Their synchronous pulsation may continue hour after hour, night after night for weeks or even
months on end. Weather conditions have no effect, save that
the flashing ceases on bright moonlit nights.

Figure 71.
Fire-fly *Pyrophorus* with two luminous organs on the thorax, and
with a luminous organ on the lower surface of the abdomen illumi-
nating the leaf on which it rests (Grandi).

Many different organs and tissues may be used for light
production. In the larva of the fungus gnat *Bolitophila* the
ends of the excretory organs, the Malpighian tubes, have
been converted into thick, rod-shaped, light-producing structures. In *Phengodes* it is the clumps of 'oenocytes', specially
modified epidermal cells, which are the source of light. In
the primitive Collembola it is the 'fat body' which gives

out the steady glow, and it is generally believed that even the most highly specialized luminous organs are made up of modified 'fat-body' cells. These masses of luminous cells, the 'photogenic cells', are covered by a transparent window in the cuticle of the insect, through which the light shines (figure 72). They are commonly backed by a different type of cell, stuffed with white granules of uric acid, which serve as a reflector.

It has often been suggested that the light of these organs is due to luminous bacteria which maintain a symbiotic existence within the cells. The photogenic cells are, in fact, filled with uniform granules which bear a superficial resemblance to micro-organisms. In the male of *Photinus*

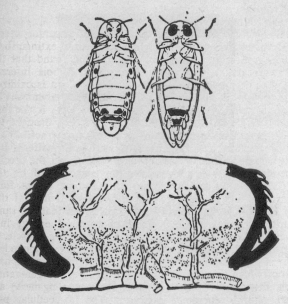

Figure 72.
The glow-worm *Lamprovhiza splendidula* seen from below, female (to the left) and male. The luminous areas are marked in black; note the small eyes of the female, the large globular eyes of the male. To the right is a somewhat diagrammatic section through one of the luminous organs. There is a translucent window in the cuticle above; below this are the light-producing cells, richly supplied with nerves (shown as black threads) and tracheae; below the luminous cells is a mass of cells filled with granules of uric acid which serve as a reflector (Bütschli).

the granules are round like cocci, in the female they are rod-shaped like bacilli. If the luminous organ is excised from the larva, the usual glowing of the pupa is eliminated—but perfectly normal photogenic organs develop nonetheless in the adult beetle. Unless, therefore, it is supposed that the bacteria go through a developmental stage in which they are not luminous, it must be concluded that micro-organisms are not responsible for the light production.

The light shows a superficial resemblance to the light of phosphorus, and Sir Humphry Davy attributed it to a sub-stance containing phosphorus, secreted by the insect and glowing by slow combustion in the air. But it was Dubois in 1886 who made the first real step towards an understanding of 'living light'. He removed the two luminous organs in the thorax of *Pyrophorus*. One he ground up and kept until the light had disappeared, presumably through the exhaustion of the photogenic material. The other he immersed for a few seconds in boiling water; its light also became extinguished. He then ground the two organs together and found that the light reappeared. From these experiments Dubois inferred that the cells contain a substance 'luciferin' which is oxidized by an enzyme 'luciferase' to produce light. The enzyme is destroyed by heat. The 'luciferin' on which it acts is not thus affected, so when the two treated organs were brought to-gether the two substances could once more interact.

Within recent years the chemical nature of luciferin has been elucidated and the substance synthesized, but the precise biochemical mechanism by which the energy used by the body is caused to appear in the form of light is not fully understood—and in any case that is not the province of this book. But it is perhaps of interest to point out that the same obscurity surrounds the conversion of chemical energy into mechanical work which happens in a contracting muscle. It is known that in a muscle the chemical energy is supplied in the form of adenosine triphosphate (ATP), the phosphate bonds of which serve as stores for energy. For the generation of this energy certain salts (of magnesium or manganese) are needed, and so ultimately is oxygen. The intracellular par-ticles called 'mitochondria' are chiefly responsible for produc-ing the energy and 'packaging' it in the form of ATP. In the luminous organs, oxygen is likewise necessary for light pro-duction; there are abundant mitochondria in the organs (at one time mistaken for bacteria); ATP and magnesium or manganese are also needed. In a muscle the chemical energy is fed into the contracting system; in the light organ it is fed into the luciferase–luciferin system, and appears not as mechanical work but as visible light with virtually no waste heat.

Light production in insects normally occurs only within the living cells. There has been much argument as to what factors limit the activity of the luminous organ of the living insect; as to how, in fact, the insects control the emission of their light. It is certainly controlled by the nervous system. The European fire-fly *Luciola* puts out its light at once if it is decapitated; but it lights up again if the severed nerve cord is electrically stimulated. It has long been known that the light goes out in the absence of oxygen, and much of the argument has centred round the question whether the nerves act directly upon the photogenic cells, causing them perhaps to bring luciferin and luciferase together, or whether they act upon some intermediary mechanism which controls the access of oxygen.

Insects, as we have seen, breathe by means of tracheal tubes, which open at spiracles along the sides of the body and convey air directly to the tissues. The larger branches of these tubes may be ventilated mechanically like the lungs of vertebrates; but the supply of oxygen to the ultimate ramifications is dependent upon diffusion, which is an exceedingly active process in a system of this magnitude. The luminous organs are very richly supplied with tracheae, and it is noteworthy that such insects as *Photinus pyralis* or *Photuris pennsylvanica*, which show the most striking types of controlled flashing, have the most elaborate tracheal supply. It is characteristic of these forms that the small branches of the tracheae end in conspicuous 'tracheal cells', where they break up into 'tracheal capillaries' or 'tracheoles' which run to the photogenic cells. When studied with the electron microscope the tracheal cells are found to have a most elaborate structure. But we still do not know just how the nerves regulate the supply of oxygen and the chemical interactions which lead to the production of light.

As judged by the eye, the light of fire-flies varies in tint in different species; sometimes even in different parts of the same insect. It may be greenish, bluish, or reddish. In *Pyrophorus* the two organs on the thorax give out a light with a greenish cast; that at the base of the abdomen below has a slightly orange tint. There is a rare glow-worm in South America called *Phryxothrix*, the larva of which is known as the 'railroad worm', for it has a red light on the head and a row of greenish yellow lights on either side of the body. *Photinus pyralis* gives out an orange light, that of *Photuris pennsylvanica* is yellow—differences which probably result from the scattering of the light by the proteins in the cell, much as the varying shades in the sky at sunset are due to slight differences in the scattering of sunlight.

When it is analysed spectroscopically the light is found to be entirely free from ultra-violet and from infra-red rays; it falls wholly within a very narrow band of the visible spectrum, usually in the yellow-green zone, which is that region of the spectrum that is most stimulating and shows the greatest apparent luminosity for the human eye. There are slight differences in different species; for example in *Photinus* the light extends over the wave-lengths 520 mμ to 650 mμ, in *Pyrophorus* from 486 to 720 mμ, in *Lampyris* from 518 to 656 mμ. If the luciferin of one species is mixed with the luciferase of another the light may differ somewhat in quality. For instance, *Photinus* luciferase with *Photinus* or *Photuris* luciferin gives a reddish light. *Photuris* luciferase mixed with *Photinus* or *Photuris* luciferin gives a yellowish light. Apart from the shortness of the spectrum the light is like other light. It can be polarized, or used for photography, or for chlorophyll synthesis in plants.

The intensity of the light may be so low in some insects that it can be seen only by the completely dark-adapted eye. Indeed, if we had more sensitive eyes, perhaps we should find more insects luminous. But *Pyrophorus* gives out so bright a light that it is possible to read small print with the aid of a single insect; and Dubois estimated that thirty-seven or thirty-eight of them would be equivalent to one candle. Old books of natural history often contain an illustration purporting to show the natives of the West Indies working in their huts by the light of captive fire-flies.

The flash of the fire-fly, *Photinus pyralis,* varies from 1/400 to 1/50 of a candle, the commoner values being the smaller ones. A continuous steady glow is sometimes obtained from this insect, of the order of 1/50000 candle. If the brightness of the light given out is expressed in millilamberts, the value in *Pyrophorus* is about 45, in the larva of *Photuris pennsylvanica* 14.4. Paper properly illuminated for reading has a brightness of about 4 millilamberts, the luminous paint on watch dials 0.01–0.02 millilamberts. If the light emitted by *Pyrophorus* is analysed with a photo-electric cell it nearly always shows rapid rhythmic changes in intensity at a rate of about five per second, the fluctuations amounting to about 5–6 per cent of the maximal intensity. The records resemble those of a contracting muscle in 'incomplete tetanus' and are thought to be due to rhythmic discharges from the nerve centres to the luminous organs.

It is possible to measure the total amount of spectral radiant energy (the 'radiant flux') emitted by a given source of light, and to compare this with the amount of radiant energy which is visible to the eye, the 'luminous flux'. The ratio of luminous flux to radiant flux gives the luminous efficiency of the light source. In the case of an open gas burner the efficiency is about 0.19 per cent; of a carbon filament lamp 0.45 per cent; of a gas-filled tungsten filament lamp 5.5 per cent. In the light of *Photinus pyralis* the corresponding value is 87 per cent, and in *Photuris pennsylvanica* 92 per cent (figure 73). The light of the fire-fly has indeed a very high luminous efficiency. It is the most efficient light known; but it has been produced at the inevitable expense of colour; it would be a most disagreeable light to use for artificial illumination; all objects would have an almost uniform green hue.

These values, of course, give no indication of the efficiency with which chemical energy is converted into visible light energy. When electricity is generated by the burning of coal, and the best incandescent lamp is used, this overall efficiency is about one per cent. It is not possible to obtain a comparable figure for the fire-fly, because it is consuming energy for so many other purposes at the same time. At

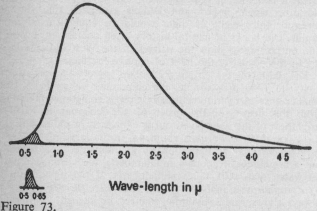

Wave-length in μ

Figure 73.
Luminous efficiency of a carbon filament lamp (upper curves) and of a fire-fly (lower curves). The shaded area of each curve represents the amount of visible light energy (the luminous flux). The total area represents the total radiant energy (the radiant flux). The ratio of luminous to radiant flux is the luminous efficiency: 0.5 per cent for the carbon filament lamp, 95 per cent for the fire-fly (Ives).

least it can be said that the heat set free in the reaction is exceedingly small. In the case of *Pyrophorus* it is judged to be less than 1/80000 of that produced by a candle flame of equivalent brightness.

The light of the fluorescent tubular lamp comes closest to that of the fire-fly. In this type of lamp, ultra-violet rays from a mercury vapour lamp are absorbed by a mixture of fluorescent chemicals incorporated in the wall of the tube, and the energy is emitted in the form of light with comparatively little heat. In the chemiluminescent reaction of the insect light-organ, the resultant energy is directed along very particular lines instead of being dissipated as heat. In recent years chemical light-producing systems have been discovered which rival the natural luciferin–luciferase in brilliance and efficiency.

As to the function of the light in the life of the insect, there can be little doubt that in the most primitive luminous forms the light is an adventitious side-product of the chemical activities within the cells and has no biological significance. In the luminous larvae of the fungus midges it probably serves as a lure to attract prey. In the glow-worms and fire-flies, as has already been described (p. 128) it is surely used as a mating signal.

Chapter 9

THE COLOURS OF INSECTS

INSECTS ARE famed for the variety and brilliance of their colours. In this chapter we shall consider how these effects are produced. We shall try to analyse what a painter would call the 'palette' of the insect—the range of basic colours that it has at its disposal and the ways in which it uses them to get the effects we admire. We shall find that many of the techniques familiar to the artist are employed by the insect, and we shall find that, although there are many pigments whose nature is unknown, the elaborate coloration of insects is mainly brought about by the ingenious use of a surprisingly limited 'palette'.

We shall not attempt to describe the structure of insect pigments in detail and will do no more than give a very general indication of their chemical nature. When we come to discuss the methods of defence among insects we shall find that these colours play an enormously important part in their lives. But most pigments do not appear to have any *physiological* function: they may be regarded as 'waste products which function in ornament'—waste products, the importance of which is biological and not physiological. A few pigments are known to play an important part in the working of the body; and it may be that others also have a physiological significance that has been overlooked.

The visible part of the insect is the integument. In its

primitive state this is soft and colourless; the store of fatty material inside can be seen through the skin, so that the termites, or 'white ants', and the vast majority of insect grubs are whitish in colour. But when the cuticle is tanned and hardened to form 'sclerotin' (p. 22) it becomes amber coloured; the depth of this colour increases to a deep brown as the hardening progresses, and the hardest parts of all, such as the tips of the mandibles and claws, may be almost black. This brown coloration is a property of hardened cuticle; many soft white grubs have sclerotized brown heads which carry the hardened mandibles; and in caves where most animals tend to become colourless, the cockroaches and crickets which abound among the excrement of bats retain their usual brown colour.

The substances used for the 'tanning' of the cuticle are derivatives of the amino acid tyrosine; other derivatives of tyrosine polymerize to form the black pigment 'melanin'. This is the pigment that is laid down in the black hair of mammals and the black feathers of birds. In insects it is laid down in the substance of the cuticle; and it is often difficult to decide, when looking at the stag beetle *Lucanus* (figure 163) for example, to what extent the dark colour is due to extreme sclerotization and to what extent it is supplemented by a true melanin. Dark colouring can be produced in both these ways.

Melanin seems always to be in the substance of the cuticle, but with very few exceptions all other pigments in insects are below the cuticle and are seen through it. They may be inside the gut; or it may be the 'fat body' or the blood that is coloured; or the pigments may be laid down as granules in the epidermal cells that lie immediately below the cuticle. In some insects, particularly the butterflies and moths, the wings and body are covered with scales—modified hairs arising from sockets in the cuticle that have become broad and flattened and overlap one another regularly like the tiles on a roof. Each scale is in origin a little flattened bladder of cuticle filled with the substance from the epidermal cell by which it has been formed. Here again the melanin of the black scales is laid down in the cuticle that forms the wall; the other pigments are always deposited inside.

Pigments are coloured because they absorb light of certain wave-lengths and reflect the rest; consequently, when viewed in white daylight, which contains the whole range of wave-lengths to which our eyes are sensitive, they appear coloured: our eyes perceive the colour complementary to that which has been absorbed. The production of colours by means of pigments is, therefore, a physical process which results in light of certain restricted wave-lengths being reflected to the eye. But there are other physical methods by which a more exact selection of wave-lengths can be brought about. Tobacco smoke appears blue when seen against a dark background, because it is the short waves of blue light which are scattered and reflected to the eye by the minute suspended particles. In the same way the intense blue of the clear sky (Tyndall blue) results from the scattering of short waves by fine particles of atmospheric dust viewed against the blackness of infinite space. A number of dragonflies and other insects have a bluish 'bloom', like the bloom on a black grape, which results from a fine waxy deposit over the outer surface of the black cuticle. This blue covering can readily be wiped off with the finger. But the enamelled blue of demoiselles and of the large Aeschnid dragonflies almost rivals the blue sky in its brilliance. It is produced in the same way as the blue of the kingfisher or of the wattles of the turkey, by the scattering of light from fine particles in the substance of the cuticle overlying a deep melanic background.

If the particles are larger, as in condensing steam or a summer cloud or the trail of ice crystals behind an aeroplane, all the wave-lengths of daylight are reflected and they appear white. The shining white of the wings of the satin moth (*Stilpnotia*) and the male of the ghost swift (*Hepialus humuli*), like the white hair of old people, owes its appearance to the bubbles of air contained within the translucent scales. And if the surface which reflects the light is sufficiently regular and smooth the wing may have a silvery sheen as on the underside of some fritillaries.

The most frequent way of securing the selective reflection of particular wave-lengths, with the production of metallic or iridescent colouring, is by the 'interference' of light waves when reflected from thin films, or from a number of thin films piled one upon another. The most familiar everyday example is the rainbow colouring given by a film of oil on the surface of water. Light falling on such a film is reflected partly from the surface of the oil and partly from the surface of the water beneath. As explained in any simple textbook of physics, given a film of a certain thickness, then light of a certain wave-length will be delayed as it passes through the oil, and is reflected at the water surface, in such a way that it will be exactly 'out of phase', that is, vibrating in exactly the opposite direction from the light reflected at the surface of the oil. Thus the two waves will cancel out, or 'interfere' with one another; no light of this wave-length will reach the eye, and the complementary colour is therefore seen.

That is how the brilliant blue green of the peacock's tail is produced; and precisely the same mechanism is met with in many insects. The wing cases of the cantharides beetle, or Spanish fly *Lytta vesicatoria* have a metallic blue-green sheen, produced in this way, which changes to yellow and copper red when the thin plates are caused to swell by exposure to ammonia. Chrysomelid beetles of the genus *Coptocycla* are normally a brassy yellow, but as the surface of the cuticle loses water and the plates shrink, the colour changes through green to blue and violet; it reverts to the original brassy yellow when water is taken up again. In the diamond beetles *Entimus,* etc, oblique lamellae fill the interior of the scales, but are differently inclined in sharply defined areas, giving corresponding patches of brilliant colour which changes as they are shifted in the line of vision.

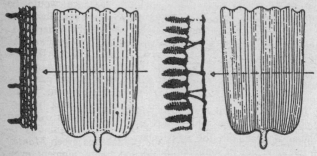

Figure 74.
Production of iridescent colours in butterfly scales through 'interference' by multiple thin plates. The detailed figures show sections across the scales as seen with the electron microscope; to the left, 'Urania' type with the plates in the substance of the scale; to the right, 'Morpho' type with the plates confined to the longitudinal ridges of the scale (Lippert and Gentil).

The formation of lamellae of just the right thickness to give these effects is probably a spontaneous process, a sort of crystallization within the structure of the cuticle. Indeed many butterfly scales, when treated in different ways, can be made to show iridescent colours which do not appear in nature. In those Lepidoptera which do show metallic colours, there are two quite different ways in which the thin films are arranged (figure 74). One is called the 'urania type' from the brilliant day-flying moths *Urania,* from Madagascar, in which the structure was first recognized. This type is found in the burnets (Zygaenidae), the swallowtails (Papilionidae), and the blues (Lycaenidae). Here the upper or the lower part of the scale is thickened and made up of a number of superimposed plates. The other type is called the 'morpho type' from the pure blue butterflies of the South American genus *Morpho,* one of the best-known insects used for butterfly jewellery. All butterfly scales have ridges that run lengthways along the scale. In *Morpho* these glass-like ridges are very high and narrow, and they are made up of innumerable oblique laminae, so that the interference colour is visible only when one looks down the long axis of the scale.

When the cuticle is not 'sclerotized', and contains no melanin in its substance, the colour of the insect depends on the pigments inside. Larvae that feed on the leaves of plants are commonly green. Much of this colour comes from the chewed foliage that fills the gut; but in addition to this the blood itself may be green and sometimes also the epidermal cells below the cuticle. The obvious inference would be that the green chlorophyll in the food has been absorbed, and while some is circulating in the blood, some is deposited within the cells. But it seems that seldom, if ever, are the green pigments of insects composed of chlorophyll. The camera can see the difference: if a green grasshopper is photographed resting on a leaf which appears to our eyes to have exactly the same hue as the insect, the tone of the grasshopper and the background in the resulting picture are quite different. The green blood of various Noctuid caterpillars or of locusts does not, in fact, contain chlorophyll. Stick insects (*Dixippus*), the predaceous green *Mantis,* and other insects develop their normal green pigment even when there is no chlorophyll in their food.

The green coloration of insects is produced in many different ways. The green pigment in the bile of mammals and birds, which is called 'biliverdin', is a breakdown product of haemoglobin, the red pigment of the blood. Haemoglobin consists chemically of a stable iron-containing pigment, 'haem', combined with colourless protein. Now the haem part of the blood pigment is present in every living cell as a component of the 'cytochromes' which play a most important part in cell respiration. It is, therefore, not surprising to find the breakdown product of haem, biliverdin, widely distributed among insects. The green Chironomid midges, which often appear in great swarms around lamps in the tropics and elsewhere, owe their colour to bile pigment in the fat body. If the scales are rubbed off the wings of a cabbage white butterfly the wing membrane shows the blue-green colour of a pigment closely related to biliverdin combined with protein to form a 'chromoprotein'.

But these bile pigments in the pure state have a blue-green tint; the green of insects, which resemble the vegetation among which they rest, is produced by a suitable admixture of yellow. The yellow component is most commonly a chromoprotein in which the coloured part may be a 'carotenoid', as in the stick insect *Dixippus,* or it may be a 'xanthophyll', as in the long-horned grasshopper *Tettigonia* or the privet hawk-moth caterpillar *Sphinx.* In yet other insects the yellow pigment may be the pterine 'xanthopterin'. In the blood these blue and yellow substances are mixed in solution like water-colour paint. But when the pigments are laid down in the epidermal cells, as in the stick insects, in grasshoppers, etc, the blue-green and the yellow lie scattered in the cells as separate granules.

This list by no means exhausts the possibilities which insects have discovered for producing green colours. Sometimes they will use other blue pigments of an unknown nature in place of biliverdin. The delicate greens of the emeralds and some other moths, which are so readily turned to a rusty brown by the acid fumes of cyanide, are of an unknown nature. We have already mentioned the structural green of the burnet moths; the green of the underside of the green hairstreak butterfly *Callophris rubi* is likewise an interference colour. The enamelled greens of dragonflies are really Tyndall blue (p. 151) seen through a thin covering that contains a yellow carotenoid. And the mottled olive-green markings on the underside of the wings of the orange-tip butterfly *Encloe cardamines* and its allies are produced after the manner of the impressionist painters by the juxtaposition of black (melanin) and yellow (xanthopterin) scales (plate 16).

In the foregoing paragraphs we have mentioned several pigments which call for further explanation. The 'carotenes', or carotenoids, are hydrocarbon pigments composed solely of carbon and hydrogen. They are widely spread in plants; the carrot and the tomato, etc, owe their colours to these substances, and the yellow-green of the spring foliage results from their presence in large amounts in leaves. They are readily absorbed by insects so that we find the same mixtures of carotenoids as are present in the tomato and the carrot, responsible for the colour of the ladybird *Coccinella* (plate 14), the potato beetle *Leptinotarsa,* the yellow and orange forms of locusts, and so forth. 'Xanthophylls' are oxidation products of carotenes; they also may be absorbed from plants, though not so readily as the carotenes.

These pigments may not only be taken up by the insect and retained in the blood, stored in the fat body, and deposited in the epidermal cells, they may also be passed on into their secretions. The golden colour of some silkworm cocoons is derived from carotene and xanthophyll taken up in the food and added to the silk (plate 14d). The predaceous bug *Perillus* is coloured by carotene pigments obtained from its victim, the larva of the potato beetle (figure 75). And the yellow cocoons of the Braconid parasite *Microgaster,* which are often seen covering the body of the cabbage white caterpillar, are pigmented with carotenoids from the blood of their host. When carotenoids are combined with different proteins, varying colours may be produced; perhaps the most striking example is the grasshopper *Oedipoda* in which different species have the hind-wing red, blue, or yellow according to the nature of the protein (plate 14d).

There are other examples of the pigments of insects being absorbed ready made from plants. The most abundant of the plant pigments, the anthocyanins responsible for the scarlet, purple, and blue colours of flowers, are rather rarely absorbed by insects; but they are assimilated by the caterpillars of the pug moths (*Eupethecia*) and cause these to resemble in colour the flowers in which they are feeding. The anthoxanthins or flavones, which vary in tint from ivory to deep yellow, are more often taken up by insects. The best-known examples are among the Satyrine butterflies (plate 14a). The ivory white colour of the marbled white butterfly *Melanargia* is a flavone taken up by the caterpillar from the cocksfoot grass on which it feeds; the buff colour of the small heath butterfly *Coenonympha pamphila* is likewise a flavone obtained from grasses.

But the most important and widespread of the insect pigments are manufactured by the insects themselves; these are the 'pterines', the 'ommochromes', and the much less common 'anthroquinone' pigments. The pterines were first recognized in Pierid butterflies. In fact almost all the white, yellow, orange, and red colours characteristic of the Pieridae are pterines (plate 14c). The white substance (leucopterine) in the scales of the common white butterflies closely resembles uric acid, with which it was long confused. The sulphur yellow of the brimstone butterfly, the deep orange of the clouded yellows, the red wing tips of *Teracolus,* etc are other examples. It is interesting to examine the underside of the wings of these butterflies and to see the varied and subtle shades and gradations, with the accurate representation of green or faded leaves, or leaves with fungal spots on them, all achieved by the use of varying shades of yellow interspersed with melanic scales where an impression of green is required. But the pterines are by no means confined to the Pieridae; they occur in some other butterflies, in the wasps, in various bugs, and in other insects.

The ommochromes are yellow, red, or brown pigments which were first recognized in the eyes of insects, where they are often associated with a red pterine. But they are found in very many parts of the body in many sorts of insects. They appear for instance in the wing scales of Nymphalid butterflies (plate 14b) such as the small tortoiseshell *Aglais* (*Vanessa*) *urticae*. And they are found in quantity in the 'meconium', the fluid excreted as the insect escapes from the pupal skin. This red pigment, splashed about on the leaves of plants when the butterflies are abundant, has given rise to reports of a rain of blood. The darkest brown ommochromes were long believed to be melanins but, as we have seen, the melanins seem always to be restricted to the substance of the cuticle, whereas the brown ommochromes form granules in the cells. In the eye they provide a dark screen to prevent the undue spreading of light in the retina; over the general surface of the body they give the brown colouring of many caterpillars, stick insects, and grasshoppers.

The anthroquinone colours are uncommon, but their interest lies in the fact that they are among the few animal pigments that have been used from ancient times for dyeing cloth. They do not normally colour the insects that produce them, but are extracted from the contents of the body. The best known of these colours is *cochineal,* or carmine, which is extracted from the dried bodies of the female scale insect *Dactylopius cacti* that feeds on various sorts of cactus in Central and South America. It is widely used as cosmetic rouge and for colouring foodstuffs. The crimson *kermes* which was used as a dye in Ancient Greece and Rome is extracted from another scale insect *Lecanium ilia* which feeds on the Mediterranean oaks. The third example is *lac dye* which is extracted, along with the resinous lac, from the oriental scale insects *Tachardia lacca* and others; it is similar to cochineal and in former times was much used in the East as a red dye for wool.

Most of these coloured substances are not known to play any part in the workings of the body of the living insect; they seem rather to be in the nature of waste products. But there is one conspicuous exception: the blood worm, the larva of *Chironomus* and related midges. The red pigment in these larvae, so common in water butts and stagnant pools, is indeed haemoglobin, closely similar in its properties to the haemoglobin in the blood of vertebrates. In vertebrates the blood pigment, of course, serves as a carrier of oxygen from the lungs or gills to the living organs and tissues. In the blood worms the general surface of the body serves as a gill; oxygen is taken up into the tracheal system and conveyed around the body by gaseous diffusion; the haemoglobin does not ordinarily come into use. But when the water contains very little oxygen, as in the mud of deep lakes, the red pigment does become important as an oxygen carrier.

Far more important is the use of pigments in forming the colour patterns of insects. The significance of these in the insect's life of struggle will form a large part of the subject matter of the next chapter. But we may here reflect for a moment on the techniques that are employed in the production of these colour patterns. Some of them are representational in the sense that they reproduce accurately the appearance of the background on which the insect rests. That is notably the case with the wing patterns or the larval and pupal skin patterns in butterflies and moths. The light and shade in these pictures is commonly achieved after the manner of the Italian primitives: the shadows are worked in monochrome by means of a varying density of dark scales and the colour is spread as a uniform 'wash' over high lights and shadows. But in some insects more sophisticated types of colour work are to be found. We have already noted the impressionist use of colour on the wings of Pierids, where green is produced by the admixture of black and yellow scales. A further striking example is the underside of the Indian leaf butterfly *Kallima inachis,* which resembles a purple brown leaf (plate 15c, d). It depicts a highly realistic representation of the mid-rib and the side veins, which stand out in convincing relief. But if the conspicuous mid-rib is examined with a lens, it is found that the appearance of relief is obtained not by monochrome painting, but by three parallel lines, one of whitish mauve, one of green, and one of orange, such as might be used by a skilful colourist.

The colours of some insects vary with the conditions under which they are living, or to which they have been exposed during their development. These changes may be brought about by the increased production of some particular pigment, or they may result from movements of pigment granules within the epidermal cells. Some are permanent, others are reversible. We shall consider again some of these colour changes when we come to discuss the part played by coloration in the concealment of insects from their enemies (p. 166); but we may look at some examples here and consider them from the standpoint of this chapter.

It is a very general observation that insects are commonly dark, and acquire an excess of melanin in the cuticle, if they develop in the pupa at a low temperature: in cold damp seasons or in cold localities butterflies tend to be darker in colour for this reason. Indeed this effect of low temperature in favouring melanin formation is seen not only in insects;

Figure 75.
The bug *Perillus bioculatus* (Pentatomidae) absorbs carotene from the Colorado beetle on which it preys. At high temperatures of 31–32°C (left) the carotene is oxidized and excreted and the insect is black and white. At medium temperatures some carotene is deposited below the cuticle and the pattern is black and yellow. At low temperatures of 21–24°C (right) much carotene is laid down in the epidermis, the insect is red, and more melanin is formed (Knight).

it is familiar in vertebrates also—as in the ears and nose and feet of the Himalayan rabbit. In the bug *Perillus*, which preys on the larvae of the potato beetle *Leptinotarsa*, there is not only an increase in black melanin pigment at low temperatures, but carotene obtained from the prey is deposited in larger amounts in the epidermal cells and the bug becomes deep red (figure 75).

When certain insects are crowded together they undergo some change which leads to an alteration both in colour and in habits. Various caterpillars such as the army worms of South Africa, *Lyphagma,* when they are present in small numbers, enter a so-called 'solitary phase' in which they are greenish or greyish. But when reared in dense crowds, not only are they more active and mobile, but far more melanin is laid down in the cuticle, and in this so-called 'gregarious phase' they become dark and velvety.

Locusts also show corresponding solitary and gregarious phases (p. 112), and here again, whereas the solitary insect is a bright green creature, the gregarious insect develops far more of the brown ommochrome pigment in the epidermal cells and far more melanin in the cuticle itself (plate 13a). If the young stages, called 'hoppers', are reared under densely crowded conditions, they become active and agitated and acquire the black and orange colouring of the gregarious phase; if they are kept singly and undisturbed, they revert to the green coloration of the solitary form; whereas if they are kept singly but are continually agitated artificially, they retain to a large extent their gregarious colouring. Evidently the change in colour is controlled in some way through the nervous system, presumably through the action of hormones (p. 112).

A very simple reversible colour change is seen in *Chrysopa,* the green lacewing-fly with golden eyes (figure 156). When it emerges in the late summer this insect has a beautiful translucent green tint. It often comes indoors in the late autumn and settles down for hibernation. As the weeks pass it becomes more and more drab in appearance; the green is obscured by a yellow or reddish coloration due to the accumulation of carotenoids. But when hibernation comes to an end the carotenoids disappear again and the lacewing-fly resumes its green colour.

The caterpillars of the hawk-moths (Sphingidae) and of the puss moth *Cerura vinula* are of a leaf-green colour while they are feeding on the foliage of trees. But when they are ready to form their cocoon and turn into the chrysalis, they deposit a large amount of a brown ommochrome pigment in the epidermis; they become chocolate brown in tint, and thus are far less conspicuous when they wander down the trunk and over the earth than they would be if they retained their green coloration.

In the stick insect *Dixippus* there is a series of colour forms ranging from green to brown which depend upon the quantities of brown (ommochrome), orange-red or yellow (carotenoid), and blue-green (biliverdin) granules in the epidermal cells. These forms are permanent and cannot be reversed. But, apart from the pure green individuals, each can undergo a striking and reversible change in colour (plate 13b). That is brought about by the movement of pigment granules within the epidermal cells. The green and yellow pigments are well scattered and do not seem to alter, but the brown pigment may migrate to the outer surface and spread out, making the insect appear dark; or it may migrate to the inner part of the cells and contract into small clumps, making the insect appear pale. The orange-red pigment like-wise may be dispersed or concentrated. It is in this way that stick insects become dark at night and pale by day. Similar movements of pigment granules cause Mantids to change colour at night in much the same fashion.

These cycles of colour change become established when the insect is exposed to a cycle of days and nights, but once established, the change may continue for several weeks even when the insect is kept in continuous darkness. And if it is kept in the dark during the daytime and exposed to artificial light at night, the cycle is reversed and the reversed rhythm also will persist in continuous darkness. For these changes to come about the light must enter the eye. In this way it presumably 'sets' a twenty-four-hour 'clock' of some kind in the brain (p. 247) and this nervous clock in turn causes, at the appropriate hour, the liberation of a hormone which provokes the movements of pigments in the epidermal cells.

Chapter 10

DEFENCE AND OFFENCE

THE MECHANISMS that have been evolved by insects for their own protection show a diversity and a complexity that is almost incredible. The provisions for this end may seem at times to be excessive; it is only when insects are closely studied in their natural state that it is possible to appreciate the intensity of their struggle for existence in the face of their numerous and resourceful enemies. Every advance in the skill of predatory birds, lizards, frogs, monkeys, and other mammals in finding insects, must be countered by some further refinement in the protective mechanisms of their prey. When Darwin visited the forests of Brazil at the age of twenty-two in the course of his voyage in the *Beagle*, he was greatly impressed by the butterflies, but was surprised that the moths appeared to be 'in much fewer number than in our own temperate region'. Modern means of collecting have revealed that these forests are, in fact, teeming with moths whose methods of concealment were so successful that they escaped the young Darwin's notice.

Vast numbers of insects, both larval and adult, live concealed in the soil, beneath stones and fallen logs, or burrowing within the stems of plants or the trunks of trees. We have no exact information about the toll which predatory enemies may levy on such species; but they certainly do not enjoy a complete immunity from attack. Such birds as wood-peckers have devised means of locating and extracting wood-boring insects; and the ichneumon *Rhyssa* (figure 76) is able to locate the larva of the giant wood-wasp *Sirex*, per-haps by sound or by a tactile sense of vibration, and to drill with the egg tube through an inch or so of timber in order to reach the larva and deposit her eggs inside it.

Insects living in more exposed situations may gain pro-tection from the form of their bodies and the nature of their integument. The body louse *Pediculus* and its allies have an exceedingly tough leathery skin which is extremely resistant

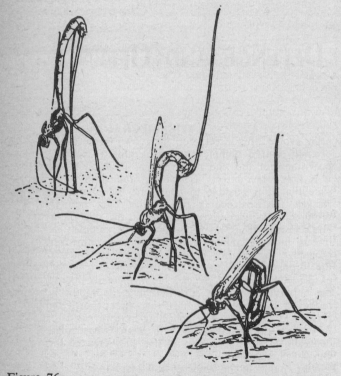

Figure 76.
The ichneumon *Rhyssa* inserting its 'ovipositor' deep into timber to lay its egg in the larva of the wood-wasp *Sirex*. The sheath of the ovipositor is used as a sense organ to locate the larva (top left) and is then lifted clear (in the middle and bottom right) (Pesson).

to crushing. The biting lice, the Mallophaga, are greatly flattened and able to insinuate themselves deeply among fur and feathers; while fleas achieve the same objective by being compressed from side to side and are again highly resistant to crushing. The heavily armoured elytra of beetles afford them much protection, but not immunity from attack—for many birds of prey, such as owls, and also bats, consume large numbers of the horniest of beetles.

With no other means of defence insects can save themselves by their exertions. The rapidity with which the housefly can take to flight constitutes in itself an invaluable method of self-preservation. We shall have more to say about this 'flight reaction' in connection with the nervous system (p. 230). Other insects react in the opposite fashion: when attacked or threatened with attack they 'freeze' and become motionless. They may drop from their resting places and become stiff and still as though dead. Beetles or caterpillars which act in this way commonly resemble a small twig, a coiled snail shell, or some other natural object. This hypnotic behaviour is often called 'death-feigning', or 'thanatosis'. If the attack continues the reaction of the insect may be abruptly changed: it 'comes to life' and makes for cover as fast as it can.

By far the most frequent method of concealment among insects living or resting in exposed situations is camouflage, or 'cryptic coloration'; but such coloration would be of little value were it not combined with appropriate behaviour. To take full advantage of its cryptic colouring the insect must rest on the proper background, it must adopt the right attitude, and it must sit still. The sort of objects that are mimicked are not so very diverse; grass stems, the bark of trees (plate 25), lichen of different colours (plate 26), leaves, green or shrivelled (plate 22a), pine needles, seeds, thorns, twigs (plate 17b), the droppings of birds (plate 21a), the dry stems of reeds—these are some of the most familiar. What is more striking is the way in which the same object is simulated by unrelated insects; so that we have a whole series of insect larvae, of Noctuid moths, of 'looper' or Geometrid caterpillars, saw-fly larvae and others, all of which resemble pine needles, with alternate stripes of pale and dark green and the proper way of resting in a straight line parallel to the pine needles themselves. Likewise there are widely unrelated moths (*Nonagria, Leucania,* and many more among the Noctuids, *Chilo,* etc, among the Pyralids, *Phragmatoecia* among the Cossids), all of which have acquired the exact appearance of dried reeds and the habit of settling with their wings closely folded to the stem. In glancing through a cabinet of moths from Northern Europe it is easy to pick out those species from widely different families, which come from the chalk downs and are in the habit of settling on the exposed chalk, or those which are on the wing in the late autumn, when the leaves are falling, and have a colouring in graded shades of yellow, orange, and brown.

A striking feature of cryptic coloration in insects is the attention to detail. Butterflies, caterpillars, leaf insects (Phasmida), grasshoppers (Tettigoniidae-Pseudophyllinae) (figure 77) which resemble leaves, not only reproduce the exact tint of the kind of leaf on which they commonly rest, together with the midrib and the side veins, but the leaf may have notches at the edge as though it had been nibbled by a caterpillar, or clear windows as though it had holes in it; or other blemishes and fungal spots may be rendered ac-

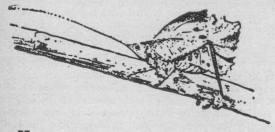

Figure 77.
Longhorned grasshopper of the group Pseudophyllinae, with leaf-like wings (Pesson).

curately in form and colour (plate 21a); or the copied leaf may be splashed with a bird dropping. And if it is a dead leaf that is simulated, the wings are often crumpled or rolled, with irregular frayed margins. Dead wood and twigs are often copied, and the broken end of a branch exactly mirrored, as by the buff-tip moth (*Phalera*) (plate 23). Stick insects (Phasmida) reproduce every detail of the knobs and thorns which characterize the plants they feed on.

There have been those in the past who have questioned whether it is possible that natural selection acting upon small chance variations could bring about such detailed copies. Could the small improvements which culminate in these ultimate refinements be of sufficient importance to lead to their preferential survival and selection? The answer is that it is quite unnecessary for any trait to give infallible or absolute protection (or anything like it) in order that natural selection may encourage its survival. If there is one occasion in a thousand when a small hereditary improvement in pattern leads to the survival of the individual which shows it, then that is enough to ensure the spread of that improvement in the population.

What first impresses the observer in the cryptic coloration of insects is the exactness of the representation of the background. Yet when a collector of moths strolls through a wood he will quickly spot the moths resting on the tree trunks. What he looks for is the triangular symmetry of the wings: if by chance a piece of bark exhibits this symmetry he will often be deceived and mistake it for a moth. This weakness in the camouflage is overcome by several means. Perhaps the most important of these is 'disruptive coloration', a principle widely used by living animals and extensively copied in military camouflage. Disruptive patterns have the effect of breaking the outline of the animal so that the parts of it fade separately into the background (figure 78). Sometimes it is used alone. In the tropics single black and white

Figure 78.
The scalloped oak moth *Crocallis elinguaria* showing how the dark bands on the fore-wings and hind-wings fit together when the wings are folded at rest (below) to form a 'coincident disruptive pattern' (Cott).

stripes may be employed, and in the bright vertical sunlight they are effective in disrupting the outline of the insect (plate 22b). But often the disruptive stripes or blotches are combined with cryptic coloration and serve to emphasize the apparent continuity of some element in the pattern of the insect with the pattern of the background (plate 17a). Of course, these disruptive patterns will be fully effective only if the insect places itself correctly. Many moths have conspicuous disruptive markings in the form of pale stripes which run lengthways along the wings. If the wings are widely spread, as in many Geometrids, this means that if the pattern is to blend with the vertical markings of the bark, the moth must always rest sideways on the trunk; and this such insects invariably do.

Another tell-tale feature of the resting insect may be the shadow around its margin. Moths at rest therefore apply themselves extremely closely to the surface, and where twig-like caterpillars, such as the larva of the brimstone moth (*Opisthograptis luteolata*) or the peppered moth (*Biston betularius*) hold to a branch by their fleshy prolegs, there is often a row of irregular protuberances which serve to bridge the gap where the body is attached to the branch and thus to eliminate the shadow (plate 11).

But the classic method for eliminating shadows is by 'countershading'. A hawk-moth caterpillar may be green, and provided with oblique stripes along the sides which resemble the veins of a leaf, and with a spine at the tail end which can look like the leaf stalk; but if there were no more to the colouring than this, the shadow below the body would at once betray the fact that it was a solid, cylindrical object and not a flat leaf. This is got over by 'countershading'; the upper part of the insect (in its natural position of rest) has a progressively deeper shade of green. This shading exactly compensates for the shadow on the lower parts, with the result that upper and lower parts show a uniform depth of colour and the caterpillar therefore appears flat and leaf-like. This can readily be demonstrated with almost any green caterpillar which rests in the open. Hawk-moth caterpillars, for example, have the lower surface more deeply coloured than the upper; they normally rest with the upper surface directed downwards and in this position they closely resemble a flat leaf (plate 12). But if they are inverted so that the light falls on the back, the illusion is destroyed and the deep shadow below makes them look rounded and conspicuous. Once again, these caterpillars must behave in the right way. All those insects, and they are very many, which have developed countershading, invariably rest with the darker surface (it is sometimes the back or dorsal surface, sometimes the belly or ventral surface) directed upward stowards the light. Plate 21b shows a Sphingid larva from Brazil which looks quite flat because of countershading. In addition it has two bright white splashes which, in the vertical tropical sun, simulate the light reflected from the shining leaves of its food plant.

Many insects rest upon somewhat different backgrounds in different parts of the country; and these differences are reflected in their coloration. Small moths such as *Malenydris didymata* which rest on brown tree trunks in Southern England are readily distinguished in the cabinet from specimens of the same moth captured in Scotland, where they rest on the grey rocks. A familiar example is the grayling butterfly (*Satyrus semele*) the underside of which has much more white in specimens from the chalk districts and much more brown in specimens from the moorlands (plate 16a). But perhaps the most striking example of all is the 'industrial melanism', the appearance of black moths that has taken place in the industrial areas of Europe during the past century.

'Industrial melanism' has appeared only in those Lepidoptera which spend the hours of daylight motionless on trunks, rocks, etc, and which depend for their survival on their cryptic coloration. Pollution of the air from heavy industry has led to the elimination of lichens and a general blackening of the resting places of these moths. Careful experiments by Kettlewell have proved that in the most polluted areas the melanic forms are better able to escape discovery by predaceous birds, while in the unpolluted areas where the trunks are coated with lichens it is the variegated forms which tend to survive (plate 29). In Great Britain where there are some 780 species of the larger Lepidoptera, 70–100 are substituting a dark or black coloration for the complicated and specialized patterns built up to perfection over thousands of years.

Most insects with cryptic patterns have a more or less standard form which occurs throughout the population, although as we have seen, there may be hereditary differences in different localities. But some can adapt themselves to the colour of their background. Locusts (*Locusta, Schistocerca,* etc) can adapt their colour from dirty white to yellow, brown, or black according to the background, the change being dependent upon the quantities of orange and yellow and black pigments formed (p. 159); and a similar change occurs in the aquatic bug *Sigara*. The amount of black pigment produced in these insects seems to depend on differences between the intensity of light entering the eyes from above and that reflected from the background below. Even adult locusts some months old can become darkened, or 'melanized', if they are kept for a few days on burnt ground. Bright green locust hoppers seem to appear only when they are kept amid green vegetation and fed with abundant moist food in a very humid atmosphere.

The pupa of the cabbage butterfly *Pieris* can become adapted to its background in a very striking manner (figure

79). The basic colour of the pupa is green, but this can be obscured to a varying extent by white pigment deposited in the epidermal cells, and black melanin pigment in the surface layers of the cuticle. The adaptation is made by the caterpillar before the chrysalis is formed; it is influenced by the background as perceived through its eyes, and if the eyes are destroyed with a cautery the chrysalis that is formed is always green. Similar changes occur in the pupae of Vanessid butterflies and the swallowtail butterflies. Of course, in the autumn the chrysalis may form on a green background which may later become brown as the vegetation dies. But that is provided for. We saw that in the autumn when the caterpillars of these butterflies are exposed to a short day the pupae go into diapause (p. 116). These diapause pupae tend always to be brown whatever the nature of the background.

The most remarkable example of this adaptive coloration is that seen in certain caterpillars such as the peppered moth (*Biston betularius*) and the lappet moth (*Gastropacha quer-*

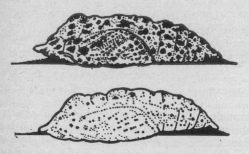

Figure 79.
Effect of background on coloration in the pupae of the large cabbage white butterfly *Pieris brassicae* (Dürken). Above, a whitish-grey pupa with much black pigmentation: black and red background. Below, pure green pupa with black pigment greatly reduced: green or orange background.

cifolia). The peppered moth caterpillar may feed on birch or oak, and the twigs among which it rests may have their natural covering or they may be coated with lichens. The background, therefore, varies greatly and the caterpillars vary accordingly. On birch they have a smooth, purplish-brown appearance with darker 'lenticels' and other markings exactly resembling a birch twig. On oak they again resemble their background, being a brownish green with suitable markings. When they feed on oak covered with lichen they have a totally different mottled appearance which reproduces exactly a lichen-covered twig. It is highly improbable that these caterpillars possess some mechanism which enables them to 'copy' the background on which they happen to rest. It is more likely that these colourforms have been evolved by natural selection; we have to do with a 'polymorphic' insect, and it is probably the perception of the general pattern of the surroundings which leads to the development of the appropriate genetic form (p. 112). The visual perception may be said to provide a 'switch mechanism' which brings into action the appropriate genes.

When a well camouflaged insect is discovered by a bird or other predator it may bring into play a second line of defence. It may suddenly spread the cryptic fore-wings and flash at the attacker the brilliant red or yellow of the concealed hind-wings. That is seen in the red underwing moth *Catocala* and many others. Brightly coloured hind-wings in an otherwise cryptic insect may have another function, which is well illustrated by the grasshoppers of the genus *Oedipoda* that are so common in the Swiss Alps. These are brown insects, so marked as to be well concealed when they settle on the stony soil. They have hind-wings of a red, blue, or yellow colour (p. 155) which render them highly conspicuous as they make their short flights (plate 14d). But the instant they land the wings are folded, the hind-wings are concealed, and the contrast is so great that the grasshopper appears to vanish.

The alarming effect of flash colouring is much greater when it takes the form of concentric rings which come to resemble a pair of eyes, such as are well seen in certain stick insects, praying mantids and in many moths. In the normal position of rest with the hind-wings concealed, the eyed hawk-moth (*Smerinthus occellatus*) resembles a cluster of dead leaves; when it suddenly displays the eye spots on the hind-wings it has a look and an expression that is well calculated to alarm (plate 18b). Careful experiments have shown that the acceptance or refusal of such moths by birds is decided by the perfection of the eye mark. This has probably been evolved by natural selection; separate genes are responsible for different elements in the eye spot, and these have doubtless become linked by natural selection to form a super-gene which operates as a unit. In the field, birds have been observed to carry off a cryptically coloured moth and lay it on the ground for a moment; whereupon the moth has been seen to flash the concealed eye spots of the hind-wings, the bird has recoiled, and the moth has flown away.

These concealed spots are sometimes called 'secondary eye marks' to distinguish them from the 'primary eye marks' that are permanently exposed. In some cases these also appear to constitute a threat mechanism. The Brazilian moth *Ophthalmophora claudiaria* has a pair of perfect staring eyes complete with pupil reflection which may well serve this purpose (plate 18a). But the common eye spots on the wings of the meadow browns and other Satyrine butterflies (figure 65), for example, seem to be 'deflection spots'; they are situated well away from the vital organs of the body and serve to invite attack on unimportant structures. In many of the 'blue' butterflies (Lycaenidae) there are eyes on the under-side of the hind-wings. Close to these are long tails attached to the wing, somewhat resembling antennae; they are kept in motion by the resting butterfly, and in combination with the eye spots they may well help in drawing the attack away from the true head.

Thus far we have been concerned only with passive modes of defence or with empty threats; but there are plenty of insects that are genuinely armed. In discussing methods of feeding we saw the development of powerful biting mandibles, the adaptation of the claws for seizing prey, the raptorial forelegs of Mantids or *Mantispa*, and many other insects, and the piercing mouth-parts of blood-sucking forms. All these

Figure 80.
'Nasute' soldier of *Eutermes* (Holmgren).

structures are used primarily for getting food, but they can all be employed to good purpose in defence against an assailant. In the soldiers of termites with their heavily armoured heads, the powerful mandibles seem to be designed primarily for defence purposes. The defensive caste of the 'nasute' termites use a different style (figure 80). The mandibles are much reduced; the head is large and tapers to a long 'nose' in front; and here are the openings of large glands that occupy much of the head. The product of these glands is not poisonous but it is ejected from a distance in the form of sticky threads which quickly entangle any small insects that may enter the nest (plate 9).

The spines on the legs of insects are used normally as an aid in walking, but they, too, may be brought into action for defence. There are hawk-moths that rely primarily on cryptic coloration, with flash colouring of the hind-wings held in reserve, which in the last resort can 'sting' by pricking their assailant with the enlarged sharp spines on the legs. In some insects such as the tiger moths (Arctiidae) these spines become contaminated at times with venom from the body, and then their effects can be severe.

Many insects are venomous. Venoms indeed are far more common among them than was suspected in the past. The facts are perhaps best interpreted along the same lines as the facts of insect colours; that is to say, we may suppose that poisonous substances have arisen by chance among the chemical products of metabolism. Certain insects have found these substances useful; their formation has, therefore, been increased and diverted for special purposes—until in the end we find insects specializing in the large-scale production of all kinds of strange poisons.

Some poisons are used primarily for killing or paralysing the prey. The larvae of certain fungus gnats (Mycetophilidae) that live below the bark of rotting logs, spin silken webs whose threads bear droplets of oxalic acid (0.15 per cent solution, with an acidity of pH 1.8) which quickly kill small insects that come into contact with them; whereas the larvae themselves are quite immune to oxalic acid.

Blood-sucking insects, mosquitoes, and the like, inject saliva into the wound as they feed (p. 75). The reactions which these bites provoke are so disagreeable that one would suppose that the salivary glands produce a poison. But it seems not to be so. It is merely that the saliva contains a 'foreign protein'. The human body becomes 'sensitized' to such proteins and the swelling and intense itching are the result of this sensitization. When one is bitten by some new and unfamiliar blood-sucking insect this may cause no reaction at all on the first occasion, whereas a second bite a week or so later may be a very different matter. I have had that experience with the bites of the sand-fly *Phlebotomus;* on the other hand it took several years, during which I occasionally allowed the bug *Rhodnius* to feed upon my arm, before I became sensitized to the bites of this insect.

We saw that the saliva of predaceous Reduviid bugs forms an important element in the mastering of their victim. It contains a nerve poison by which the prey is quickly paralysed, and digestive enzymes which quickly disperse the organs and tissues. But these bugs can use this potent saliva also for defence. Like all bugs the large assassin bug *Platymerus* has a powerful salivary pump (figure 35) by means of which it can spit out the saliva as a jet that will carry some 30 cm. This forms an effective protection against birds and reptiles; if it gets into the human eye it can cause blindness. This projectile can be accurately aimed; by rotating the head and depressing slightly the curved beak, or rostrum, it can, for example, spit 'over its shoulder' into the space above it. As many as fifteen successive jets can be fired.

The use of the poison apparatus for combined purposes of feeding and defence is equally well seen among the bees and wasps, where certain of the glands associated with the egg-laying apparatus have come to secrete venoms, and the ovipositor itself has become transformed into a sting. In solitary wasps belonging to the families Pompilidae, Sphegidae, etc, this venom is used for paralysing the prey which they provide for the nourishment of their larvae. Different families and different species specialize in different victims, usually spiders or caterpillars. After being stung they remain motionless for months, although the heart continues to beat. The venom seems to contain a nerve poison which brings about degeneration not only of the ganglion into which the sting is introduced, but of all other ganglia as well. The Braconid parasite *Habrobracon* also paralyses the caterpillar on which its own larva will develop. The caterpillar suffers a flaccid paralysis which persists unchanged until it dies; but meanwhile the muscles of the heart and gut continue to function. The wasp does not sting its host at any particular spot; the venom is carried by the circulating blood to its site of action. It is estimated that in the caterpillar of the wax moth *Galleria* one part of venom in two hundred million parts of host blood is sufficient to cause permanent paralysis—but other insects may be far more resistant. The poison seems to act at the point where the nerves join the muscles—very much like the arrow poison curare.

In social bees the sting and venom seems to play no very necessary part in normal life, but they are readily employed in the defence of the hive against invaders of all sizes. Indeed the sting and venom are now retained solely for defence purposes. An immense amount of research has been done on the venoms of these insects, but there is little agreement as to the nature of the venom and the way in which it acts. Many of the effects produced appear to be due to the poison histamine. This is not present in the venom itself but is set free from the cells of the victim (just as histamine is set free and causes many of the effects of 'shock' that follow a severe injury). Bee venom contains enzymes (phosphatases) which split off oleic acid from lecithin and thus give rise to 'lysolecithin'; it is this product which so damages the cells that histamine is liberated. But there are also present various proteins which in themselves are poisonous; notably a material called 'melittin' which likewise breaks down cell membranes. The violent and dangerous effects that occasionally follow bee sting in man are an example of 'anaphylaxis'—a generalized reaction to foreign proteins to which the body has become sensitized. The venom of wasps seems to contain a mixture of histamine, hydroxytryptamine, and other toxic substances as well as the enzyme 'hyaluronidase' which has the effect of loosening the cement which holds the cells of the body together, and thus assisting the venoms to diffuse.

The poisons of ants are equally complicated. Some families of ants possess stings which serve to inject poisons that have a painful or even dangerous effect on human beings. The minute fire ant *Solenopsis* of the Southern States of North America stings with a powerful poison whose chemistry is not yet fully understood. In the Argentine ant *Iridomyrmex,* which has been introduced and has become a pest in Southern Europe, the sting has degenerated but there are glands at the tip of the abdomen (anal glands) that produce the venom 'iridomyrmecin', the chemistry of which is now fully known; this poison kills insects with which it comes in contact and is used both for offence and defence.

Almost nothing is known about the poison of some of the most dangerous ants, such as the driver ants (Dorylinae). But it is familiar knowledge that some of the commonest ants use simply formic acid as a poison. Indeed, from Roman times until comparatively recently, ants have been used as a source of formic acid. The best-known example is the common wood ant of Europe *Formica rufa*. Here the sting is entirely absent and the venom is ejected as a spray. The concentration of formic acid that is stored in the receptacle of the venom glands is commonly 50 per cent and may be as much as 70 per cent; it is remarkable that such a universally poisonous substance can be stored at this strength, and in a quantity that may amount to 20 per cent of the whole body weight of the insect, without injury to the ant itself.

Along with these ant poisons there are often other odorous substances which probably serve to repel enemies, to warn other members of the colony, and sometimes perhaps to hold the community together. An interesting example that has recently come to light is the production of the terpene citral (closely related to the citronella obtained from plants and widely used as an insect repellent) which is secreted by the mandibular glands of the leaf-cutting ant *Atta sexdens*.

Perhaps the best way to give some idea of the diversity of the chemical defences of insects will be simply to catalogue a few of these, selected more or less at random. Certain conspicuously coloured grasshoppers (plate 19) discharge an offensive foam from the spiracles or from special glands (figure 81). The water-beetle *Dytiscus* and its allies produce a milky white secretion from glands at the sides of the thorax; this contains a very active nerve poison; a full-sized frog can be killed by injecting the secretion from a single beetle;

Figure 81.
The shorthorned grasshopper *Dictyophorus* gives out an offensive brown foam when alarmed (Grassé).

but under normal circumstances a predator is not permanently injured, it is merely repelled. This is an important point to which we shall return later, that 'repellents' are 'toxins' received in small doses. The arrow poison used by the bushmen of the Kalahari desert is a toxic saponin extracted from the beetle *Diamphidia locusta*, a minute quantity of which will cause paralysis in a small mammal. The cantharidin extracted from the body of the beetle *Lytta* known as 'Spanish fly' is an article of commerce used as a blistering fluid. The Staphylinid beetles of the widespread genus *Paederus* produce a different poison known as 'pederin' which also causes severe blistering if it contaminates the skin. If the small beetles of the family Paussidae, readily recognized by their large swollen antennae, are picked up, there is an explosive sound and they emit a brown cloud which stains the fingers and is said to contain iodine. If the larva of the beetle *Chrysomela populi* is disturbed, a row of glistening white globules of foam appear along the back; these have been discharged from special glands which prepare and store salicyl-aldehyde derived from the salicin of the poplars or willows on which it feeds. The musk beetle *Aromia moschata* similarly prepares an ester of salicylic acid which is discharged from glands opening on the hind-legs.

The caterpillars of Papilionid butterflies have a forked organ called the 'osmeterium' which is withdrawn into a pouch on the prothorax. This glandular organ accumulates essential oils obtained from the food plant and if disturbed, the osmeterium, commonly coloured a bright yellow or red, is suddenly everted and the odour dispersed. It seems likely that we have here a threatening act and a repellent odour as part of a defence mechanism. The same type of behaviour is seen in the caterpillar of the puss moth *Cerura vinula*. In its normal position of rest the puss-moth caterpillar is a fine example of cryptic coloration; it resembles a curled poplar leaf with a blackened margin, and the two prongs of the tail held together look like the leaf stalk. But when it is attacked it goes over from passive crypsis to active threat: the head is thrown up to display the crimson front of the prothorax with its two eye spots, the forked tail is spread and red whip-like threads are everted from its ends and flourished in the air; and finally, if the attack persists, a burning colourless fluid containing 40 per cent of formic acid is forcibly projected from the prothoracic gland.

A remarkable transformation of the same sort is seen in the larva of the Sphingid *Leucorhampha ornatus* as described by Miles Moss in Brazil (figure 82). At rest on a lichen-covered branch this caterpillar provides an exact representation of its background; but when disturbed it twists the fore-parts of its body and blows up the front segment, at the same time revealing the markings and assuming the threatening attitude of a snake, swaying gently from side to side.

Many caterpillars have found protection by developing a coat of long hairs which render them unacceptable to most predatory birds; and this effect may be enhanced by including 'urticating hairs' among their armour. In the processionary caterpillar of Southern Europe *Cnetocampa pytiocampa,* for example, these organs consist of a series of transverse oval buttons along the back, known as 'mirrors', which are normally concealed by lip-like folds. If the caterpillar is alarmed the 'lips' open and the mirror projects. Its surface is covered with delicate hollow hairs each containing a minute quantity of venom secreted by the gland at their base. On the lips of the mirror there are in addition a number of long branched hairs, and as the caterpillar moves, with the mirrors projecting, these larger hairs brush against the fragile urticating hairs and detach and break them up and so disperse these tiny poisoned barbs. The nature of their irritating poison, which causes intense itching, is not known; it seems to liberate histamine in the tissues but not to supply it.

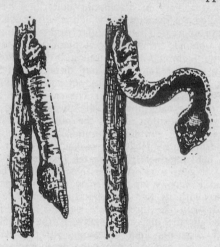

Figure 82.
The hawk-moth caterpillar *Leucorhampha ornatus* of Brazil, at rest on a twig (left) and alarmed (right) (Miles Moss).

Among the commonest components of the repellents of insects are quinones of various sorts. The repellent secreted by the flour beetles *Tribolium* is a mixture of quinones. In the cockroach *Diploptera* certain of the tracheae have become transformed into odoriferous glands producing another mixture of quinones. Some cockroaches, and the earwig *Forficula*, have stink glands at the sides of the abdomen from which they can eject the repellent secretion up to a distance of 5–10 cm. The bombardier beetle *Brauhinus*, when attacked by predators, always responds instantly by ejecting spray from the tip of the abdomen. This spray is not discharged at random, but by rotating the end of the abdomen is accurately aimed towards the limb or other part of the body that has been seized (plate 8). A single bombardier beetle may let off as many as twenty consecutive discharges, and the common predators such as ants, Carabids, Mantids, and spiders are nearly all repelled. The chemistry of the explosive reaction in *Brachinus crepitans* is interesting. The gland consists of a chamber into which is secreted a mixture of hydro-quinones which are oxidized by hydrogen peroxide in the presence of enzymes. An explosive reaction takes place and the oxygen suddenly liberated provides the pressure that expels the cloud of quinones and projects them at the enemy.

One of the most curious examples of the use of the chemical weapon for securing prey is that of the Javan bug *Ptilocerus*. This insect has a tuft of bright red hairs which mark the point where a gland opens beneath the abdomen. The coloured tuft provides an additional attraction for ants which come to feed on the secretion. But this secretion has a narcotic action; the ant collapses, and is then pierced through the neck by the proboscis of the bug and sucked dry.

It is a common though not universal feature of venomous insects that they are brightly and conspicuously coloured and make no pretence to cryptic coloration. It has long been supposed that the association of conspicuous coloration with dangerous or distasteful qualities, has been favoured by natural selection on the grounds that potential predators will thereby more quickly learn which are the insects to be avoided, and thus the numbers of the distasteful insects which are killed during the learning process will be reduced. A typical example that has been tested experimentally is the black and yellow banded caterpillar of the cinnabar moth *Hipocrita jacobaeae*. It seems to be the integument of this larva which renders it distasteful. It is certainly avoided by birds; and if mealworm larvae, which are very readily eaten by birds, are coloured to resemble the caterpillars of the cinnabar they too are avoided. This type of colouring is therefore called 'warning coloration' (plate 20a).

Birds in the wild state, offered a selection of insects, choose mainly those with dull and obscure patterns; those, in fact, which are cryptically coloured; and they tend to avoid those with brighter colours and bolder patterns of the type commonly interpreted as 'warning coloration'. Such experiments do not give any indication as to whether the birds are relying on past experience. But starlings, which normally accept mealworm larvae, quickly learn to reject larvae which have been dipped in quinine, if these bitter larvae are artificially coloured with green bands. And they will continue to reject most of such banded larvae even when 60 per cent of them are 'mimics', which have not in fact been treated with quinine.

The adult cinnabar moth also is conspicuously coloured, with bright red spots and stripes on a blue-grey background, and it, too, is highly distasteful; according to Miss Rothschild it is the one insect which birds never forget. That is due to the body fluid, or to a glandular secretion which exudes through openings in the thorax. These moths are certainly venomous. Their tissues contain high concentrations of histamine, as indeed do the bodies of some other 'warningly coloured' moths such as the burnets (Zygaenidae) and the white ermine *Lubriciperda menthastri*. The burnet moths discharge a yellow fluid, resembling their blood, from the neck or prothoracic region, and if a minute quantity of this is injected into the human arm it produces most alarming and dangerous symptoms. Among other poisons it contains prussic acid (hydrogen cyanide) to which, as every collector knows, these moths are highly resistant. The garden tiger moth (*Arctia caja*), surely a classic example of warning coloration, is also a rich source of poisons: a substance closely resembling acrylylcholine is present in the secretion of the prothoracic glands, and a highly dangerous poison of a different kind can be extracted from the tissues.

Even in the normal position of rest such insects as the tiger moths expose their warning coloration. But if they are threatened with attack, they take up a characteristic attitude which displays the colouring on the fore- and hind-wings, on the legs or thorax, and elsewhere, to the maximum degree, and at the same time the warning scent is given out by the discharging of the prothoracic glands (plate 24b). In the white ermine moth, secretion from the prothoracic glands may be combined with 'death feigning'.

We have already quoted examples of the fallibility of even the most elaborate means of protection. The same applies, naturally enough, to unpleasant tastes, repellent or toxic secretions, coupled with warning coloration. When a species becomes unduly abundant as the result of unpalatability, it is not uncommon to find that some particular predator has modified its feeding habits and come to specialize upon this one insect. The preferred diet of the European cuckoo consists of caterpillars with poisonous hairs which other birds will not touch. Locusts in their solitary phase are cryptically coloured; when they become transformed into the gregarious phase (p. 112) they are enormously more abundant and are conspicuously coloured, often in orange and black. It has been suggested that this represents a switch from cryptic to warning coloration; but if, indeed, the gregarious locusts are relatively distasteful their unpalatability is far from absolute, for some birds destroy great numbers of them. It may simply be that the gregarious phase is so plentiful that the species can afford a heavy mortality, and there has, therefore, been no selection for cryptic coloration or other protective mechanism. But it is well to emphasize that absolute security is never attained; according to the theory of natural selection it is because certain characteristics ensure an *increased chance of survival* that they become established in the population.

Supposedly distasteful qualities combined with 'warning coloration' are most frequent among insects which are active by day; they are much less common among nocturnal insects which remain at rest during the day and are cryptically coloured. It is not uncommon to find other insects which are active by day, and which give no evidence of being harmful or distasteful in any way, which closely resemble a distasteful species. Birds which have learned to avoid wasps, with their conspicuous black and yellow banding, will also avoid the larva of the cinnabar moth which can be said to mimic the appearance of the wasps. Clearly any small change in the appearance of a cryptic insect, towards the colours of a warningly coloured insect, would increase the risk of attack by predators, and the disadvantage of this would be greater than any advantage that would accrue from possible confusion with a warningly coloured species. On the other hand, such insects as butterflies which fly by day are so conspicuous in any case that a change in colour pattern in the direction of some distasteful species can only be an advantage. Under these circumstances there would be no need for a perfect imitation, or 'mimetic pattern', to be produced in a single step by one 'mutation'. This change could come about gradually, those intermediates which were most often mistaken for a distasteful 'model' being avoided by predators. This progressive imitation will extend not only to colour pattern but to shape, behaviour, odour perhaps, and other characters.

There are two points of special interest to note about such a process. A palatable insect which comes to resemble, or 'mimic', an unpalatable and warningly coloured insect will gain an advantage—but the model itself will not. Selection, therefore, will favour the development by the model of a pattern that will be very easily recognized and learned. By the same argument the mimic will begin to lose its protective advantage if it becomes too numerous, for predators will find that many insects of this appearance are, in fact, quite palatable. Palatable butterflies which mimic distasteful species are, therefore, as a rule far less common than their models. Or, alternatively, they may become 'polymorphic'; a particular mimetic form will increase in abundance only up to a certain point; beyond that point it loses its advantage, and thus a so-called 'balanced polymorphism' is established. The mimetic form makes up a more or less constant proportion of the whole species; and this percentage will vary in different geographical regions depending on the local abundance of the model. Meanwhile the same species may be evolving other forms which mimic quite different distasteful species.

All this may lead to results of extraordinary complexity. The African swallowtail butterfly *Papilio dardanus*, for example, has some half dozen forms of the female which mimic various distasteful Danaine butterflies in different parts of Africa. In each region there is a different balance, and a different assortment of these mimicking forms, which is made still more complicated by the fact that other species, too, may be producing mimics of the same distasteful models! In plate 10, *a* represents the normal black and yellow type of *Papilio dardanus; b* and *c* represent two of the many mimicking varieties that exist: *b'* and *c'* are supposedly distasteful species that are models for these two varieties. *b* is the *planemoides* form which makes up 20 per cent of the females in Uganda, where its model *Amauris albimaculata* (*b'*) is plentiful; it is unknown in South Africa, where this model does not extend. In South Africa 85 per cent of the female *dardanus* belong to the *cenea* form (*c*) which makes up only 7 per cent in Uganda. This form mimics *Bematistes poggei* (*c'*).

The whole relationship can be very plausibly interpreted by what is known about the effects of natural selection in influencing the distribution of mutant genes in a population, and the selection of further genes (modifiers) which modify the action of the primary genes. What experimental work has so far been done in cross-breeding the different forms supports this interpretation. As the geneticist would describe the situation: a polymorphism for several mimetic forms has been evolved, with single genes 'switching' one pattern to another —a situation comparable with that believed to exist in the cryptic coloration of caterpillars on different backgrounds

(p. 168); though here it is the appearance of the surroundings that is responsible for the 'switching'.

The other point of special interest is that in most butterflies mimicry is confined to the female. This is difficult to explain. As we have seen (p. 128) the males of butterflies are attracted to the female at first by the general colour pattern and then, at close quarters, by odour. And yet, in a 'polymorphic' species, the males will mate readily enough with all the very different forms of the female. It can be argued that the female is more selective in accepting a male with the right colour pattern—but that remains to be tested by experiment.

It was pointed out long ago by Gowland Hopkins, my former teacher, who is often referred to as the 'father of biochemistry', that the chemistry of the pigments used by the mimic may be quite different from those employed by the model, although the colour patterns are closely similar. That presents no difficulty in the interpretation of mimicry and its evolution along the lines that have just been sketched; but it rules out some other interpretations that have been put forward from time to time.

This type of mimicry, where a palatable, unprotected species comes to resemble an unpalatable, venomous, or otherwise protected insect, was first observed by H. W. Bates on the Amazon in 1862 and is often called 'Batesian mimicry'. But there is a second type, noted by Müller, also in Brazil, and usually called 'Müllerian mimicry', in which a group of more or less unrelated insects, all of them supposedly distasteful, come to mimic one another. The advantage of such a state of affairs is evident, for a predator may make several trials before he learns to recognize the butterfly patterns that are to be avoided. If a group of species band together, and all sail under the same flag, each species will benefit, since the number of attacks that are needed for the learning process will be shared between them.

It is becoming increasingly evident that odours may be as important as colour patterns in these processes of recognition. Some insect odours seem to us repulsive, such as those of the Pentatomid bugs, most of which are also warningly coloured; others, such as that of the garden tiger *Arctia caja* may be agreeable—but they all stick in the mind, and therefore (if the memory of them is as well retained by other predators) they are well calculated to recall a previous unpleasant experience and so to protect the insect from further attack.

All these odours seem to have three characteristic components: a very volatile element which helps rapid dispersal, an oily element which makes for long persistence, and an element which provides the long-lasting smell. Persons with a sensitive and analytical nose can detect that the odours are usually complex and made up of a variety of components, and certain of these components can be recognized as being the same in widely dissimilar insects. This conclusion has been confirmed by the analysis of the odours by gas chromatography, so that, for example, the same quinolene-like scent appears in the tiger moth and in the ladybirds. These observations suggest that the defensive odours of insects may fall into scent patterns which are shared by different insect species—just as the warning colour patterns of wasps are shared. In other words that there may be something in the nature of a Müllerian mimicry of odours among protected insects, which will make it all the easier for a predator to recognize a member of the group.

The protective measures used by insects are indeed exceedingly complex. Although it is convenient to speak of Batesian and Müllerian mimicry, the two phenomena merge into one another. For 'distastefulness' is only relative; no insect is completely inedible to all predators; and many insects which serve as 'mimics' of distasteful models are often themselves in some degree distasteful—so that it is possible to speak of them as 'Müllerian mimics'. Likewise many cryptic insects, particularly those with variable colour patterns, have disagreeable qualities in reserve; we have already seen how, under some circumstances, many of them can switch over from reliance on concealment to reliance on their distasteful or venomous properties.

Chapter 11

INSECT VISION

THE VERY existence and survival of insects depends on their behaviour: their ability to find safe retreats, to locate their food, to discover a mate, to capture their prey, or to escape their enemies. If they are to do these things they require on the one hand a set of sense organs by which to perceive all the happenings in their surroundings, and on the other a nervous system which will integrate these varied perceptions and translate them into appropriate action. 'Sense organs' and 'behaviour', therefore, cannot really be separated; the one depends upon the other; indeed it is possible to form some idea about the sensory perceptions of insects only by observing their behaviour or 'reaction' when the organs of sense are stimulated in a particular way. In this chapter we shall consider the ways in which insects can detect differences in light and shade, pattern and colour—in short, what we call vision. But it will be impossible to avoid some discussion of their behaviour, which will be treated in more general terms in a later chapter.

There are many chemical reactions brought about by light. The reactions made use of in photography are only one example among many. If light-sensitive chemicals of this kind were present in certain parts of the body, and if the substances produced by their illumination were to stimulate the nerves, we should have the simplest rudiments of an organ of vision. Indeed, many living things including insects have a primitive general sensitivity to light of this kind.

We have seen that caterpillars will take up such a position of rest that the darker surface of the body is directed towards the brightest light, and they can thus compensate by 'countershading' for the appearance of solidity or relief (p. 166). In such caterpillars it is the general surface of the body that is sensitive to light; the eyes are not concerned in this particular reaction. Similarly there are many insects such as cockroaches, or the mealworm *Tenebrio*, which will avoid the light even after they have been blinded or decapitated; and the blind cave-dwelling beetles of the genus *Anophthalmus* will still respond to illumination. In the aquatic larvae of the water-beetles *Acilius* and *Dytiscus* the skin is sensitive to light all over the body, but it is particularly sensitive in the region of the spiracles at the tip of the abdomen, the area which makes contact with the surface of the water when the larva comes up to breathe (figure 34).

We saw that certain Aphids would assume the parthenogenetic form, and proceed to reproduce indefinitely without the presence of a male, if they are exposed to a long day of fourteen hours, and then give rise to sexual forms if the length of day is diminished (p. 134). It is supposed that here again some photosensitive chemical is concerned, the accumulated products of which serve to advertise the fact that the insect has been exposed to a long day. But the light that is effective for this purpose does not enter through the eyes; it passes through the cuticle of the head and acts directly upon some centre in the brain. It may well be that the length of day which controls the appearance of diapause in many insects (p. 117) is perceived in the same way.

It is the concentration of photosensitive chemicals of this kind in certain groups of cells, and their connection with sensory nerves, which leads to the formation of eyes. In their simplest form, as seen in some insect larvae, such as those of mosquitoes and other midges, the eyes appear only as small 'pigment spots'. These are cells filled with granules of dark pigment which surround and shelter the photosensitive cells themselves, often not more than two or three in number. Eyes of this kind are commonly called 'lateral ocelli'. In the maggots of the house-fly and its relatives no eyes at all are visible at the surface; but deeply set in the head region is a group of innervated cells. Maggots are able to make straight for the dark by turning so that these cells are kept in the shade of the rest of the body.

In their more elaborate form, as in saw-fly larvae (Tenthredinidae) or the larvae of beetles, each lateral ocellus is covered by a clear lens-like thickening of the cuticle below which is a group of fifty or more light-sensitive or visual cells closely packed together. Eyes of this sort reach their most complex state in the larva of the tiger beetles (*Cicindela*) (figure 83). On each side of the head of these larvae there are six lateral ocelli two of which are quite large and contain more than six thousand visual cells. It is generally supposed that these eyes are incapable of perceiving anything like a clear image of outside objects. But tiger-beetle larvae live in vertical burrows in sandy soil, where they rest with the head level with the surface. They can perceive their prey from a distance of 3–6 cm provided it is moving; and they snap and seize the prey only when it comes within reach of the mandibles. Evidently the two groups of lateral ocelli work together as a unit and enable the larva to make an accurate judgement

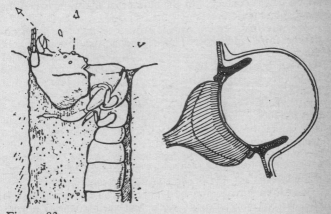

Figure 83.
The larva of the tiger beetle *Cicindela* seen in side view at the mouth of its burrow, showing the group of simple eyes (ocelli) on the head. The arrows indicate the line of vision of some of the ocelli. To the right is a section through a single ocellus showing the numerous retinal rods below the prominent lens (Friederichs).

of the distance of the prey—and also of its size, for if it exceeds three or four millimetres across, the tiger-beetle larva does not snap but hastily retreats into its burrow.

The large lateral ocelli of the tiger-beetle larvae are covered by a tolerably efficient lens; but this does not focus a clear image upon the sense cells; indeed the image which is formed falls too far back. It is difficult for us to judge how clearly these larvae can see; but it is probably safe to assume that they can gain much more information about what they see than we might suppose from our limited knowledge of their sense organs—just as a man who has been deprived of a large part of his sense organs (the eyes or the ears for example) can become extraordinarily adept at getting information about his surroundings by means of the organs that remain.

A remarkable example of this is provided by the vision of caterpillars. These have a group of five or six lateral ocelli on each side of the head (figure 84). Each ocellus contains only a single light-perceiving element or 'retinal rod' (p. 187); each is covered by a lens which will concentrate the light

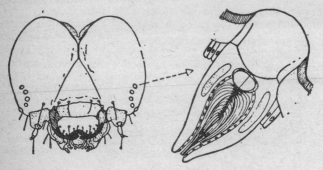

Figure 84.
The head of a caterpillar seen from in front showing the row of five simple eyes (ocelli) on each side; and the detailed structure of a single ocellus seen in section. Note that there is only a single retinal rod (shown as cross bars) below the lens (Demoll).

received from a particular area of the outside world. But a single light-sensitive element cannot possibly perceive a pattern. All that the caterpillar can perceive will be twelve points of light, six received on each side of the head. And yet a caterpillar can recognize vertical pillars, as it were tree trunks, and if offered the choice of two pillars of the same width but of different height it will choose the taller and crawl towards this. Moreover it is able to make this choice, which clearly requires some capacity for distinguishing different forms and patterns, even when eleven of the lateral ocelli have been covered with black paint and only one remains in operation. The explanation of the apparent paradox is that the caterpillar 'scans' the scene and builds up a composite picture of it, like a television camera: by moving its head in different directions it is able to estimate approximately the shape of a dark object, although at a given moment it can perceive only a single point of light.

The eyes of the primitive Collembola, as well as some other insect larvae, such as the ant-lion *Myrmeleon,* are of the same type as those of caterpillars. They consist of six or eight lateral ocelli each of which contains seven retinal cells grouped in a ring and co-operating to produce a central visual rod (retinal rod); above this is a tiny crystalline lens, and outside this again a large lens or cornea formed out of the cuticle. The system of lenses concentrates the light upon the visual rod. The visual rod probably contains the light-sensitive chemical of the eye; this chemical is altered by exposure to the light, and the resulting products stimulate the retinal cells, which are connected by nerves to the brain.

This type of visual element, or ocellus, may be regarded as the model on which all the more elaborate eyes of insects are based (figure 85). These are termed 'compound eyes' and consist of a large number of visual elements built on the same plan as the ocellus of a caterpillar, but small and elongated and packed closely together. The individual element of the compound eye is called an 'ommatidium'; in the compound eye of the house-fly there are something like 4,000 hexagonal facets, like a diminutive honey-comb, which are the corneal lenses of the ommatidia; in the great globular eyes of large dragonflies there may be as many as 28,000 ommatidia in a single eye.

As in the lateral ocelli of caterpillars, each ommatidium admits a point of light, received from a certain area of the outside world, which is concentrated by the lens upon the retinal rod. There are so many of these points of light that, taken all together, they will make up a mosaic which will represent a tolerably good image of the objects viewed. Of course the tiny lens of each facet, placed in the right position, will itself produce an inverted image of the whole object in front of it. One often sees in books photographs taken by means of these little lenses, showing a myriad representations of the same object. But such pictures bear no relation to what the insect sees: in the living insect each facet collects the light from a little patch of the outside world, and what the single retinal rod perceives is the average intensity of light from that little patch. These points of light falling on the convex retina, that is, on the ends of the retinal rods, will build up an erect image of the whole field of view.

This is the so-called 'mosaic theory' of insect vision, which was put forward by Johannes Müller in 1829 and is now, with certain modifications, generally accepted. The mechanism can be approximately imitated by holding a bundle of straws with blackened walls in front of a ground glass screen; an erect image is thrown on the screen, the amount of detail which it shows being greater the smaller the diameter of the tubes.

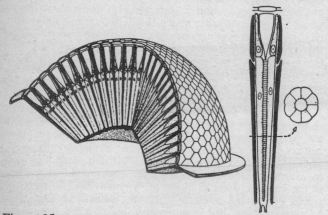

Figure 85.
Schematic figure of the compound eye of an insect showing the multiple visual elements, or 'ommatidia', each with its own lens, separated from their neighbours by a screen of pigment. The figure on the right shows a single ommatidium with the 'corneal lens' and 'crystalline cone' above, and below this the retinal rod, or 'rhabdom' (marked with transverse lines). The cross-section shows how the retinal rod is formed by eight retinal cells leading to nerves below. The whole ommatidium is enclosed by 'pigment cells' (von Frisch).

The lens part of each ommatidium consists of the 'corneal lens', composed of cuticle, and the so-called 'crystalline cone' lying below it (figure 85). In most diurnal insects, Hymenoptera, Diptera, Odonata, many Coleoptera and day-flying Lepidoptera, the crystalline cones are surrounded by pigmented cells, the so-called iris cells, so that light can emerge to reach the retinal rod only at the central point; and the retinular cells which produce the retinal rod are likewise sheathed in cells loaded with pigment. The light from each facet, therefore, falls only upon its own retinal rod, and the compound image is formed as described above. This is known as the 'apposition type' of visual image (figure 86).

But in many nocturnal insects, the glow-worms (Lampyridae) and other beetles, Noctuidae and other Lepidoptera, the ommatidia are greatly elongated. The retinal rods do not lie immediately behind and in contact with the crystalline cones, but are separated from them by a long interval, and the pigment of the iris cells may move outwards and be concen-

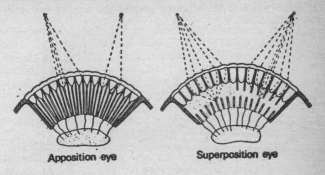

Apposition eye   **Superposition eye**

Figure 86.
The two types of insect eye (diagrammatic). In the apposition eye each retinal rod receives light only through its own lens, or facet; light from neighbouring facets is intercepted by the screen of pigment. In the superposition eye the short retinal rods receive light entering a group of facets (in the 'dark adapted' state, to the left). But in the 'light adapted' state (to the right), when the pigment extends inwards to form a screen, this eye acts like the apposition eye.

trated between the crystalline cones. Without going into details about the rather complicated properties of the lens in this type of eye, it can be said that the retinal rod of a single ommatidium receives light not only from its own facet, but rays of light entering quite a group of adjacent facets all converge upon it (figure 86). This will almost certainly mean that the mosaic image in this so-called 'superposition type' of eye will be less sharply defined than in the 'apposition type'. But since the light that reaches a particular retinal rod has entered through perhaps thirty adjacent lenses, the image produced will be very much brighter. Hence the adoption of this type of eye by nocturnal insects. During the daytime the pigment in the iris cells of these insects migrates inwards to form a curtain that extends far beyond the crystalline cones. This effectually prevents the spread of light from adjacent facets, and the image produced is now of the apposition type.

The collector of moths, who searches for Noctuids feeding after dark in the flowers of ivy or sallow, is familiar with the fact that as the eyes of these insects catch the light of the lamp they appear like glowing coals. That is because they have a rich supply of small tracheae at the inner end of the retinal rods, and running outwards between the retinal cells. These tracheae form a 'tapetum', or mirror, comparable with the tapetum in the eyes of cats and other mammals, which has the effect of reflecting the light outwards, so that it passes twice along the retinal rod, and can thus double its effect in producing chemical breakdown in the light-sensitive substance of the eye. There is indirect evidence for the existence of at least three different light-sensitive chemicals in the insect eye, but only one has been conclusively demonstrated. That is 'retinene' which has been extracted from the heads of bees. Retinene is a constituent of 'rhodopsin', the visual pigment in the retina of man and animals. It is a chemical closely related to vitamin A; it is common knowledge that serious lack of vitamin A in human diet can lead to night blindness.

We should like to know just how good the perception of the form of objects by insects may be. The image cast on the retina, as we have seen, consists of a mosaic of points of light of varying brightness; a mosaic which will be coarse or fine depending on the number of facets per unit area. Plate 27b shows the well known photograph, obtained by Exner in 1891, of the retinal image in the male glow-worm Lampyris. It represents a window with a letter R on one pane, at a distance of rather more than six feet, and a church tower beyond. The detail of this picture (the degree of resolution) is estimated to be about 1/60–1/80 that of the normal human eye. This is an insect with 2,500 facets in the eye. Some insects have less than this; the wingless female of Lampyris has only 300; but some have more: the water-beetle Dytiscus 9,000, the cockchafer Melolontha 5,100, the house-fly Musca 4,000, dragonflies 10,000–28,000.

More important than the absolute number of facets will be the area of the outside scene which is covered by each (the 'ommatidial angle'). In the honey-bee this angle is 1°, in the earwig 8°, so that the earwig will obtain only a single point of light from an object which the bee will resolve into sixty-four points. As the angle becomes smaller the amount of detail seen, the 'resolving power', will increase, but less light will enter each facet and the image will then be much less bright. However, if the eye is large it will be less curved; the facets remain of more or less the same size, but each covers a smaller angle and, therefore, the eye will have an improved resolving power without any loss of brightness. (In recent years it has been found that a single ommatidium receives light from a far wider area, something like 20°, than is usually supposed. This means that there must be a large amount of overlap between adjacent facets; but it is difficult to visualize the impression this will give.)

The curvature of the eye may differ in different directions. For example, in the honey-bee the eye is more convex, and the ommatidial angle twice or three times as great, in the transverse or horizontal plane of the eye than in the vertical plane. This means that resolution will be much better in the vertical direction than in the horizontal, and the effect produced will be like that of astigmatism in man. There is in fact some evidence that the acuteness of vision in the bee is greater in the vertical axis than in the horizontal.

In some insects the facet size is greater in some parts of the eye than in others: in males of the horse-fly *Tabanus* the facets are larger over the upper and anterior parts (plate 16b, c); in the black-fly *Simulium* and St Mark's fly *Bibio,* the two areas of different-sized facets are distinctly separated; and in the whirligig beetle *Gyrinus* and the male may-fly *Cloëon* (figure 87) there are in effect two compound eyes on each side of the head, one fine-grained and one coarse-grained.

In nocturnal insects, as we have seen, the brightness of the image is increased by the superposition of light from adjacent facets. Presumably this must entail a large sacrifice in the sharpness of the image. In the praying mantis, which must be able to get as accurate a view of its prey as possible before it strikes, the front of the eye is of the apposition type; but the sides of the eye are of the superposition type, and will give a bright but more diffuse image of the surrounding scene. From inspection of the photograph of the retinal image of the glow-worm, it was estimated that the resolving power of the insect eye is perhaps one-eightieth that of the normal human eye. By a different method, dependent on the behaviour of the insect when faced with moving stripes, the resolving power of the bee is judged to be about one-hundredth that of man, and in the fruit-fly *Drosophila* about one-thousandth.

It is not entirely satisfactory to try to calculate the acuteness of insect vision from the size and distribution of the facets of the compound eye. We saw how, by moving its head in all directions, a caterpillar can gain some idea of the form of objects in its field of view. The same thing happens in the compound eye. The desert locust *Schistocerca,* when surveying an object, will sit swaying the body from side to side. This curious 'peering' behaviour may be concerned in part with estimating the distance of the object,

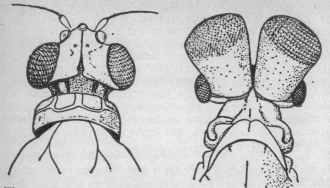

Figure 87.
The head of the may-fly *Cloëon dipterum*. To the left the female with a single pair of compound eyes. To the right, the male with a pair of eyes with small facets at the side of the head, and a pair with large facets on the top (Verrier).

but may also represent a scanning of the scene to provide information about its finer details. The insect eye has a re- markable capacity for seeing different successive images at very short intervals. This may compensate to some extent for the relative coarseness of the image of a stationary object, for it will greatly increase the capacity of the eye for 'scan- ning' a moving object. Indeed, it has been claimed that the insect will be able to resolve a finer pattern when it is flying than when it is at rest.

The compound eye is usually regarded as a rather in- efficient structure as compared with the simple camera-like eye of vertebrates. But on purely physical grounds it can be shown that for very small eyes the compound eye of insects is probably the more efficient—but as the size increases the acuteness of vision increases much more rapidly in the vertebrate, or single lens, type of eye and this soon becomes the more effective of the two.

This account of vision by the compound eye has been generally accepted for many years; but recent researches sug- gest that it may not represent the whole story. The eye of a blowfly or of a locust, which is usually described as an ap- position type of eye, besides forming an apposition image as already outlined, forms in addition at least two further images in the deeper levels of the eye. These newly discovered images are of a modified superposition type; they are formed

a

13. (a) Larvae or 'hoppers' of the desert locust *Schistocerca gregaria*, solitary phase to right, gregarious phase to left (Anti-Locust Research Centre, London).

(b) 'Physiological' or reversible colour change in the stick insect *Dixippus morosus*: pale form from light surroundings; black form from dark surroundings; and intermediate form.

b

14. (a) (left) Examples of an-
thoxanthin, or flavone, pigments in the wings of Satyrine
butterflies.

(b) (right) Wings of Nymphalid butterflies showing ommochrome pigments.

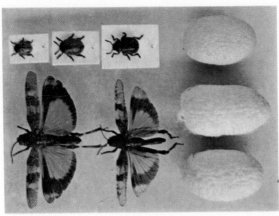

(c) (left) Wings of Pierid butterflies showing pterine pigments.

(d) (right) Examples of carotenoid pigments in the hindwings of the grasshoppers *Oedipoda*, in the ladybird beetle *Coccinella*, the Chrysomelid beetles *Melasoma* and *Leptinotarsa* (the potato beetle) and in the cocoons of the silkworm (a white Japanese race, a faintly pigmented European race, a bright yellow Chinese race).

d

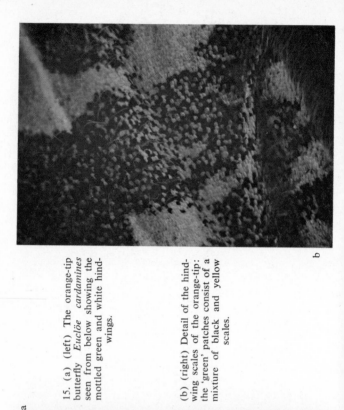

a

b

15. (a) (left) The orange-tip butterfly *Euclöe cardamines* seen from below showing the mottled green and white hind-wings.

(b) (right) Detail of the hind-wing scales of the orange-tip: the 'green' patches consist of a mixture of black and yellow scales.

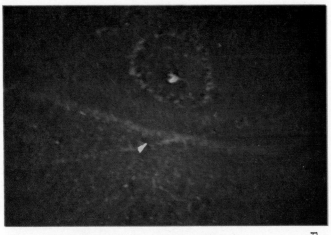

d

(c) (left) The Indian leaf butterfly *Kallima* showing the line resembling the mid-rib of a leaf.

(d) (right) Shows the detail of the 'mid-rib' consisting of a line of whitish scales, a line of green scales and a line of orange scales. The picture also shows the detail of a simulated 'fungus spot'.

c

16. (a) The grayling butterfly *Satyrus semele*: above, a male upper surface showing the dark 'brand' of scent scales on the fore-wings; in the middle, lower surface of specimen taken by the author on moorland at Arnside, Lancashire in 1910; below, a specimen taken by author on the chalk near Cambridge in 1920. (b) Head of a female horse-fly *Tabanus* showing the large compound eyes; (c) head of a male *Tabanus* showing the compound eyes with large facets above, and small facets below.

a

17. (a) Brazilian moth *Euglyphis braganza* at rest on bark; the hind-wings extend beyond the fore-wings; the pattern on the two wings merges together and thus obscures the outline of the insect; (b) the moth *Lirimiris lignitecta* mimicking a broken twig.

b

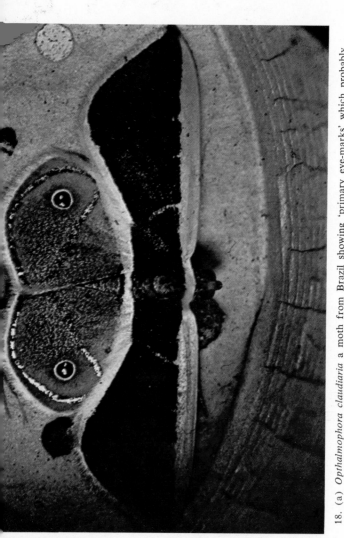

18. (a) *Opthalmophora claudiaria* a moth from Brazil showing 'primary eye-marks' which probably act as a 'threat' (photograph by H. B. D. Kettlewell).

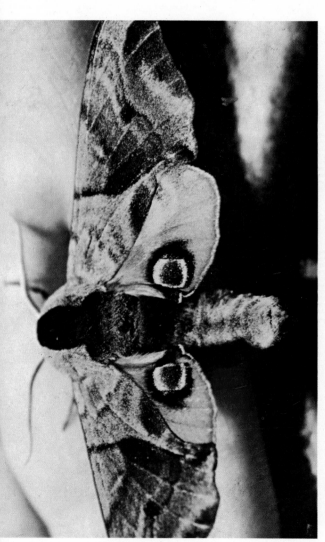

(b) The eyed hawk-moth *Smerinthus ocellatus* with 'secondary eye-spots' displayed in threat.

19. (a) The grasshopper *Phymateus viridipes* in full warning display.

(b) The warningly coloured grasshopper *Poekilocerus heiroglyphicus* exuding bubbles of a repellent froth.

a

20. (a) *Trosia dimas* of Brazil; warning coloration; (b) *Macroneme immanans,* a moth that mimics a wasp in Brazil.

b

a

21. (a) The moth *Anophylla magnifica* from Brazil; an example of disruptive pattern and representation of a splash of bird excreta; (b) an unidentified Sphingid larva from Brazil; a fine example of 'countershading'.

b

a

22. (a) A longhorned grasshopper, *Phyolloptera* species, resembling a leaf with mould-like markings; (b) *Automolis angulosa* a moth from Brazil showing a 'disruptive pattern' of black and white stripes.

b

a

23. (a) The buff-tip moth (*Phalera bucephala*) at rest, showing the rounded twig-like form of the wings; (b) shows a comparison of the wing-tip of *P. bucephala* with the exposed end of a twig.

b

24. (a) The large elephant hawk-moth *Chaerocampa elpenor* at rest on a flower; (b) the cream spot tiger moth *Arctia villica* in full warning display with the front of the body raised to show the red markings and the hind-wings and abdomen exposed.

by the diffraction of light received from groups of adjacent facets. How the insect interprets this confusing array of images it is impossible for us to judge. It may perhaps use different images for different purposes or at different ranges from the object.

There is another feature of the compound eye that is most important—its capacity for perceiving distance. One of the ways in which we perceive the distance of an object is by the extent to which our eyes converge as we look at it. In the insect the eyes are fixed and cannot be moved independently of one another. But if the insect faces an object and then gradually approaches it, the image on the retina will gradually move towards the inner part of the two eyes. The insect will therefore have at its disposal an absolutely exact method of judging distance. The larva of the dragonfly *Aeschna,* for example, always turns to face any moving object which attracts its attention. The visual angle of the ommatidia becomes progressively less over the inner part of the eye, and this will improve the definition as the object is approached. The larva knows by experience the points on the retina of the two eyes that will perceive the prey when it is exactly within striking distance of the labium, or mask (figure 88). It does not matter how dim the light may be, the accuracy with which these larvae seize their prey is unimpaired. But if one eye is covered with black paint the capacity for judging distance becomes very poor.

What evidence is there from the behaviour of insects that they are able to distinguish forms and patterns? One of the standard methods of judging the sensory perceptions of the honey-bee is to train bees to associate a particular feature or signal with the presence of food and then, without any food, to offer them this signal in competition with other signals, and count the percentage of bees which choose the original signal to which they have been trained. Bees can be trained to associate certain black figures on a white ground with the presence of food; they are attracted to any mark which contrasts with the colour of the background to which they have become accustomed, just as they are attracted by the 'honey-guides' in flowers—that is, the dark marks at the base of the petals which serve to lead them to the source of the nectar. But such figures as triangles, squares, circles, and ellipses, which are well within the capacity of the optical equipment of the bee to differentiate, and which appear very different to our eyes, are apparently not distinguished by the bee. On the other hand, it can readily distinguish from these

Figure 88.
The head of a dragonfly larva *Aeschna* with the 'mask', or labium, extended. The dotted lines show the line of vision from various facets of the compound eye. The sharpest vision is obtained when the object is between the pincers of the extended mask; the larva can judge the distance accurately in this way (Baldus).

any figures that are broken up into many black and white areas—rows of stripes, chequers, flower patterns, etc (figure 89). Bees show a natural preference for such divided figures; like butterflies, they are attracted to flowers divided up into numerous petals, and by flowers shaken in the wind or artificially kept in motion. They seem to associate a flickering appearance with the presence of nectar, and these experiments with black figures probably do not give a true measure of the capacity of the bee for distinguishing shapes.

When insects are studied under natural conditions it is evident that they can perceive forms and patterns. Whereas the dragonfly larva *Aeschna* will snap repeatedly at any moving object, and hunting wasps will fly at nails hammered in a wall, mistaking them for flies, *Aeschna* adults, which will turn towards a paper pellet thrown in the air, attracted by its movement, will instantly turn away from it when its image is perceived. Bees and ants utilize visual landmarks in finding their way back to the nest. The solitary wasp *Philanthus* locates the entrance to its nest by the arrangement of visual marks around it, and by moving these it can be led astray at will. Bees which can recognize their hive by coloured marks at the entrance, can appreciate the difference if a given colour is on the right or left of the entrance hole. In fact the bee is able to differentiate the same three spatial co-ordinates as we can; it can distinguish left and right, before and behind, above and below, and so form a general appreciation of its surroundings.

Figure 89.
Perception of form by the honey-bee. The bee cannot distinguish the figures in the upper row from one another; the same applies to the lower row. But the figures of the lower row are readily distinguished from those of the upper (Hertz).

There are other features in the vision of insects with which we are familiar in ourselves. Their eyes become adapted to a dim or a bright light. This is partly the result of the movement of pigment in the iris cells of the ommatidia, partly the result of some change in the brain itself, which after a time ceases to react to a particular stimulus received by the eyes. They also experience the phenomenon of 'simultaneous contrast'; that is, a particular object appears darker on a bright background than it does on a grey. The humming-bird hawk-moth *Macroglossa* seeks dark crevices in which to retreat at night and in the autumn; if a series of dark discs of suitable size are set up in a room, it makes for the darker ones; and if two of equal darkness are set up side by side, one on a dull grey background and one on white, the moths regularly make for the latter.

One of the most interesting comparisons between the vision of insects and of ourselves concerns their perception of colour. The first question is how much of the spectrum can insects see? Most of the ultra-violet light in the sun's rays is filtered out by the ozone in the upper atmosphere; only the near ultra-violet (down to a wave-length of 300 mμ) reaches the surface of the earth and this is invisible to our eyes; we cannot see beyond the violet of the spectrum (400 mμ). At the red end of the spectrum, we can see to a wave-length of about 750 mμ.

It is characteristic of insects that they are sensitive to the shorter wave-lengths of the spectrum. It was shown many years ago by Sir John Lubbock that for ants the visible spectrum extends well into the ultra-violet. Ants which seek the dark will shelter below a flask filled with carbon disulphide, which cuts out the ultra-violet, and avoid a zone covered by a sheet of violet glass, which appears quite dark to the human eye. They will choose a light green or yellow zone and avoid a zone covered with deep violet glass. But if a layer of carbon disulphide or quinine sulphate solution is placed over the violet glass (making no perceptible difference to the human eye) they will all collect under the violet shade. If an ants' nest is illuminated with the colours of the spectrum, the ants carry their pupae and deposit them at the infra-red end, just at the limit of our visible spectrum, whereas at the opposite end they leave vacant a considerable zone beyond our visible range. By covering the eyes Forel showed that it is the eyes themselves which are responsible for this sensitivity to ultra-violet.

Similar conclusions have been reached with many other insects. Moths and other light-seeking insects will fly to illuminated glass that allows ultra-violet to pass through, even when it appears opaque to us, in preference to bright blue glass. The honey-bee, the blowfly *Calliphora*, etc, will react to light with a wave-length of 297 mμ, at the lower limit of the solar spectrum. Lutz carried out an experiment in which he had two white notices painted on a black background; one read: 'Bees may feed here', and the other read: 'No bees allowed here'. He had no difficulty in training the bee *Trigona* to collect only around the former notice—because in this the letters were painted with process white which reflects ultra-violet, whereas the letters in the other notice were painted with Chinese white which does not.

At the other end of the spectrum there are great differences between different insects. Most seem to be insensitive to the deeper shades of red. The honey-bee, for instance, will not respond to light of a wave-length greater than 650 mμ (on the border of red and orange). Wasps (*Vespa*) after being trained to visit a black surface, can be diverted equally to black or red. On the other hand, some butterflies (*Pieris, Vanessa*, etc) can certainly perceive red and will visit deep red flowers or red paper models of flowers. The fire-fly *Photinus* will respond to flashes of light from some point between 520–560 mμ in the green, up to at least 690 mμ in the deep red. That is the longest wave-length yet recorded as visible to any insect.

When we view the spectrum the brightest point is in the yellow zone. It is difficult to be sure which region appears brightest for insects. Various methods, some consisting of observing their behaviour towards light of different wavelengths, others consisting of measuring the electric responses in the eye under these conditions, commonly show several peaks of sensitivity along the course of the spectrum. In the honey-bee there is a very high peak in the far ultra-violet at 360 mμ and another in the green at 540 mμ. In the blowfly *Calliphora* there are three peaks; one in the ultra-violet at 340 mμ, one in the blue-green at 500 mμ, and a third in the red at 650 mμ. But it is not altogether certain which if any of these peaks really represents the brightest region of the spectrum.

What is quite certain is that the perception of ultra-violet must alter the entire colour of the outside world. There is no doubt that flower-visiting insects are able to perceive colour. The bee-fly *Bombylius* visiting blue *Muscari* in the spring will fly rapidly from flower to flower; they are equally attracted to flowers enclosed in glass tubes or to pieces of blue paper. The fritillary butterfly *Argynnis* feeding in the field on flowers of blue bugle will turn aside to visit violet or purple flowers made of paper. It was established by Lubbock that bees can distinguish one colour from another; they can learn to associate the finding of honey with blue or orange papers, and they will continue to visit the colour to which they have been accustomed although no honey is present. By exposing the colours to which the bees had been trained on a chequer board made up of a complete range of grey shades, von Frisch excluded the possibility that the colours might be distinguished simply by differences in their apparent brightness. And he covered the chequer board with a glass plate so that smell was excluded. Incidentally he showed that bees could *not* be trained to come to any particular shade of grey. Bees can also be trained to visit bands of spectral light in a large projected spectrum, so that it was not a question of different amounts of ultra-violet light being reflected from the papers.

Bees tested by training to bands of spectral light seem able to distinguish four main regions of the spectrum: red—yellow—green (650–500 mμ); blue-green (500–480 mμ); blue-violet (480–400 mμ); and ultra-violet (400–310 mμ). At the red end of the spectrum their perceptions are much like those of a man with red-green colour blindness. They can distinguish certain red flowers, such as the poppy *Papaver rhoeas;* but that is only because these reflect ultra-violet

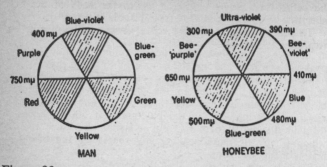

Figure 90.
To the left, the colour circle as experienced by man. The shaded sectors represent the three primary colours; and the sectors opposite to these are the complementary colours. To the right, the colour circle of the honey-bee in which 'ultra-violet' appears as a colour (Daumer).

(plate 28); bees trained to visit such flowers are equally attracted to a black glass emitting ultra-violet rays invisible to man. Indeed, red flowers appear to the bee either 'bee ultra-violet' or 'bee black' depending on the degree of ultra-violet reflection. Among flowers which appear blue or violet to man there is so much variety in ultra-violet reflection that bees see them in no less than four colour tones.

The ultra-violet region is probably perceived as a true colour. Reflected daylight will, therefore, appear colourless to the bee only when its composition approximates to sunlight; if it is deficient in ultra-violet, 'white' light will appear coloured. The colours of papers remain unchanged to our eyes when covered with glass; but to the bee they may be totally changed, grey papers appearing coloured. Indeed ultra-violet is just one normal component in a system of four principal colours as seen by the bee; white paper or white flowers which do not reflect much ultra-violet will appear bluish-green to the bee. Bees experience also the phenomenon of 'simultaneous contrast': a grey area surrounded by yellow appears blue and is visited by bees trained to this colour; surrounded by blue it appears yellow. Blue (or 'bee violet') and yellow, therefore, form complementary colours which, combined in the right proportions, will give the appearance of white; and probably blue-green and ultra-violet are also complementary to produce 'bee white'. A mixture of yellow and ultra-violet gives a new colour for the bee which might be called 'bee purple', since it unites the ends of the bee spectrum to give the complete colour circle (figure 90).

To sum the matter up, the colour system of man may be expressed as follows:

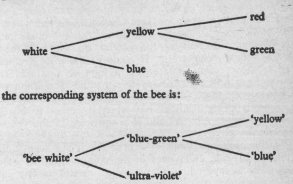

the corresponding system of the bee is:

It was suggested by Lutz that flowers may well possess patterns of ultra-violet reflection invisible to us but visible to the bee; and it has in fact been shown in recent years that many pure yellow flowers, such as *Oenothera* or *Potentilla,* reflect ultra-violet over the greater part of their petals but have patches at the base of the petals which fail to do so. To the bee these will appear as dark areas which will serve as 'honey guides' visible only to the bee (plate 28).

Butterflies offered paper flowers of various gay colours obviously prefer these to grey paper flowers. The tortoiseshell butterfly *Vanessa urticae* shows two preferences: for the blue-purple group and the yellow-red group; and it can be trained to show increased preference for either one group or the other; green and greenish flowers are unattractive. The cabbage butterfly *Pieris brassicae* shows a similar preference and disregards green, blue-green, and grey. But the egg-laying female of *Pieris* has a peculiar 'drumming' reaction of the fore-legs, with which she tests the leaves of the foodplant; and for this reaction she chooses emerald green to greenish-blue papers; yellow and blue are neglected; though she will sometimes show the 'drumming' behaviour at the margin of a purple paper—evidently in response to the green contrast colour. In this behaviour and in the recognition of red, the colour vision of *Pieris* approximates more closely to our own than does that of the bee. For butterflies, ultra-violet does not seem to play such an important role as it does for the bee, but it is probably visible to them; and in many Pierid butterflies, such as the brimstone *Gonepteryx*, the wings of the male reflect far more ultra-violet than those of the female, and sometimes this reflection is arranged in striking patterns invisible to the human eye but visible to the insect. Some butterflies, such as the meadow browns, etc (Satyrinae) and the skippers (Hesperidae) are insensitive to red.

The hawk-moth *Deilephila* can distinguish the blue-violet-purple group of colours of the flowers on which it feeds, from the yellow-green group. It feeds in the dusk and can recognize these colour differences in light so dim that the human eye can no longer see any colour at all. The humming-bird hawk-moth *Macroglossa* shows the same preference for blue flowers during feeding; but when it comes to lay its eggs its preference changes and it is attracted to the yellow-ish-green tints.

By various other methods of experiment it has been found that there are wide differences in the colour vision of other insects. The plant-feeding Chrysomelid beetles clearly distinguish green tints from one another, as well as yellow and orange from blue-violet and green. Some flying aphids are attracted to the yellow colour in foliage and therefore tend to alight for preference on young leaves. They can often be seen settling in large numbers on yellow objects, such as yellow cigarette cartons lying on the ground, and they can be caught in large numbers in yellow-painted trays containing water. The nocturnal stick insect *Dixippus* and the bug *Troilus* on the other hand appear to possess no colour vision at all; and in the water-boatman *Notonecta*, part of the eye (the upper and back part) is sensitive to colour, whereas the lower and front parts appear to be colour blind. What is quite unknown is the nature of the differences inside the eye, the various 'chemical receptor substances', which account for these varying capacities for colour vision.

Another remarkable property of the insect eye which has been recognized only in recent years is that of being able to detect the direction in which light is polarized. It might be supposed that this capacity to recognize light that has passed through a nicol prism or through a sheet of polaroid, and become 'polarized', would be of little value in the normal life of the insect. But it was observed by Santschi as long ago as 1923 that ants could orientate their movements in relation to the sun when only the blue sky was visible to them. He made the suggestion that they might be able to perceive the stars (like an observer looking up the shaft of a mine) and were navigating by these. It happens, how-

ever, that the light coming from a blue sky shows a regular
pattern of polarization (readily observed if the sky is viewed
through a sheet of polaroid) which depends on the position
of the sun. The ability of insects to see this pattern was first
recognized by von Frisch when he found that bees and ants
could steer equally well by an artificial pattern of polarization produced by a polaroid screen. (Bees can also see the
position of the sun through quite thick cloud; but that is
because they can see the ultra-violet rays.)

Since then it has been found that all insects have this
ability. It is not confined to the compound eye; for the larvae
of saw-flies and Lepidoptera, which have only lateral ocelli,
can also steer by the pattern of polarized light. Exactly how
the insect eye perceives the plane of polarization is not entirely understood, but it seems that something resembling
'polaroid' is built into the retinal rod. The study of the compound eye with the electron microscope suggests that there
is a regular molecular pattern in the retinal rod which is
serving this purpose.

Another puzzling feature of insect vision is the presence
in many adult insects of simple eyes or ocelli side by side

Figure 91.
The fruit-fly *Drosophila melanogaster* showing the triangular group
of ocelli on the top of the head (Müller).

with the compound eyes (figure 91). In the house-fly or the
honey-bee, for example, there is a group of three tiny ocelli
set in the form of a triangle on the top of the head. The
structure of these ocelli resembles that of the lateral ocelli
in many larvae, where a single lens covers a large group of
light-sensitive cells. The old belief was that the compound
eyes are used for distant vision and the ocelli for viewing

objects at close range. But in most insects it has proved impossible to get any evidence that insects see anything at all with their 'dorsal ocelli'. The only idea which has any experimental evidence to support it is that these organs are concerned with recording rapid changes in illumination, and that they serve as so-called 'stimulatory organs' which as it were 'wake up' the nervous system and bring the insect into a state in which it can react quickly to what it sees through the compound eyes.

Chapter **12**

HEARING, SMELL, AND OTHER SENSES

THE WHOLE body of the insect is encased in cuticle, horny and rigid in some parts, more or less flexible in others. The primary task of the epidermal cells is to lay down this protective covering. But if the body were enclosed in an unbroken sheet of armour, like that which forms the elytra of some beetles, the insect would be wholly cut off from the outside world. The epidermal cells, however, have another function: to keep the insect informed about what is going on in the surroundings. For this purpose there are points in the cuticle that are modified to form sense organs. Specialized epidermal cells build these organs and connect them by nerves to the central nervous system.

The 'central nervous system' is a general term which includes the brain and all the other nerve centres that will be discussed in the next chapter. In all animals the central nervous system arises during development as an ingrowth from the outermost cell layer (the 'ectoderm'). It comes to lie deep in the body of the animal and is connected to all parts by nerves (figure 92). In insects one can see this development continuing throughout their growth. During the moulting process a single cell in the epidermis will divide to form a little group, usually four cells. One of these gives off a slender, thread-like structure which grows inwards. This thread is indeed a nerve fibre, or 'axon', and as it grows it soon meets a nerve (which is a bundle of nerve fibres), and joining the bundle and growing along with it the new fibre readily finds its way to the central nervous system. The remainder of the little group of cells proceed to build a tiny structure in the cuticle designed to serve one or other of the senses.

In discussing vision we referred to the retinular cells and their retinal rod. These in origin are epidermal cells which have become sense cells; a great number of them are crowded together to form the compound eye. But most of the sense organs of insects are small structures with a single sense cell and a single nerve fibre. These 'little sense organs', or 'sensilla' ('sensillum' in the singular) are scattered over the surface of the body. They are the sensitive points of contact with the outside world; the cuticle between them is quite insensitive. Of course they may be concentrated in certain regions of the body, such as the legs, the antennae, the 'palpi' around the mouth-parts, the 'tail feelers' or

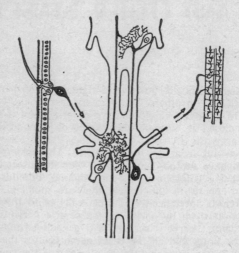

Figure 92.
Schematic figure of the nervous system in an insect. To the left is a sense organ ('sensillum') on the cuticle. The sense cell (in black) sends an 'axon' along a nerve to a 'ganglion' of the central nervous system. By means of fine branches the sensory axon makes contact with 'association nerve cells' (in white), and by way of these connects up with the fine branches of a 'motor nerve cell' (in black) the axon from which leaves the ganglion along a nerve and ends in a muscle (to the right).

'cerci', and so forth, and in this way large sense organs are formed.

The nerve fibres convey electrical vibrations, oscillations of electrical potential, which follow one another in rapid succession along the nerve. In this respect all nerves seem to be alike. But the little sense organs are of many different kinds; some are so constituted that they respond to mechanical pressure or touch, others to high temperature, taste, or smell. By some means that we do not begin to understand the central nervous system can sort out the electrical vibrations it receives, and distinguish them according to the nature of the receptive organ from which they come; and thus light and colour, contact, sound, heat, cold, taste, and smell are interpreted as representing quite different things in the outside world—although all are transmitted in the same electric code.

When the range and sensitivity of this equipment are closely studied it is at once apparent that the insect has at its disposal an immense amount of information about the outside world. In this chapter we shall consider some of the ways in which this information is obtained and some of the evidence that the information is indeed reaching the central nervous system.

The tiny bristles or hairs which project everywhere from the surface of the insect are all sense organs. The base of the bristle is joined to the cuticle by a ball and socket joint (figure 93). The movement of the hair in its socket compresses or stretches the ending of the nerve and provides the sense of touch. Hairs of this kind are plentiful on the feet of insects and enable them to sense their contact with the ground. But they are often particularly numerous on the antennae and the tail filaments, which can then properly be called 'feelers'. When a cockroach is sitting at rest, its long whip-like antennae are nearly all the time reaching out in this direction and in that, so that any movement of objects in the neighbourhood is instantly detected.

These tactile hairs are often so sensitive that they will respond to slight movements of the air. Flies will take off instantly if a hand is moved towards them; but if they are the other side of glass they pay no attention. It is the movement of the air that they perceive. It has even been suggested that insects in flight may be able to avoid collisions with other objects by the disturbance in the air currents which these produce; but the readiness with which flying insects bumble into glass does not lend support to this idea. On the other hand there is no doubt of the importance of tactile hairs in the flying insect. Many insects can be kept in so-called 'stationary flight' by suspending them on a wire sealed to the thorax by wax; but it is often necessary to direct a jet of air against the front of the head to simulate the air stream produced in flight. Flies, butterflies, locusts, and other insects have slender tactile hairs on the face or antennae that are stimulated by the flowing air. A locust can no longer be maintained in stationary flight by a jet of air if these sensory hairs are covered with cellulose paint. In the pond skater *Gerris* (figure 15) the numerous tactile hairs on the legs help the insect to maintain its proper position on the water surface, and in addition they serve to detect the vibrations in the surface film set up by other insects on which the pond skater preys; and the water-boatman *Notonecta* (figure 16) has air cushions in contact with sensory hairs at the base of the antennae, which help it to keep its inverted position of rest at the water surface.

There is another source of air-movement, and that is sound. Sound consists of waves of increased pressure which pass through the air succeeding one another at very short intervals. Our ears respond to these waves of pressure. But the differences in pressure will lead to small *movements* of the air, which will begin to flow from points of high pressure to points of low pressure. The detection of these rapid movements of air affords a second method of perceiving sound. The more delicate tactile hairs of insects are sensitive enough to react in this way. Caterpillars, even those with relatively few hairs, will react to sounds by becoming still and contracting the body; if the hairs are removed, or are loaded with powder or with droplets of water, they will no longer respond.

Many other insects have tactile hairs that are sensitive to sound; but those most carefully studied are on the tail filaments, or cerci, of crickets and cockroaches. Here the method of study has been to record the electrical changes in the nerves with a loudspeaker or an oscillograph, and then compare these records with the sounds to which the sense organs are exposed. It is quite clear that it is the tactile hairs which are the sensitive organs; they will respond to notes of so low a pitch as to be quite inaudible to the human ear, and they will keep pace with the vibration in the air up to a frequency as high as four hundred per second, so that if the cerci are exposed to the humming of a suitable tune, this can easily be recognized in the loudspeaker recording the electrical changes in the nerve. It seems likely, however, that in the normal life of the cricket the auditory function of the tail filaments is merely incidental, and their main use is to perceive earth-borne vibrations. In the cockroach, in which the cercus is held upright, it is probably used as a wind gauge for detecting draughts.

The tactile hair is the most characteristic sense organ of insects, but it can become modified in various ways and still respond to mechanical effects. One common type is the 'campaniform', or bell-shaped, organ in which the hair is absent and all that remains is a round or oval dome-like structure lying flush with the cuticle (figure 93). These organs are so constructed that when the cuticle is bent the nerve

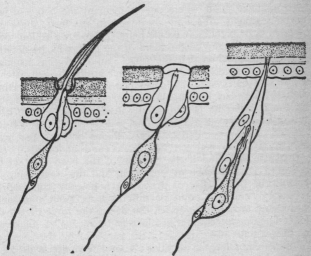

Figure 93.
Three types of mechanical sense organ. To the left, a 'tactile hair' with its sense cell giving off the nerve fibre (axon) that will connect it to the central nervous system. In the middle a 'campaniform organ' consisting of a dome of thin cuticle connected to the sense cell. On the right a 'chordotonal organ' in which the sense cell is attached to the cuticle but there is no structure visible from the outside.

ending is stretched, and in this way they serve to detect strains in the cuticle. The evolutionary process may go a stage further. There may be no external structure at all that is visible from the outside. There is simply a strand that runs across from one point in the cuticle to another. Movements of the body or external pressure upon it may pull upon these strands which are called 'chordotonal organs' (figure 93).

Sense organs are needed not only to give information about the surroundings but about the position of the parts of the body. We know the position of our own limbs at a given moment only from the evidence of our senses; we rely particularly upon the sense organs which detect tension in the different muscles and tendons. In some insects, also, certain muscles have become transformed into sense organs, so-called 'stretch receptors'; but most of the sense organs used in self-perception (what physiologists call 'proprioception') belong to the types of mechanical sensilla derived from the cuticle and its cells, which have already been discussed.

Around the joints where one segment of the body, or one of the segments of a limb, is linked to the next, there are often rows or patches of tactile hairs. There are cushions covered with such hairs on the front of the thorax in the dragonfly or the locust, so that the insect can know that its head is being held straight and in the proper position. Such patches of sensory hairs are well developed in the praying mantis (figure 142) and here again they serve to keep the insect informed about the position of its head, and so enable it to strike accurately at a fly to one side or the other of the body. There are similar sensory cushions between the head and thorax, and between the thorax and abdomen in the bee (figure 94); and if the position of the head is upset by attaching a small piece of lead to it, and thus increasing its weight, the bee's sense of gravity is hopelessly confused.

There is another point of difference between our sense organs and those of the insect. We detect the force of gravity and maintain our equilibrium largely by means of the semicircular canals associated with the ear, and by the sense of tension in muscles and tendons. A very few insects do have 'statocyst organs' which are concerned solely with the detection of gravity, but most of them depend on the mechanical senses at the surface of their bodies: sensory hairs detect contact and pressure; campaniform organs detect forces bending the cuticle; chordotonal organs detect tension between one part and another. By taking all this information into account the insect can build up a 'sense of gravity'. Staphylinid beetles of the genus *Bledius*, which make vertical burrows in the sand, are guided solely by gravity; they are able to judge the direction of gravity with an error of less than 1°.

We saw how the semi-hydrofuge hairs on aquatic insects, when set in rows, will form barriers with water on one side and air on the other (p. 51). These same hairs are also tactile sense organs; they play a most important part in enabling the insect to perceive the force of surface tension, and thus to know when its body has made contact with the

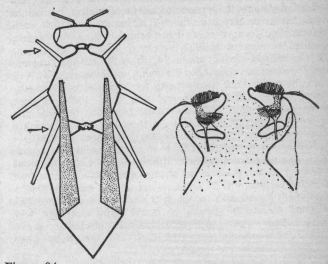

Figure 94.
Schematic figure of a honey-bee showing the cushions of sensory hairs between the head and thorax, and between thorax and abdomen which are mainly responsible for the perception of gravity by the bee. The figure to the right shows the detail of the patches of hairs at the front of the thorax and the nerves supplying them (Lindauer and Nedel).

surface of the water. The same equipment can also be used to help the insect to keep itself on an even keel while it is submerged. The best known example of this is in the water scorpion *Nepa* (figure 24). Without going into precise detail it can be said that air in the tracheal system is separated from the surrounding water by barriers of mechanical sense organs in the region of the spiracles. If the water scorpion is tilted in the water, the barrier will tend to be pressed inwards where the spiracles are deeper in the water and the pressure is greater, and outwards where they are nearer the surface and the pressure is less; the insect can thus easily recognize whether it is in a horizontal position and whether it is crawling upwards or downwards. The Naucorid bug *Aphelocheirus* (figure 27) uses a similar mechanism not only for keeping its body level in the water but for recognizing the absolute hydrostatic pressure to which it is exposed and thus knowing how deep it is under water.

So far as we know insects have no means of detecting changes in barometric pressure. But it is obvious that successful flight must depend on an informative instrument panel. As in an aeroplane this will not matter so much in the more primitive sort of flying machine, which has a large degree of inherent stability, such as a glider or a long-legged, slowly flying crane-fly; it will become increasingly important in an unstable flying machine such as a jet aircraft or a stout two-winged fly such as a bluebottle. We have seen that locusts and flies (and doubtless many other insects) must have the tactile hairs on the face stimulated by a steady flow of air, if they are to keep going in sustained flight. These same organs serve also as stabilizers during flight: if the locust finds that the flowing air is striking it obliquely from one side, it immediately alters the movements of its wings so as to change direction and turn itself into the air current. In addition, the insect must be able to appreciate the stresses to which the wings are exposed. That is done mainly by means of tactile hairs over the wing surface, and by campaniform organs and chordotonal organs in the wing membranes, particularly in the veins where the wing is attached to the body.

One of the most interesting sensory controls for the regulation of flight is found in the Diptera. In the 'two-winged flies' the second pair of wings has been lost, and is represented only by a pair of little knobbed organs, the 'balancers', or halteres. The halteres are jointed to the thorax like the wings, and during flight they vibrate up and down at the same rate as the wings. Where they join the thorax they have a great number of campaniform organs set in regular rows in the cuticle (figure 95). When the haltere oscillates up and down during normal flight there is no strain in the cuticle around the joint, and these campaniform organs are not affected. But the slightest deflection of the haltere to one side or the other will at once set up a strain in the cuticle, and will stimulate the campaniform organs. Now it is well known that a spinning top has a gyroscopic action: it resists any attempt to change the direction of the axis in which it is revolving. An object that is vibrating rapidly up and down in one plane, like the haltere, reacts in the same way; it behaves as an 'alternating gyroscope'. If, therefore, the flying insect is tipped or inclined so that the plane in which the haltere is vibrating is changed, then strains will be set up in the cuticle, and these will be detected by the campaniform organs. By this means the blowfly can maintain its equilibrium in the air. If the halteres are snipped off its stability is lost and it can no longer fly without crashing to the ground. But if a cotton thread is attached to the tip of the abdomen this restores stability to the insect (like the tail of a kite) and it can now fly without the halteres. Of

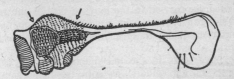

Figure 95.
The haltere (or modified hind-wing) of the blowfly *Calliphora* seen from below, showing the two groups of campaniform organs set in regular rows near the attachment of the haltere to the thorax (Lowne).

course, the halteres are not the only organs that help the fly to maintain its equilibrium; the eyes, tactile hairs, and other sense organs are also important.

It is obvious that the same mechanical sense organs can serve either as organs of self-perception or for the detection of disturbances in their surroundings. That certainly applies to the chordotonal organs. These are plentiful in the legs of insects, and they probably give information about the position of the joints. But they are also stimulated by vibration. The sensitivity of insects to vibration is more or less proportional to the numbers of chordotonal organs in the legs. It is well known that low-pitched sounds will cause the floor to vibrate—and thus what were in origin perhaps organs of self-perception become in part organs of hearing; indeed, the more elaborate organs of hearing are generally believed to have arisen by specialization and adaptation of 'proprioceptive organs'.

The same sort of adaptation is seen in the antennae of insects. Most of the movements of the antenna take place beyond the second segment from the base. At the joint between the second segment and the rest of the antenna (called the 'flagellum') there is always a group of chordotonal organs. This group is known as 'Johnston's organ'; it serves to provide information about the position of the antenna at any moment. But, of course, it is sensitive not only to the movements of the antenna that are made by the insect itself, but also to movements brought about, for instance, by air currents. In fact Johnston's organ is one of the chief sense organs used for detecting movements of the air. It is used by aphids for the control of flight: if the 'flagellum' is cut off beyond the second segment flight becomes quite erratic. Normal flight is restored if an 'artificial antenna' is reattached; but the aphid again becomes incapable of flight if this is removed. In the whirligig beetle *Gyrinus* (figure 17) the antennae are carried in the surface film of the water, and Johnston's organ seems to be used to detect changes in the curvature of the surface, and thus help the beetle to avoid collisions.

As we have seen, in the tail filaments of crickets or the tactile hairs of caterpillars, as soon as an organ becomes sensitive to air movements, it becomes sensitive to sound. It is not surprising, therefore, that Johnston's organ develops into an organ of hearing. That is best seen in the males of Chironomid midges and mosquitoes (figure 96). The second segment of the antenna contains a most elaborate Johnston's organ, and the main shaft of the antenna in these male insects is feathered with long hairs. When exposed to sound waves the whole antenna is set into rapid vibrations, that are received by Johnston's organ. We have already seen how the male mosquito is particularly sensitive to the note given out by the beating wings of the female, that is, a note of about 500 cycles per second, and how the mating male will fly towards the source of such a sound. But very young females of *Aedes* can fly unmolested in a cage with sexually active males, because the sound produced by the recently emerged female is outside the range that will induce the male to copulate.

The more specialized organs of hearing in insects, however, are of a different type. They, too, seem to have arisen by the evolution of chordotonal organs serving originally for proprioception. But these organs have increased in number, and become attached to a thin taut membrane in the cuticle —a drum, or 'tympanum', which is set into vibration by the waves of air-borne sound. The most frequent site for these ear-drums is one on each side of the abdomen just behind the thorax, or on the last segment of the thorax itself. This is where they are found in many moths (Noctuidae, Geometridae, Arctiidae, Notodontidae, etc), in the short-horned grasshoppers (Acridiidae), in the cicadas (Homoptera), and in some aquatic bugs. The other site for the ears is on the tibiae of the fore-legs. In the long-horned grasshoppers (Tettigoniidae) there is a slight swelling on the first pair of legs, with two fine slits on the front of it; these slits are the open-

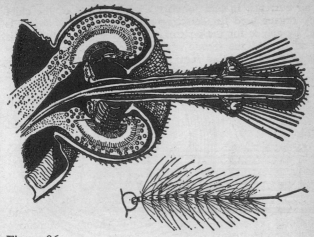

Figure 96.
Below, the antenna of a male mosquito showing the large globular segment at the base. Above, section through this globular segment in a male *Anopheles* showing the elaborate sense organ (Johnston's organ) which detects movements of the shaft of the antenna (Risler).

ings of deep pockets, and the drums form the inner walls of the pockets, which are separated by two large tracheae (figure 97). In crickets (Gryllidae) the placing of the ears is similar, but there is no infolding to form pockets. The long-horned grasshopper *Tettigonia* and its allies will 'scan' the surroundings by swinging the legs. At certain points in this movement there will be a rapid change in the loudness of a sound, and this makes possible the accurate localization of the source from which the sound is coming, even with a single leg (figure 98).

There is good evidence that insects which possess these so-called 'tympanal organs' are really capable of hearing. Various Noctuids and other moths will vibrate their wings and fly away if exposed to the high pitched notes of a Galton whistle, even when every care is taken that only air-borne conduction of the sound is taking place. There is no response if the ear-drums at the sides of the abdomen are pierced with a needle; and there is no response in butterflies or in hawk-moths (Sphingidae) or other moths which do not possess drums.

A more difficult question concerns the use to which these

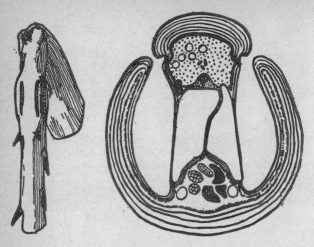

Figure 97.
Ear of the long-horned grasshopper *Tettigonia*. The fore-leg seen
from in front shows the two slits in the tibia. On the right is a section through the leg at the level of the slits showing the two
pockets into which they lead, and the two ear-drums forming the
inner walls of these pockets, with two large tracheae between them
(Weber; Schwabe).

organs of hearing are put during the everyday life of insects. Among the grasshoppers, crickets, and cicadas, in
which the ear-drums are particularly well developed, so also
is the capacity for song. The males of short-horned grasshoppers 'stridulate' by drawing a series of pegs on the hind-
legs across a stiff vein on the outer surface of the fore-
wing (figure 99). In long-horned grasshoppers, in *Ephippiger*
(figure 100) for example, and in crickets, two modified areas
on the fore-wings, forming a 'ridge' and a 'file', are rubbed
together and set the wing in vibration. In the water-bug
Corixa a group of teeth on the front femur is rubbed against
a ridge on the head—and in all these insects the female responds to the call.

The males of the cicadas produce their sounds in quite a
different way. They have a pair of ridged drums or 'tymbals'
at the base of the abdomen, which are convex outwards
and have a powerful muscle attached to the inner concave
surface (figure 101). When the drum is drawn inwards and

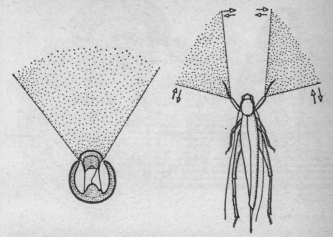

Figure 98.
Sound location in the long-horned grasshopper *Tettigonia cantans*.
Directly in front of the fore-legs (as seen in section on the left) there
is a sector of reduced sound, about 70° wide. Immediately beyond
this sector the sound enters the slits and appears much louder. The
figure on the right shows how the locust can scan the surroundings
by swinging its legs as it walks (Autrum).

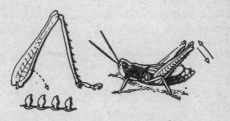

Figure 99.
The method of 'stridulation' in the short-horned grasshoppers. To the
left, the row of pegs on the inner surface of the femur. To the right,
the movement of the legs which sweeps the pegs across the margins
of the wings (Weber).

Figure 100.
In the katydid, or long-horned grasshopper, *Ephippiger*, the hind-wings are absent; the fore-wings, or 'tegmina', are very small (just visible behind the prothorax in the figure) and are used solely for stridulation (Robert).

then released, it produces sound by the same mechanism as a rounded tin lid pressed inwards by the finger. The purpose of the cicada's song is to assemble the local population of one species, males and females, into a small group.

In crickets and grasshoppers there are three main types of song. The ordinary spontaneous song of sexually mature males; the wooing song of the males of many species when the female is close, which induces the female to mount the male and mate with him; and the rival duet of males—a sort of 'ritual battle', which may be long continued before mating begins. In some species there is a 'triumphal song' just before mating, and a copulatory song during pairing. In quite a number of Acridiidae and Tettigoniidae the female also stridulates—but only during a very restricted period when she is ready to receive the male. This song is, therefore, easily missed.

The song of any one species of insect thus differs with the circumstances; and the different species produce songs that are unlike, and that are recognized by their own kind. In order to appreciate the sort of difference that the insect uses in distinguishing one song from another, we must consider a little more closely just how these songs are produced.

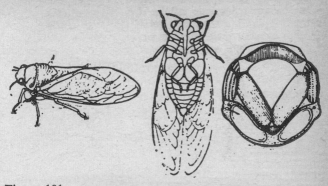

Figure 101.
Sound production and hearing in the cicada (Robert). In the middle is the cicada viewed from below. Above the hind-legs are a pair of oval plates which conceal the 'tymbals' and the ear-drums. On the right is a section through the back of the thorax showing the powerful muscles which are attached to the ridged tymbals (at the sides, above) and which produce the song; and the two ear-drums, or 'mirrors', below (Weber).

Most commonly, in the grasshopper, the impact of each tooth produces a succession of vibrations in the wing, which partially die away before the next tooth strikes and a new chain of vibrations begins (figure 102: *Ephippiger*). The result is a very complex noise, which consists of a succession of loud trills, or pulses of sound, each of which marks the impact of a new tooth. The whole pattern of sound is, therefore, decided by the anatomy of the insect (the nature of the vibrating wing membrane and the number and spacing of the teeth) and by the frequency and rapidity of movement of the legs or the other structures that carry the teeth.

In the song of some crickets each trill is produced by some ten or twenty oscillations of the wing membrane. The structure is so arranged that the time between the impact of one tooth and the next corresponds with the resonant frequency of the wing. The result is that one sound wave is given out as each tooth strikes the wing, and a relatively pure note of 2,000–3,000 cycles per second is produced (figure 102: *Oecanthus*).

In the cicadas the tymbals vibrate naturally at a frequency of about 4,500 cycles per second. They are set in vibration,

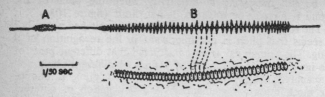

Ephippiger bitterensis

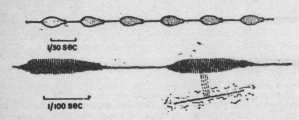

Oecanthus pellucens
Figure 102.
Above, electric recording (oscillogram) of the song of the katydid
Ephippiger (figure 100) and the file on the small fore-wings (tegmina) which produce the sound. A, is the sound caused by opening
the tegmina, B, the sound produced by closing them. This is made
up of a series of sound 'pulses' each of which is produced by one
tooth of the file.
Below, slow and fast oscillograms of the song of the tree cricket
Oecanthus. Each pulse of sound is here produced by one stroke of
the file. As shown in the fast recording each tooth on the file produces a single sound wave giving a pure note at a frequency of about
2,500 cycles per second (Busnel).

as we have seen, by the contractions of the tymbal muscles.
These muscles resemble the wing muscles of flies (p. 62) in
being capable of exceedingly rapid rates of contraction,
approaching four hundred per second. The result is that at
each of these contractions the tymbal gives out a 'pulse' of
sound which is at the high frequency of its natural vibration.

We saw that the tactile hairs which serve as occasional
organs of hearing respond to relatively low-pitched sounds.
But it is characteristic of the tympanal organs of insects that
they are most sensitive to exceedingly high notes. In *Locusta*,
notes with a frequency higher than 90,000 cycles per second
can still be heard; this is more than two octaves higher than
the human ear can detect. Indeed the grasshopper ear seems

to be still increasing in sensitivity when the pitch of the sound is already beyond the human limit (figure 103).

The songs of insects are rich in these high-pitched notes, but it seems that pitch is not important in the recognition of a song. The human ear is so constructed that different parts of the inner ear are stimulated by sounds of different pitch, and the analysis of sounds according to their pitch is one of the most important elements in the recognition of different sounds. But in insects such a mechanism is almost non-existent, and electrical studies of the nerve from the tympanal organs have shown that what the insect is perceiving is a succession of volleys of nerve impulses, corresponding to the rapid pulses of sound given out by the stridulating organ (figure 102). The important factor in the recognition of a specific song is the rate of repetition of these pulses of sound—and that, as we have seen, is largely dependent on the anatomy of the sound-producing organs.

It was shown by Regen many years ago that the female cricket, which is attracted to the male by his chirping from a distance of more than 30 feet, will be equally attracted to chirps transmitted by telephone, and these will cause her to go to the receiver. But during this transmission the high-frequency notes in the chirps are lost; indeed the sound is so distorted as to be quite unrecognizable to the human ear. What remains unchanged is the rhythm, the frequency with which the sound as a whole waxes and wanes; it is this 'frequency modulation' which the cricket recognizes as characteristic of her mate. The sounds of high frequency, which are given out by the stridulating insect, act as a 'carrier' for a low-frequency modulation.

The insect is thus in striking contrast to ourselves; our ears are almost insensitive to the frequency of modulation. That is because of the large difference between the insect ear and the human ear in the time taken for the ear to recover from one stimulus in readiness for the next (the so-called 'time constant'). This is at least ten times longer in the human ear—with the result that, whereas we can only distinguish two sounds when they are separated by an interval of not less than 1/10 second, insects can distinguish sounds separated by intervals as small as 1/100 second. They can easily distinguish the separate pulses of sound of which insect songs are made up.

It is when we turn to insects that have no songs, that the purpose of their elaborate tympanal organs is more puzzling. This applies particularly to the Lepidoptera. It is well known that bats in flight continually give out brief pulses

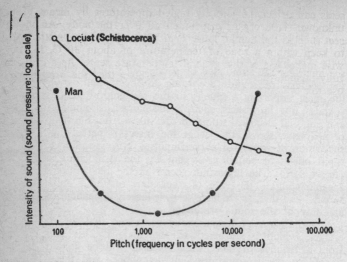

Figure 103.
Graphs showing the 'auditory threshold' (the lowest intensity of sound that can be heard) with sounds of different pitch. The most sensitive region for the human ear is at about 1,000 cycles per second. In the locust *Schistocerca* the threshold is still falling when the pitch is too high to be audible for man.

of sound at a very high pitch of 30,000–80,000 cycles per second, at the limit of human hearing and beyond. They use the reflected echoes of these sounds to locate obstructions in the dark and to hunt their prey. When Noctuid or Geometrid moths are exposed to such sounds, they react by flight, or by becoming motionless and 'feigning death'; and it has been shown by electrical methods that the tympanic organs can detect the cries of an approaching bat. It has, therefore, been suggested that they use their ears to escape from bats. In addition to this the tympanic organs are stimulated by the sounds given out by another moth in flight, and an alternative suggestion is that they might use the reflection of their own flight sounds to detect objects in the dark. But there has been no proof of this idea.

The perception of temperature is sometimes classed among the mechanical senses on the ground that heat and cold depend on differing rates of vibration of molecules. But very little is known about how sense organs are able to recognize temperature differences. It is certain that insects can detect dangerously high temperatures by means of unknown sense organs distributed all over the body. An insect such as the human louse *Pediculus,* which always strives to keep within a zone of temperature of about 30°C, likewise makes use of this general temperature sense. Bees carefully regulate the temperature of the hive; they too probably use this widespread sense of temperature.

We saw (p. 33) how locusts and other insects can orient themselves so that they can collect much radiant heat from the sun if they are too cold, and a minimum of radiant heat if they are too hot. This perception has been ascribed to certain areas of the body surface where there are windows of thin and transparent cuticle; but the nerve supply and the sense organs in these special areas have not been fully described, and there is some doubt about this explanation.

There are insects, however, with an exceedingly delicate temperature sense that is carried by the antennae. The bedbug *Cimex* (figure 35) and its large relative from South America, the blood-sucking bug *Rhodnius,* feed upon warm-blooded animals; and the warmth of the air in their neighbourhood is one of the main guides which leads them to their victims. When these insects are kept in a hungry state in a glass jar, they can often be seen to approach and probe with their 'proboscis' those places where the glass has been warmed by holding in the fingers. This behaviour disappears if the antennae are cut off. It seems likely that the innumerable fine hairs on the antenna are responsible for this very sensitive perception.

The perception of moisture in the air is another sense which it has proved difficult to locate exactly. The general tendency is for insects to avoid humid places. The earwig, for example, seems to have organs of some kind on the lower surface of the abdomen which detect moisture and enable it to avoid unsuitable resting places. The human louse *Pediculus* likewise avoids a high humidity, and here the organs responsible have been recognized. They take the form of minute tufts of excessively fine hairs carried on the tips of the antennae; if these are covered with cellulose paint the louse no longer avoids moist air. Somewhat similar organs are found on the lower surface of house-fly maggots. Other insects, such as the larvae of wireworms, are adapted to live in very moist conditions. They have sense organs which seem to be very sensitive to drying, and the larvae avoid low humidities. But here, and in many other insects, it has proved impossible to distinguish between the organs which detect humidity, and the organs of smell.

Very much more is known about the chemical senses of insects, for these play a most important part in their lives. So far as we ourselves are concerned, pungent chemicals such as acid fumes or ammonia will produce smarting of the eyes or at any point where the skin is broken. Likewise in insects, materials of this kind will cause irritation in all parts of the body. They are sometimes said to be perceived by a 'general chemical sense'.

Apart from this we classify our chemical senses into taste and smell. Taste, properly speaking, comprises the four sensations of salt, sweet, sour, and bitter that are perceived by the nose. But what are commonly called 'tastes', or 'flavours', are a complex mixture of true tastes recognized by the tongue combined with odours that are simultaneously being analysed by the nose. It is a matter of opinion whether the distinction between taste and smell can be maintained in the insect, when the same organs may be concerned with both sensations, and where in aquatic insects both groups of substances are dissolved in water when they are tested by the sense organ. But since we draw a clear distinction between true tastes and odours it is convenient to use the same terms in thinking about the senses of insects.

Organs of taste are certainly associated with the mouth in many insects. Bees will reject honey treated with quinine or salt; caterpillars make vigorous spitting movements of the mouth in response to salt, acid, or bitter substances. In the bee, sensory pits at the base of the tongue are perhaps the sensitive organs; in caterpillars the response disappears if certain of the mouth-parts are removed; and in plant-sucking bugs there are organs of taste within or behind the cavity of the mouth. In the cockroach the taste organs, or 'contact chemoreceptors' as they are often called, are on the tips of the maxillary and labial palps as well as inside the upper lip, or labrum. The same applies to many beetles.

It is possible for the water-beetle *Dytiscus* to learn to associate a particular taste with the presence of food. The beetle is submitted to a course of training in which it is either rewarded with sweetened meat or punished with quinine-treated meat. After several months, if accustomed to being fed with the sweetened meat after a salt taste, *Dytiscus* will disregard cotton wool containing sugar, but respond to wool containing salt. In this way it can be shown that this beetle can distinguish the four taste qualities. Many of the sensilla concerned are carried by the palps, but others (inside the mouth) remain after the palps have been removed.

When a wasp settles on a smear of jam it can often be observed to sweep the surface with its antennae. That suggests that the antennae also can serve as organs of taste. It has, indeed, been proved by experiment that ants, bees, and wasps can distinguish plain and sweetened water by means of the antennae, and this response to sugar is prevented if acid or quinine are added.

But a much more frequent site for organs of taste, and a rather surprising one, is on the feet, notably on the tarsus and the lower end of the tibia. Many butterflies and moths, the honey-bee, the fruit-fly *Drosophila*, the blowflies *Calliphora* and *Phormia*, and many others, immediately extend the proboscis in search of food if the tarsi come into contact with the sweetened water (figure 104). This response can sometimes be prevented if quinine is added to the sugar; but in general it seems that the tarsal sense organs are concerned mainly with recognizing the presence of sugar and calling attention to it; the more careful analysis of the material as a possible source of food is done by the sense organs in the mouth-parts themselves. These sense organs on the feet are commonly sensitive to sugar solutions far more dilute, sometimes over two hundred times more dilute, than the human tongue can detect.

The complexity of the analysis that can be made by a single sensillum is well illustrated in the blowfly *Phormia*. These flies have long, thin-walled hairs on the tarsi and on the margins of the 'tongue' (the lobes of the labella, p. 75). If

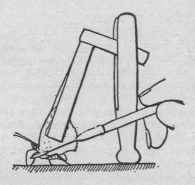

Figure 104.
The red admiral butterfly *Pyrameis atalanta* extends its proboscis when the tarsus is touched with a brush carrying sugar and water (Minnich).

a tiny droplet of sugar solution is rolled along the shaft of one of these hairs nothing happens until the drop reaches the tip, and then the proboscis is extended. This experiment shows that only the tip is sensitive, and that the stimulation of a single sensory hair is sufficient to produce the characteristic response. Furthermore, each of these hairs has three sense cells, with three corresponding nerve fibers running to the brain, and three sensory endings in the single hair (figure 105). One of these endings is sensitive to sugar alone, and when it is stimulated it leads to extension of the proboscis and the imbibition of liquid. The second ending is not concerned with sugar; it is stimulated by a great variety of substances and always causes retraction of the proboscis and the cessation of feeding. The third ending is not a taste receptor at all but is sensitive to mechanical stimulation.

The sense of taste has been studied in much detail in the honey-bee. It has been found that most substances which appear sweet to us are apparently tasteless to the bee. For example, out of thirty-four sugars and closely related substances that have been tested, thirty appear sweet to the human tongue, but only nine appear sweet to the bee, and all these nine are substances present in the natural food of the bee. All artificial sweet substances, such as saccharin, are tasteless when in dilute solution and repellent at higher concentration.

Among plant-eating insects the choice of food-plant is influenced or decided by many kinds of strongly tasting substances which cannot be classed simply as sweet, salt, sour, or bitter. The suggestion was made many years ago that the accumulation of strongly flavoured chemicals by plants, such as glucosides, tannins, alkaloids, essential oils, etc, was brought about by natural selection because they gave protection against plant-eating animals. But natural selection worked both ways; certain insects developed a tolerance for these repellent substances so that they were able to feed upon the protected plants. Finally tolerance changed to preference for the substances in question and these have come to serve as *attractants*. We find different species of insects invariably feeding upon plants which contain 'repellent' chemicals of a particular type. The white butterflies of the genus *Pieris,* and the diamond-back moth *Plutella* will eat only plants which contain the glucosides of mustard oils (sinigrin and sinalbin); they will feed on cabbage and other Cruciferae and on 'nasturtiums' (*Tropaeolum*). These larvae can be induced to eat filter paper if it is impregnated with sinigrin.

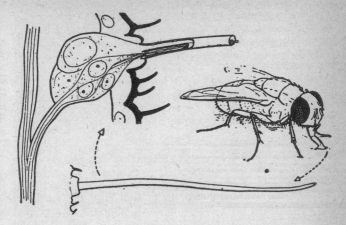

Figure 105.
A single hair (below) from the margin of the tongue of the blowfly showing the sensory tip. Above, a microscopic section through the hair showing the three sense cells and the two nerve endings running in an inner tube to the tip of the hair (Hodgson).

The caterpillars of many swallowtail butterflies, *Papilio*, feed on Umbelliferae containing characteristic essential oils.

Caterpillars of the silkworm are attracted to mulberry leaves from a distance by certain volatile substances (α-β-hexenol and β-γ-hexenol) which are of common occurrence in many kinds of leaves. But their specific choice of mulberry seems to be due to other types of compound which are recognized by taste rather than smell. Some of these substances stimulate the biting action of the caterpillars; others stimulate continuous swallowing. By the use of these stimulants extracted from mulberry leaves the larvae have been induced to feed on agar. Conversely, if silkworms are deprived of their maxillae, they will feed readily on cherry, cabbage, or other leaves: they can no longer taste the repellent substances which these leaves contain.

The sense of smell in insects is located chiefly in the antennae. This was clearly proved by Lefebvre in 1838 when he showed that the antennae of the bee are extended in any direction towards a needle dipped in ether; while in the absence of the antennae there was no response to odours at all. Observations of this kind have since been made on many sorts of insects. The cockroach *Periplaneta* will locate cheese from a distance with its antennae, with which it reaches out in all directions as the source of smell is moved. The males of Bombycid and Saturniid moths such as the silkworm moths, as we have seen, locate the female by smell, and this sense is confined to the highly branched antennae. Females of the parasitic wasp *Habrobracon* discover their host, the mealmoth *Ephestia,* by smell, and the males find the females by the same means; if the antennae are cut off or covered with varnish these reactions fail. When the dung-rolling beetle *Scarabaeus* is searching for dung in which to lay its eggs it holds the antennae aloft with the clubs spread open.

But in many insects the palps also bear organs of smell. There is a deep olfactory pit well supplied with sensilla at the tip of the palps in butterflies; it is estimated that in *Pieris* the sense of smell is not reduced by much more than half if the antennae are amputated. In beetles, also, the maxillary and labial palps carry organs of smell, although as a general rule these are much less important than the antennae, and are probably used mainly for the examination of foods during the act of eating.

It is interesting to consider the distribution of the olfactory organs in the blowfly *Cynomyia.* These organs are confined to the antennae and the 'labella' which form the extremity of the proboscis. This has been proved by training the fly to associate the odour of coumarin (a substance with a strong persistent scent resembling fresh hay) with contact of the tarsi with sugar. After training, when the fly has developed a 'conditioned reflex', it will extend the proboscis on exposure to the odour alone without any sugar being present. If now both the antennae and the labella are removed, the response to the odour of coumarin is eliminated, and flies so treated cannot learn. But if either the antennae or the labella alone remain, the response continues. It may be that the combined stimulation of the sense organs of the labella by odours as described here, and by simple tastes of sweetness, etc, as described earlier, will produce an effect comparable with the perception of tastes and flavours by ourselves.

This experimental procedure of training insects to associate some desirable experience, such as the presence of sugar, with some other kind of stimulus, is a standard method for discovering whether this other kind of stimulus can be perceived by the insect or not. The powers of smell in the honey-bee have been studied in great detail by training foraging bees to associate particular scents, mostly flower scents and essential oils, with the presence of honey. By this means it has been found that the bee can distinguish, for example, essence of orange from forty-three other ethereal oils. There seems to be much in common between this sense in the bee and the human sense of smell. The olfactory acuity—that is, the lowest concentration of a scent that can be perceived—does not seem to be very different in the bee and in man. But there are some divergences. The human nose seems to be about five times more sensitive to oil of rosemary than is the bee; whereas the bee is far more sensitive to the smell of beeswax or to the scent of other bees; and the bee is far more efficient at detecting a particular odour in a mixture of others. This is probably important in the recognition of hive mates by their complex mixture of scents.

As a general rule, substances which appear odorous to us appear scented to the bee; flowers such as those of red currants or *Vaccinium* which seem odourless to us are either odourless or relatively weakly scented for the bee. It is particularly interesting that nitrobenzol, which has an odour resembling oil of almonds (it is commonly used to make an unpleasant substitute for marzipan), can be confused with oil of almonds also by the bee. It is of interest, also, to note that while bees can learn to associate many ethereal scents with the presence of sugar, they cannot be trained in this way with foul-smelling substances such as skatol or asafoetida. When the antennae are removed the bee can no longer detect even powerful odours.

The recognition of odours is equally important in other groups of insects. Caterpillars of the large cabbage white butterfly are attracted by the odour of their own species and so form dense colonies; and they will follow trails of this scent leading to such a colony. Many Lepidoptera, when they come to lay their eggs, are guided by the smell of their special food-plant: probably that is why certain species lay their eggs always on plants belonging to the same natural family. For example, the deaths-head hawk-moth *Acherontia* chooses Solenaceae—potato or nightshade. Ants, like bees, recognize by smell the members of their own community, and ants of different genera, which normally fight, will feed amicably together after removal of their antennae.

Chapter **13**

THE WISDOM OF THE INSECT

THE 'WISDOM of the body' is a poetic phrase which comprehends all those intricate and co-ordinated workings of the living machine that form the subject of physiology. Every figure in this elaborate pattern of activity seems to be predetermined. The response to any interference, changes of temperature, lack of oxygen, the infliction of injuries, and many more, can be predicted. The task of the physiologist is to formulate the 'laws' which make such predictions possible.

But when he turns to the workings of the mind and brain, and the different kinds of behaviour to which thought can lead, the physiologist finds himself out of his depth. It may be that in course of time it will become possible to describe and perhaps predict all these acts of thought and behaviour on the basis of 'laws', not necessarily laws of physiology, but of psychology.

This chapter has been named 'the wisdom of the insect' in order to emphasize the parallel with the wisdom of the body as defined above. The behaviour of insects gives the impression of being stereotyped. The insect seems to have a set of prearranged acts, each well suited to its normal conditions of life. When faced with a given situation it produces the appropriate 'act'. These acts, or 'patterns of behaviour', are built into the nervous system in some way that we do not

229

in the least understand, and they are inherited like any other character in the form or colour of the body, so that on the first occasion they are called for they can be performed with absolute precision—in exactly the same way as a growing insect can form a perfect head or brain without having had any previous practice or experience. These acts of behaviour are commonly called 'instincts'.

It is not easy to compare this kind of behaviour with our own, which seems to be so much more dependent upon practice and experience. But it is well to remember that most of our own activities from minute to minute are of exactly the same preformed type as those of the insect; that it may well be that many others which we believe to be based on 'reason' are really of the same kind; and that in any case the brain and nervous system which operate our behaviour are preformed in precisely the same fashion as those of the insect and certainly work on the same general principles.

The chief difference between the brain of an insect and the human brain is one of quantity. We have immeasurably more brain cells and connecting fibres. This vast supply of nerve cells and connections provides for a corresponding variety in behaviour, and capacity for learning. The insect with its *relatively* few nerve cells is compelled to economize its equipment and to organize its behaviour along set lines, all closely adapted to the situations it will meet in its normal life, and with comparatively little scope for individual learning from experience. Indeed it can be argued that in an animal as short-lived as most insects the ability to learn is of far less importance in survival than an efficient set of 'built-in' reactions.

The emphasis in these statements should be on the words 'relatively' and 'comparatively'. When at the end of the last century the great Spanish student of the nervous system, Ramon y Cajal, was trying to understand the connections of the eye with the brain, he turned to the eye of the fly hoping to find there the nervous basis of vision 'in relative simplicity'. But after studying this for two years he wrote: 'The complexity of the nerve structure for vision is even in the insect something incredibly stupendous . . . The intricacy of the connections defies description. Before it the mind halts abased'. That is the experience of anyone who actually looks inside the insect brain in the hope of finding a simple structure.

One curious feature of the insect nervous system (shared with many other invertebrate animals) may be mentioned here. If the insect is to save itself from its enemies it must be able to act quickly. A few thousandths of a second may make all the difference between life and death. But small nerve fibres conduct nervous impulses rather slowly. The speed of conduction is roughly proportional to the diameter of the fibre. We therefore find that most insects have a few 'giant fibres', which run through the whole length of the nervous system and convey very rapidly the information needed for a quick response. Refinements in perception, that would have been given by a large number of small fibres, have been sacrificed to speed. The time required for a fly to get away when alarmed is about a twentieth of a second. The time needed for the complete strike of a praying mantis (p. 322) is about the same.

Admitting that we do not understand the workings of the brain, we can at least appreciate that what it is largely doing is receiving information by means of the nerves coming from the sense organs scattered all over the surface of the body, co-ordinating this information and acting accordingly, or turning on the behaviour pattern best suited for the situation on hand (figure 92). In this chapter on insect behaviour we shall be continually looking at these dual aspects: the information, or nervous signals, from the sense organs, and the inborn patterns, or instincts, which this information provokes.

One functon of the sense organs seems to be to keep the nervous system 'awake' and ready to react. Some insects are exceedingly lethargic in the dark. The humming-bird hawk-moth (*Macroglossa*) will fly in a room lit with electric light, but immediately falls to the ground if the light is switched off; or, if the eyes are blackened over, it settles, folds its wings, and lays back its antennae.

This often seems to be the chief function of the simple eyes, or ocelli: these are little concerned in vision themselves, but they quicken the response of the insect to changes in the brightness of light as seen by the compound eyes. The antennae have a similar function; it is probably the movements of the air, which disturb the antennae and stimulate John-ston's organ (p. 212), that keep the insect awake. The blood-sucking bug *Rhodnius* without its antennae becomes extraor-dinarily sluggish and difficult to arouse, as though it had fallen into a deep sleep. And we saw how flying insects need the stimulating effect of air blowing against tactile hairs on the head and antennae, if they are to be kept in continuous flight. In the two-winged flies, the reduced hind-wings or 'halteres', besides acting as organs of equilibrium (p. 210), seem also to have a comparable stimulating effect.

During the early years of the present century there was a

school of thought led by Jacques Loeb which aimed at proving that there was a more or less mechanical and inevitable connection between the stimuli received by the sense organs, and the resulting muscular movements set going by the brain. According to his view the muscles were 'forced' to make particular movements when particular nerve stimuli were given. This was the theory of 'tropisms, taxes, or forced movements' in which the living body was compared with a mechanical model of a dog furnished with photoelectric cells behind its model eyes, so wired to suitable electric motors that it would turn towards a flash lamp and follow this in all directions.

In the development of this theory the insects played a prominent part. Indeed it is possible to describe the behaviour of many insects as though they were working in this sort of way. When the caterpillar of the browntail moth *Euproctis* hatches from the egg it has a strong reaction towards light. Light seems to provoke a 'forced movement' and the young larvae invariably crawl towards the source of illumination. If they are placed in the middle of a tube with a light at one end and a supply of leaves at the other, they will crawl towards the illuminated end and die of starvation. We saw how the male silkworm moth is excited and attracted by the female scent, which it perceives with its bushy antennae. If both antennae are intact it will make straight towards the female. If one antenna is cut off it will circle towards the sound antenna and never reach the female at all. It behaves just like the model dog with one of its model eyes blacked out, when it is exposed to a bright light.

But although experiments of this kind are impressive, the theory of 'forced movements' has proved unsatisfactory. The more closely these simple acts of behaviour are studied the more complex do they appear. We can get a truer picture if we say that the young *Euproctis* caterpillar has a built-in behaviour pattern which consists in crawling against gravity and towards the light. In normal circumstances, in the forest, these reactions will cause it to move up the trunk towards the tree top where the leaves are. The male silkworm moth has a very rigid behaviour pattern which consists in crawling and fluttering towards the female scent. These descriptions are no less scientific in spite of the fact that we do not understand how a 'behaviour pattern' is constructed.

What is of lasting value about the theories of 'tropisms' and 'taxes' are the ideas they give us about how the insect makes use of its sense organs in finding its way about. The caterpillar swings its head from side to side scanning the field of view (p. 186) as it walks, moving in the direction of the light. If there are two lights, well separated, it will go towards a point between them. But when it has advanced a certain distance it can satisfy its need of going towards the light only by turning and crawling towards one light or the other. The male silkmoth with its antennae more or less fixed and spread out in front of it, follows its antennae when the two are equally stimulated by the scent. When one antenna is cut off all the scent appears to lie towards the sound side and the moth circles in that direction.

The sense organs may be used in other ways. Many insects, such as the earwig, the bed-bug, and some moths, creep into crevices for concealment. They are not necessarily impelled by the avoidance of light, as might have been supposed (the moth *Amphipyra* for example is perfectly content to settle down between two sheets of glass), but they come to rest when as many as possible of their tactile hairs are touching some solid object. An earwig in a plain rounded dish will finally come to rest with its body curved and pressed into the angle between the wall and the floor (figure 106). Most insects will settle down only when the feet are in contact with the ground. A fly suspended on a wire fixed to the thorax with wax, will vibrate its wings in flight. The wings come to rest at once if it is given a little ball of cotton wool to hold in its feet; in the house-fly *Musca*, contact with a

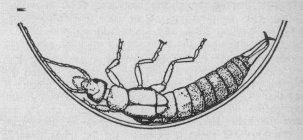

Figure 106.
The earwig at rest in a glass dish: it brings as much of its body as possible into contact with the glass (Weyrauch).

single claw of one leg is enough to inhibit flight. Some moths firmly settled on a tree trunk, with the wings, legs, and antennae closely applied to the surface, are in a sleep-like state from which they may be quite difficult to arouse. They wake up at once if the feet are detached from the surface. Other senses besides touch may be used to inhibit movement and cause the insect to settle down. The earwig *Forficula* is agitated by moist surfaces and will settle only in dry surroundings; the mealworm *Tenebrio* behaves in the same way; but the wireworm *Agriotes,* which lives in the soil, reacts in just the reverse fashion, it shows intense burrowing activity in dry soil but is quickly immobilized if this is moist.

In some insects the need for contact to inhibit movement may be replaced on suitable occasions by a totally different pattern of behaviour. When suddenly disturbed by a potential enemy, they fall instantly into a motionless hypnotic state with the legs in any chance position. This is the 'death-feigning' reaction already discussed (p. 163). It may be brought on in many insects by sudden loss of contact between the feet and the ground, as when the plant on which the insect is resting is suddenly jarred; or by touch or rolling between the fingers as in the water scorpion *Ranatra.* The 'warning' attitudes assumed by some caterpillars and saw-fly larvae when disturbed (p. 176) seem to be special forms of the same response. The stick insect *Dixippus* and various caterpillars, which are protectively coloured against their background, assume a comparable hypnotic state which shows a diurnal rhythm and comes on during daylight. In this state the stick insect seems to be more or less insensitive; the muscles are in a condition resembling that of catalepsy in man: the limbs can be forced into any queer position and will remain there as though the joints were made of wax.

Some of the simplest methods of using the sense organs by which insects find their way about can be well illustrated from the behaviour of the body louse *Pediculus.* The louse is accustomed to live in a temperature of 30°C which is the usual temperature between the clothes and the skin. When crawling at this temperature it moves in a more or less straight line; but if it comes to a place with a slightly higher or a slightly lower temperature, say 32°C or 28°C, it no longer walks straight but begins to turn at random to right and left. As soon as it re-enters an area with a more favourable temperature it crawls in a straight line again (figure 107). Of course, if the louse continued indefinitely to turn rapidly to right and left when it found itself in uncomfortable surroundings, it could be trapped and remain there turning indefinitely. But after a time it becomes hardened, or 'adapted', to the unpleasant conditions, and begins again to crawl in a straight line, and continues to do so as long as conditions remain the same or improve. But if they become less favourable, it repeats the same procedure and starts turning again.

The louse adopts this procedure of random turning followed by 'adaptation', in many kinds of mildly unfavourable conditions: temperatures that are rather too high or too low; air that is rather too moist; surfaces that are somewhat too smooth, as when it moves from rough wool to smooth silk; the absence of the odour of human sweat or the smell of other lice and their excrement. When conditions become more strongly disagreeable the frequency of turning increases. And when they become very strong indeed, the first turn may be so abrupt and complete that the louse immediately reverses its direction and returns to the favourable environment. This extreme form of the response is called an 'avoiding reaction' and appears in the presence of all kinds of harmful stimuli.

These turning reactions are used by many insects for finding their way about among diffuse odours, areas of unfavourable temperature or humidity, and so forth. Male Bombycid or Saturniid moths attracted by the female scent from great distances make use of the same procedure. So long as they are flying upwind into the scent they continue flying in a straight line; but if they lose the scent they begin a zigzag flight, and if they overshoot the mark so that the scent sud-

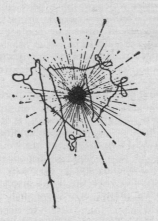

Figure 107.
Diagram of the track followed by the louse *Pediculus* in approaching a favourable stimulus, such as a source of warmth. It moves in a straight line so long as the favourable stimulus remains constant or increases in strength; it shows random turning movements when the strength of the stimulus diminishes (Wigglesworth).

denly disappears they instantly stop flying, and alight, and reverse on foot.

When the location of the smell or source of heat is more definite, insects may use their sense organs in a different way. They may be able to compare conditions on the two sides of the body simultaneously by means of the two antennae, and then move in such a direction that both antennae are equally stimulated. The male silkworm moth seeking the female at short range is an example of that. We saw that removal of one antenna causes circling towards the opposite side.

Or insects may make successive comparisons in different directions by means of the antennae. The blood-sucking bug *Rhodnius* is attracted to its host by the warm, scented air around it. When offered the choice of a tube of warm water and a similar warm tube covered with a fresh mouse skin, *Rhodnius* will extend the antennae first in one direction and then in another and finally move off towards the mouse skin and probe this with its proboscis.

These different ways of using the sense organs are all classified and given different names; but that is apt to make them appear more fixed and rigid than they really are. Obviously the insect may change over from one procedure to another in the course of a single act.

Most of the senses which we have been considering so far, touch, temperature, humidity, smell, or taste, can be used only to detect changes in immediate contact with the insect. The insect cannot normally infer from what direction these stimuli are coming. An exception to this is when such stimuli as warmth, moisture, or odour are carried from their source on a stream of air. Some insects, such as fruit-flies, dung-beetles, and flesh-flies which breed in carrion pay no attention to a stream of plain air, but will immediately turn into the air stream and crawl against it, if it carries the attractive odour. This seems to be a combination of the turning reaction (with straight line movement in favourable surroundings) and the use of tactile hairs as a guide to the direction of the wind. That can only apply, of course, so long as the insect is on the ground. How the flying insect orientates itself in a wind is another matter, which we shall consider a little later.

We must first say something about the use of senses, notably vision and hearing, which operate from a distance and may, therefore, give a clear indication of direction. Of course the eyes can be used after the manner of the antennae of the male silkworm moth. The insect may be attracted to light, or it may be repelled by light and attracted by darkness. In the former case, if one eye is blackened, the insect will circle towards the uncovered eye; in the latter case it will circle towards the blackened eye. Insects can be described as positive or negative towards light, and this simple response will lead them into light or darkness as the case may be.

Aquatic insects, such as larvae of the may-fly *Cloëon* (figure 19) or the Naucorid bug *Aphelocheirus* (figure 27) keep their position when swimming freely in the water by making sure that the eyes are receiving the light from above the head and in equal amounts in the two eyes. If they are placed in an aquarium which is illuminated from below they will swim upside down. Indeed, the larvae of the water-beetles *Acilius* and *Dytiscus* have a dermal light sense (p. 184) which is sensitive enough to ensure that they swim with their backs to the light even if they are totally blind.

But the eye is provided with a retina; it can locate precisely the direction of objects or of a source of light. This provides the insect with an entirely new way of orienting itself. If a beetle is placed on a sheet of white paper exposed to the sun it will crawl in a straight line. If it is covered with a black box it immediately becomes disoriented and moves in any direction. But if it is once more exposed to the sunlight it will again begin to crawl in a straight line in the same direction as before. This is called the 'sun-compass' reaction and is widely used by insects. They quickly become accus-

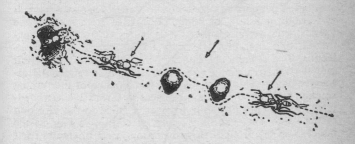

Figure 108.
Ants using the 'sun-compass' to steer a more or less straight course to and from the nest (Berland).

tomed to receiving the image of the sun at some fixed part of the retina, and they continue to move so that this state of affairs remains unchanged. Ants make use of this procedure in finding their way to and from the nest (figure 108). Moths which fly by night will steer by the moon in the same way; and since the moon is so far off they will fly more or less in a straight line at a fixed angle to it. But if on a dark night they make use of a lamp for this purpose, they will turn towards it as they get near to it, so as to keep the angle of approach the same. They will in fact approach the light in a spiral (a 'logarithmic spiral') which ends in their colliding with the flame (figure 109).

(Some insects, such as caterpillars, apparently steering by the sun-compass may in fact be following the plane of polarization in the blue sky; or the radiant heat from the sun—going directly towards the sun when they are cool, turning more and more away from it as they become warmer, and finally moving directly away from it when overheated.)

Insects do not use the sun and moon alone for this sort of compass reaction; they may attempt to fix quite near objects on their retina in the same way. If a fly is allowed to sit on a revolving table facing a window or some other conspicuous object, and the table is then made to rotate slowly, the fly will move round in such a way that it remains facing the object. Similarly a water-boatman *Notonecta* placed in a stream

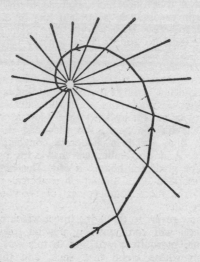

Figure 109.
Diagram of the course followed by a moth approaching a lamp. It keeps the light falling on its retina at a constant angle to the direction of flight, and thus flies into the lamp along a 'logarithmic spiral' (v. Buddenbrock).

of flowing water will 'fix' with its eyes some object on the bank and turn round and swim against the current so as to maintain a constant position.

This tendency to avoid change in the visual pattern as received by the retina seems to recur again and again in the behaviour of insects. Caterpillars and other insects will creep along the edge of black bars painted on paper and follow the bar if it changes direction. The earwig, the louse, and other insects will be attracted to small dark areas in a white background. Perhaps the most striking example is the behaviour of locusts. Migrating locusts, whether as marching bands of 'hoppers' on the ground, or as winged adults in the air, tend to keep a constant image of neighbouring locusts on their retina. Hence they move along in the same direction as their companions. This is certainly one factor which helps to maintain the cohesion of locust swarms; but such swarms are also making use of distant objects, including the sun, to steer themselves on a straight course. That can be shown very strikingly with a marching band of hoppers moving to the north with the sun shining from the east. If they are shaded from the sun with a blanket, and a mirror is placed on the opposite side so as to reflect the light of the sun from the west, the hoppers will turn round and march to the south. Indeed, by changing the apparent position of the sun they can be made to march to and fro like soldiers on the parade ground.

It is obvious that such insects must have some degree of memory as to what part of the retina was receiving the light. A more complicated form of the same reaction is seen in the whirligig beetles *Gyrinus*. These also will maintain their position in a pool or stream by keeping in view a constant pattern of objects on the bank. But they can do this while swimming at high speed in elaborate convolutions in the water surface. And dragonflies will hawk for prey up and down the same glade for hours on end. This behaviour can hardly be described as a simple physiological response. It leads us into the more complex acts of behaviour that we must consider later.

We may now revert to the flying insect which orients itself upwind. Insects will commonly fly upwind towards an attractive odour: mosquitoes will find in this way the warm-blooded hosts whose blood they suck, and the males of Saturniid or Bombycid moths fly upwind to the female. How do they recognize the direction of the wind once they have taken off? The answer is that they do so with their eyes. Mosquitoes in a stream of air over a series of stripes will fly upwind so that the image of the stripes moves backwards over the retina. In the yellow fever mosquito (*Aedes aegypti*) the maximum speed of flight is about $3\frac{1}{3}$ miles per hour. If the wind speed exceeds this they are carried backwards, and the stripes will move from behind forwards over the retina. This the insect will not tolerate; and it immediately alights. Of course, this mechanism will only operate when insects are near the ground; at higher altitudes they are swept along by the wind.

It is a common experience for anyone who has experimented with the behaviour of insects that they do not always show the reaction that is expected of them. They are not in the right 'mood'. This indeed is a fundamental character of their behaviour. Insects can generally be relied upon to show 'avoiding reactions' when exposed to some strongly disagreeable stimulus; but more subtle reactions require that the nervous system must be in the appropriate state. The state of the nervous system is commonly decided by the experience of the insect in the immediate past; this experience may cause a complete reversal in behaviour.

Take the example of the blood-sucking bug *Rhodnius*. The innumerable delicate sense organs on the antennae which respond to warmth and odours are protected by long tactile hairs that project above them. If these long bristles are lightly touched with a pencil the antennae are immediately withdrawn and the bug may retreat. But suppose the insect has been placed near a tube of warm water covered with a mouse skin; it has quickly reacted to this and is moving towards it with the antennae extended. If the protective bristles of the antennae are now touched with a pencil, there is no withdrawal but the proboscis is at once extended in an attempt to probe. The experience of warmth and smell had started the feeding response. The next step in this response would have been contact with the warm host and would have led to immediate probing. But the nervous system was now in such a sensitized state that the probing reaction was elicited even when the antenna touched a cold object.

There are any number of examples of such 'chain reactions', in which each response prepares or sensitizes the nervous system for the next response in the chain. Each instinctive response is commonly called forth by some special 'releaser stimulus'. If the 'releaser' does not come, the instinctive reaction may be triggered off by some very mild or quite inappropriate stimulus. Sometimes it is changes within the body which alter the responsiveness of the nervous system, sometimes it is the impact of the outside world.

Hunger itself is an example of a change in responsiveness due to altered conditions within the body. One of the strongest reactions of the blowfly *Phormia* is the drinking of syrup. But if a sweet fluid is present in the fore-gut, a certain nerve, the 'recurrent nerve', carries information to the brain which suppresses this hunger for sugar. If the recurrent nerve is cut, this inhibition is removed and the flies feed continuously until they die. Parasitic insects are commonly attracted to the food of the insects in which they seek to lay their eggs; but this response will vary with the state of the egg-laying female. Thus the ichneumon fly *Pimpla* which is a parasite of the pine-shoot moth *Rhyacionia buoliana* is repelled by the smell of pine oil early in its adult life; but as soon as the ovaries ripen it is strongly attracted by the oil.

The hunting wasp *Philanthus* stocks its solitary nest solely with honey-bees. It hunts these by sight, and is often attracted momentarily to bumble-bees or other insects. It may perceive a bumble-bee a foot away, but as soon as this comes within an inch or two it is recognized by its smell and left alone, whereas a honey-bee is seized. Smell is evidently very important in obtaining prey; but it is brought into play only when the expected victim has been seen; during the process of searching, *Philanthus* pays no attention at all to honey-bee odour.

Cocoon spinning by caterpillars affords a good example of a succession of instinctive responses controlled by both internal and external stimuli. In the giant cecropia silkmoth, for example, spinning consists of a progression of instinctive activities so organized that no stage can be omitted and no stage repeated. A predetermined amount of silk is utilized for the outer envelope of the cocoon, a set amount for the loose intermediate layer, and the greater part for the compact inner envelope. The steps in this sequence seem to be controlled by the amount of silk that has been ejected from the silk glands. Spinning is carried out by means of set movements, of which the most important are an alternate stretching and bending, and an alternate swinging of the head from side to side, coupled with the turning round of the body from time to time. The details of these movements must, of course, be influenced by the surroundings; but the mechanical nature of the spinning movements is well illustrated by experiments on the domestic silkworm *Bombyx*, in which the body of the caterpillar was splinted with wax in different positions so as to restrict the swinging movements of the head. Under the different conditions produced, the caterpillar may spin a very small cocoon, a very large cocoon, or even a flat cocoon with no inside.

But besides these mechanical influences, and the state of the silk glands, spinning activity may be influenced by hormones. When the young wax moth caterpillar (*Galleria*) is going to moult into a caterpillar again, it spins just a loose web on which it rests. But before the full-grown caterpillar moults into a pupa it spins a firm cocoon. If, however, the full-grown larva receives an extra amount of juvenile hormone, its spinning behaviour is changed and it prepares only a flimsy web.

The nest-building and provisioning activities of the solitary wasps and bees provide the supreme examples of complex sequences of elaborate behaviour patterns. The leaf-cutter bee *Megachile* (figure 110) must first locate a suitable site for the nest in soil or rotten wood, and shape this into

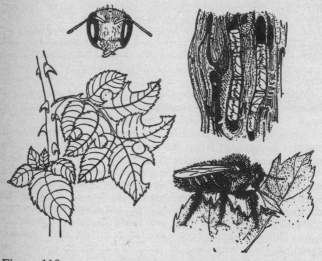

Figure 110.
The leaf-cutter bee *Megachile*, showing the large mandibles in front view (top left); the bee in action (bottom right); a rose leaf with discs and pear-shaped pieces cut out; and the tunnels in soft wood with the rows of completed brood cells in position (A. Smith).

a long tunnel. It must then find the preferred flower or shrub from which to cut the leaves or petals to form the cells. An exact disc is cut to form the cap of the cell, and a series of uniform oval pieces are cut and applied to form the walls. Then a mixture of pollen and honey is prepared and stored in the cell, the egg is laid, and the cell closed down with more cut leaves. The sequence is repeated and more cells added until the nest is filled. Each act in this process can be performed only in its proper sequence; if the work is disturbed and partially undone, the bee continues its behaviour sequence as though nothing had happened.

The solitary wasp *Ammophila campestris* (figure 111) digs a vertical tunnel in the ground and seals it with pebbles. It then searches out a caterpillar that will serve as food for its larva and proceeds to sting this deliberately in successive segments of the body to induce paralysis (p. 172). It then crushes the neck of its victim with its mandibles to complete the immobilization, and drags the caterpillar back to its nest, deposits an egg on the middle segments of the body and seals the tunnel again with small stones and earth. In this behaviour sequence there seems to be a considerable degree of flexibility. Not only will the wasp temporarily leave its prey while it reconnoitres the position of the nest, but it will maintain two or three nests at once, each in a different state of development. Once more we have a series of preformed acts of behaviour; but these are subject to wide variation in detail according to circumstances; and the order in which they are performed can be changed according to the needs of the situation. This behaviour comes a long way towards the flexible behaviour of the honey-bee which we shall consider later.

When we reflect upon their different levels of behaviour it is at once apparent that insects must have a capacity for learning and remembering, and a remarkable capacity for finding their way about. In discussing the function of the different sense organs we saw that many insects could learn to associate the presence of food, or the location of the nest, or the imminence of disagreeable or punishing experiences, with other stimuli; and they can use these latter signals, or 'token stimuli', accordingly—just as many of their in-born reactions in seeking food or sites for laying their eggs are directed by 'token stimuli' of one kind or another. The larva of the dragonfly *Anax* soon learns to associate the sight of its keeper outside its aquarium with the supply of food. In this state of anticipation it may even snap for food before this is seen.

Solitary wasps or bees constructing and provisioning their nests can remember the landmarks in the immediate surroundings of the entrance, and can remember the general ter-

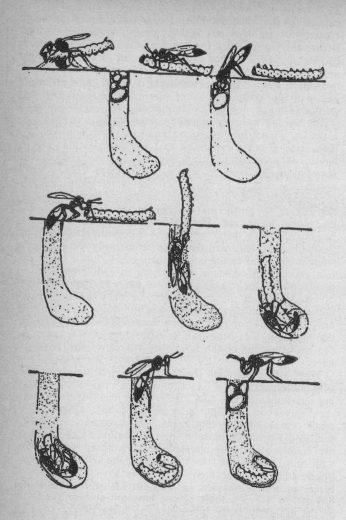

Figure 111.
The successive acts of the solitary wasp *Ammophila campestris* in the provisioning of its nest. It captures, stings, and paralyses a caterpillar and drags it to the prepared nest. It removes the stones from the entrance to the nest; pulls in the caterpillar; lays an egg upon it; climbs out of the nest; and closes the entrance again with stones (Baerends).

rain of the neighbourhood. *Ammophila* may fly off to secure a caterpillar and then return dragging this to the nest on foot. Before leaving the nest these insects, like honey-bees before leaving a newly placed hive, make an orientation flight around it to imprint its features in the memory.

In these route-finding activities all sorts of clues are made use of at the same time or at successive moments. Ants of the genus *Lasius* make use of the light reflected from their surroundings; they use the position of the sun and the pattern of polarized light in the blue sky as a guide, they use the general odour of the background, and they run with the tips of the antennae continually touching the surface in order to follow the scent trails laid down by other ants of their colony. They have an appreciation of distance; foraging ants guiding themselves back to the nest by the sun-

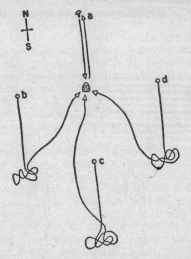

Figure 112.
Return of bees to the hive in a countryside without landmarks. Bees feeding at a site about 150 m due north at *a* fly straight to and from the hive. If removed from the feeding table to *b*, *c*, or *d* they always fly south for the same distance before circling around and eventually finding their way back to the hive (Wolf).

compass will start searching in circles when they have come the appropriate distance; they may then discover a known scent trail which will lead them to the nest. If the finger is drawn across such a track the ants refuse to cross the half-inch gap; they are repelled by the new scent; but if the scent trail has been interrupted by wiping with cotton wool they go straight ahead and soon find the trail again.

Foraging honey-bees use similar methods. They steer the way to and from the hive and the collecting grounds by the sky-compass and by conspicuous features in the landscape. They, also, can form a pretty good appreciation of the distance they have flown. For if, in a countryside devoid of landmarks, the bees are captured at the foraging site and liberated some distance away, they will fly in the customary direction (perhaps directly south), and when they have flown the usual distance they will circle around before eventually finding their way back to the hive (figure 112).

When they are making use of landmarks, the outward flight and the return flight to the hive must be learned separately. This has been confirmed in experiments with bees and wasps in a labyrinth in the laboratory. If the zigzag track to the source of honey was indicated by coloured marks on the ground, the bees quickly learned to make use of them on the outward journey, but were unable to do so on the return journey. In other experiments they had to turn left to get round a blue obstruction and right to get round a yellow obstruction, whereas for the return journey they could run straight forward. They soon learned this faultlessly. But if opposed by a blue or yellow obstruction on the return journey they had to learn the problem all over again (figure 113).

The ability of bees and other insects to appreciate the points of the compass has long been a source of wonder. This ability is dependent on their sense of time. An instinctive sense of time is poorly developed in civilized man, but insects and many other animals, including even single-celled protozoa, are able to appreciate the twenty-four hours' period from one day to the next with extraordinary accuracy. It was noted that foraging bees, which were provided with syrup at only one fixed time of day, stayed resting in the hive and did not appear again at the feeding table until the same hour next day. Normal bees start foraging soon after sunrise; but when a colony was flown across the Atlantic or flown from New York to California they continued to set out at their old time as determined by their own 'physiological clock'. It was several days before they became adjusted to the new sun-time and their clock was reset.

Diurnal rhythms of activity have long been known in many insects. One of the most familiar examples is the emergence of insects from the pupa at a set time of day, often extending over no more than an hour or two. The fruit-fly *Drosophila* emerges between six and nine a.m., and this happens even if the pupae are kept in continuous darkness—but only if the larvae at some time of their life have been exposed to a daily cycle of illumination. If *Drosophila* is reared from the egg in continuous darkness the daily rhythm of emergence disappears. If, however, the larva is exposed to light for a single period this is sufficient to establish an emergence rhythm, the cycles of twenty-four hours being measured from the beginning of the period of illumination. Even a single flash of light lasting a fraction of a second is enough. Alternatively a sudden change of temperature may serve to start a rhythm.

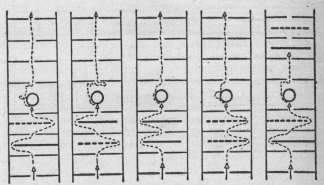

Figure 113.
Orientation of bees in a maze. A dish of syrup is in the centre of the maze. The bees entering the maze learn always to turn left when confronted with a blue screen (continuous thick line) and right when confronted with a yellow screen (broken thick line) no matter what order these screens are in. But when (in the experiment to the extreme right) they meet screens of blue or yellow on their way out from the maze, they are confused and do not know which way to turn (K. Weiss).

Clearly the insect is provided with some kind of internal 'clock' which can be set going at any time and which thereafter measures intervals of twenty-four hours. The nature of this clock is not really known, but some of its effects can be seen in the cockroach *Periplaneta*. Like many other insects the cockroach is inactive during the day-time and becomes active at night. This diurnal rhythm of activity will persist for some days in continuous light or continuous darkness, but eventually it disappears. While the cockroach is kept in continuous darkness at an unchanging temperature its movements may be recorded by means of a diminutive 'burglar alarm': every time it moves across a beam of infra-red light (which is invisible to the cockroach) and prevents the beam shining on a photoelectric cell across the animal's cage, its activity is recorded on a moving band. Figure 114 shows such a record from one cockroach obtained by Dr Janet Harker. This insect became active in the evening and was able to measure off time-intervals, not of exactly twenty-four hours but of twenty-three hours and fifty-three minutes. A small deviation of this sort from twenty-four hours is quite common, and varies slightly from one individual to another.

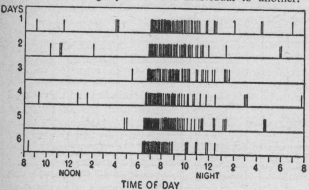

Figure 114.
Record of activity in a cockroach kept in continuous darkness in an unchanging environment. It became active each evening between 6 and 7 o'clock; but its measurement of twenty-four hours was not exact: activity began about seven minutes earlier each day (Harker).

The increase in activity of the cockroach is brought about by a hormone circulating in the blood; and this hormone comes from a group of secreting nerve cells ('neurosecretory cells') in the lower ganglion of the head, the 'suboesophageal ganglion'. This group of cells constitutes the 'clock', and if this clock is cut out from a cockroach which has a well marked diurnal rhythm of activity, and implanted into another cockroach with no rhythm, the second cockroach at once assumes the activity rhythm of the first. The secreting 'clock' in the normal cockroach is 'set' by means of the stimulus of light received by the ocelli and the compound eyes. But this is by no means a simple business; it seems likely that an elaborate system of other 'clocks' and internal secretions are concerned in the process.

Given a sense of time, and eyes that can judge direction, the insect is provided with all the equipment needed for a simple process of astronomical navigation. Certain Carabid beetles living on the sea-shore in Italy, always run in a direction away from the sea when they are alarmed; and this movement is independent of the slope of the shore. They can do this at all times of day, for they can instinctively calculate the hour, and steer themselves by the position of the sun or by the corresponding pattern of polarized light in the blue sky.

This method of steering by the sun was first discovered in ants, and the ability to use, as an alternative, the pattern of polarized light in the blue sky was first described in the honey-bee by Karl von Frisch. But it is now realized that these abilities are widely spread among insects, as also is the capacity to utilize the sense of time to compensate for the apparent movement of the sun. We have seen that bees in a countryside devoid of landmarks steer their way to the collecting ground, and back to the hive, by the position of the sun. If bees are captured at the collecting site and imprisoned for an hour or so and then released, they at once fly off in the direction of the hive. They are clearly able to calculate the position of the sun according to the changed time of day and to orient themselves accordingly. In the same way, bees which have been trained, during the afternoon alone, to fly westwards to a feeding site, and obliged to rely on the sun for their navigation, will again fly westwards when they set out the next morning. They have been able instinctively to make the necessary computation.

In the Northern Hemisphere the sun appears to move round in a clockwise direction; but in the Southern Hemisphere the apparent direction of movement is reversed. Honey-bees were trained in Ceylon, which is south of the equator, to forage at a collecting ground to the south of the hive. They were then moved overnight to Poona which is an equal distance north of the equator. When liberated from the hive they flew north, for the sun was in the wrong position. But this understanding of the apparent movement of the sun is not irrevocably fixed for the bee. Honey-bees carried from Ceylon to Munich had learned within six weeks (or their successors had learned) that in the Northern Hemisphere the sun moves in a clockwise direction. If they had not this ability to learn, bees living between the tropics, where the apparent movement of the sun changes direction twice a year, would be at a serious disadvantage.

Chapter 14

THE ORGANIZATION OF INSECT SOCIETIES

ALL INSECT societies are overgrown families. The sixty or eighty thousand worker bees in a flourishing hive are one family, the progeny of a single female. The same is true of the four or five hundred thousands of ants or of termites which form a single colony and populate a single nest; and even the one and a half million driver ants of the genus *Eciton* (figure 115) forming a marching column several hundred yards long are all the progeny of one queen.

The distinguishing feature of a true society is division of labour. Division of labour may or may not be combined with differences in form (polymorphism) and the appearance of separate 'castes' devoted to different duties. But in all such societies, if they are to be effectively administered, the members of the community must do the work required at the proper time. This means that the needs of the society as a whole must be communicated to the individual and the individual must act accordingly.

The complicated acts which are called for in the maintenance of a large society are of the same nature as the inborn patterns of behaviour which formed the subject of the preceding chapter. The prime essential of social life is the communication of the needs of the society from one individual to another. These needs may sometimes be met simply by a temporary change in *behaviour* during which the appropriate inborn acts are performed. Sometimes they may be met by a change in *development* leading to the appearance of the appropriate inborn forms or castes. In this chapter we shall be concerned chiefly in discussing the methods of communication. Since the days of the Greek philosophers it has been a common practice to compare the organization of society with the organization of the living body. Among social insects this analogy is so close that the insect community is often spoken of as a 'superorganism'.

Many insects are more or less gregarious. Caterpillars of the large cabbage white butterfly (*Pieris brassicae*) in their young stages are herded together in clusters derived from a single batch of eggs. They scatter to some extent during feeding, but are brought together again by mutual attraction to the species odour. Some caterpillars live together in tents made by webbing the leaves together with silk; and in the cooperative building of these nests we have perhaps the germ of a society. The small ermine moths (*Hyponomeuta*) which have this habit, leave their nests at night for feeding and then find their way back mainly by smell but partly by vision and by following the course of the silk threads. The processionary caterpillars *Thaumetopoea* form marching columns regularly aligned head to tail. These also make use of silken threads but they seem to be guided mainly by an instinctive tendency to maintain head-to-tail contact. The huge aggregations of migrating locusts are held together by mutual visual attraction, by a common response to the environment, and doubtless by other unrecognized factors. In these and many more examples there is aggregation but no division of labour, no trace of social life.

So far as complexity of behaviour is concerned, the solitary wasps and bees, such as *Ammophila* and *Megachile* (p. 242) are the equals of the social wasps or of the honey-bee. Nest-building, provisioning, recognition, and location of the nesting site, are all highly efficient. The solitary wasps of the genus *Bembix* leave the brood cells uncovered and continue to catch flies and feed them to their young throughout larval life; and they are gregarious, building their nests in close proximity to form a colony. But there is no vestige of social life here.

Among the solitary bees, however, there are species which show the first signs of communal activity. In the mining bee *Halictus marginatus*, for example, the female that builds the nest leaves the brood cells open and feeds her larvae. She lives on, and when the young females emerge they remain in the nest and share in the work of collecting food and defending the home. Each female cares for her own offspring independently, but joint nest-building and defence are the first beginnings of a social life.

In the related Halictine bee (*Augochloropsis sparsilis*) the females remain together in the nest during the summer. Something like 10 per cent of these, apparently from some accidental cause, fail to mate, and these unmated females become industrious workers confining their activities to nest-building and foraging.

A further step forward is seen in *Halictus malachurus* where unmated females are more numerous and always smaller in size than the fertile females. It is only one step more to the state of affairs found in the colonies of the bumble-bees, *Bombus*. Now for the first time the division of labour is essential for the survival of the species. The large fertilized female, the queen, passes the winter sheltering in the earth. In the spring she is able to found a colony on her own, to select a suitable mouse hole or other cavity, to build a few rounded waxen cells and rear a small brood of small-sized worker bees. In order to raise the large, sexually mature individuals she must have the collaboration of workers. As in the social wasps and hornets (*Vespa*) these societies come to an end in the autumn; a certain number of the large females are fertilized and these go into hibernation to found a new colony in the following spring.

The highest state is reached in the honey-bee, *Apis mellifera*, where the queen survives for several seasons but the males, or drones, and the infertile females, or workers, are short-lived. From time to time new queens are reared; the old queen leads out a large contingent of workers as a swarm fully prepared to establish a new community; and one of the new queens, after a 'marriage flight' in which she mates with one or more of the males (p. 129), takes over the task of egg production for the old hive.

Among the four thousand or so known species of ants all are social insects. As a rule the sexual pair alone are winged; but after the nuptial flight each mated pair shed their wings (these are so constructed that they are easily snapped off at the base) and settle down to found a new colony. The workers in these colonies are always wingless and usually much smaller than the queen. They may vary greatly in structure among themselves and so constitute a range of castes. Insects, like many other animals, exhibit the phenomenon known as 'allometry': when they increase in size certain parts of the body become disproportionately large. Thus the well-fed large workers among many sorts of ants develop enormous heads and mandibles which are simply the result of this allometric growth. In the driver ant *Anomma* the largest workers may be seventy-five times the volume of the smallest (figure 115). These very large workers constitute a 'soldier' caste.

The termites, or 'white ants', are related to the cockroaches, a far more primitive group than the Hymenoptera among which most of the social insects are to be found. But it is remarkable how similar is their social organization to that of the true ants. Of course, the young stages of termites, like young cockroaches, are active creatures of the same general form as the adults, and they fend for themselves; whereas the larvae of the social Hymenoptera are helpless grubs which have to be nursed continuously. It is sometimes said that the termites differ from the ants in relying wholly upon child labour for the maintenance of their societies. Up to a point that is true; many of the termite workers are larvae that will eventually become winged adults;

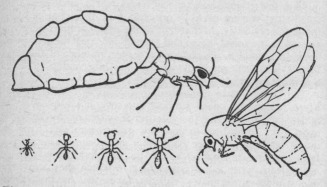

Figure 115.
Polymorphism in the driver ant *Eciton;* all drawn to the same scale. Above, the gravid female or queen. To the right, the winged male. Below, four sizes of sterile workers. Note the disproportionately large head and mandibles of the larger workers ('allometry') (Bruch).

others are larvae which will probably never grow up (pseudoworkers, or 'pseudergates' as they are called); but in some species of termites there is a true caste of sterile adult workers. In addition there is a true soldier caste with powerful mandibles, so greatly developed that they can no longer be used for feeding purposes, or with conical heads (nasute soldiers) which eject a sticky secretion (p. 170). In some termite species the colony may contain two types of workers and up to three types of soldiers.

But in spite of these structural differences between ants and termites the similarities are striking. The winged adults of termites also make nuptial flights in vast swarms. The mated sexual forms likewise shed their wings before founding a new colony of which they will be the royal pair. There is the closely parallel development of workers and soldiers; there are many likenesses in colony formation and nest construction; both exhibit food exchange, or 'trophallaxis', which as we shall see plays a large part in their social organization; and certain members of both groups have acquired the habit of fungus cultivation, along almost identical lines. (The leaf-carrying ants *Atta*, of South America, collect fragments of leaf which are mixed with excreta and serve as the medium for growing fungi in special gardens or chambers, the fruiting bodies being harvested as food.)

We are now in a position to consider the means of integration within these societies. Up to a point it is possible to consider separately the influence of the needs of the community on the production of different forms or castes, and on the activities and behaviour of individual members. But these two aspects of the division of labour often merge into one another. In the last analysis form and behaviour are inseparable.

In the chapter on growth (p. 112) we discussed the question of 'polymorphism', the occurrence of alternative forms within a single species, and concluded that we often have to do with two or more sets of genes, or genes with multiple effects, which are brought into action under different circumstances. The classic example is the distinction between queen and worker in the honey-bee; the many differences between the two are brought about by differences in the nutrition of the larva, notably the continued feeding of 'royal jelly' to the potential queen. Differences in feeding are presumably responsible for the small differences between the queens and workers among the social wasps. It is only towards the end of the summer season that the larvae are sufficiently well fed to develop into normal sexual adults. The ordinary worker wasps are hard put to it to provide sufficient food for the brood. They possess ovaries but the eggs in them do not ripen; the food collected is given to the young larvae instead; the workers are said to be suffering from 'nutricial' castration, that is, sterility resulting from their continuous nursing activities. But the ovaries of wasp workers are capable of functioning, and if deprived of their brood as many as one-third of the workers become fertile and lay eggs.

The same applies to the honey-bee workers. So long as the queen is present the ovaries of the workers do not ripen; but if the queen is removed many of the workers begin to lay eggs. That brings us to the question of how some 50,000 workers in the hive can know whether the queen is present or not. Bees and ants and other social insects are continually regurgitating and passing food from one to another. When some six foraging bees were allowed to feed on honey containing radioactive phosphorus, it was found that within twenty-four hours 60 per cent of the members of the hive, a colony of 25,000, had become radioactive. This food exchange is the most primitive and perhaps the most important single factor in the integration of insect societies. It may serve to convey information about the nature and source of the food being brought in by the foragers, but it also serves to transmit information of a more specific kind.

Chemical substances with characteristic odours or tastes are widely used by insects in communicating with one another. We have had occasion to mention the female scent that attracts the male (p. 124), the male scent that excites the female (p. 126), the odours that hold aggregations of caterpillars together (p. 227), the warning scents emitted by the stink glands and osmeteria (p. 175). A general name has been given to these chemical messengers that pass from one individual to another; they are called 'pheromones'. This term carries with it the implication that these substances may act like the hormones of the body; they are indeed 'social hormones' by means of which the members of insect societies may be suitably excited and controlled. Their effect may be to produce a change in behaviour or a change in growth and development. Whether 'pheromones' act like hormones in the body and influence growth directly, or whether they merely stimulate the nervous system of the insect and cause this to modify the action of its own hormone system, or whether they control directly the activities of particular systems of genes (p. 112) remains to be proved.

Among the social insects one of the best-known chemical messengers of this kind is the 'queen substance' (oxodecenoic acid) secreted by the mandibular glands of the queen bee. This secretion is smeared over the integument of the queen during her grooming activities. The queen is usually surrounded by a circle of workers, all facing her and licking her and passing on the material in the course of food exchange

25. The African hawk-moth *Xanthopan* at rest on bark showing how the disruptive black lines in the wing pattern help in making it disappear into the background.

a

b

26. The weevil *Lithinus nigrocristatus* is conspicuous against a plain background but the two specimens shown resting on lichen are less easily seen.

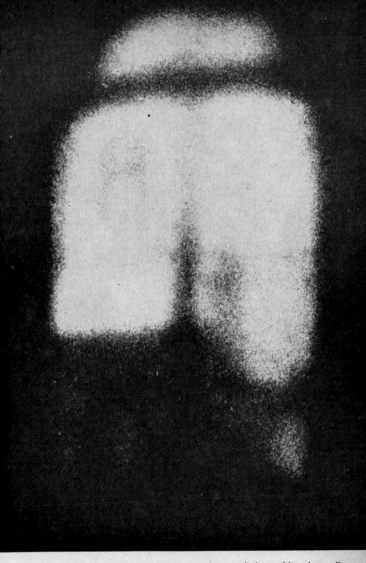

27. Photograph by S. Exner (1891) showing a window with a letter R on one pane and a church beyond as produced on the retina of the compound eye of the glow-worm *Lampyris*.

28. (a) Flowers of *Iris;* (b) evening primrose *Oenothera;* and (c) poppy *Papaver rhoeas* photographed in yellow light (on the left) and ultraviolet light (on the right). *Iris* and *Oenothera* show 'honey-guides' which fail to reflect ultraviolet and therefore appear dark to the bee, as in the right-hand pictures. The red poppy is almost invisible in yellow light but reflects ultraviolet light strongly and will therefore be conspicuous to the bee although the eye of the bee cannot see red.

29. The two forms of the peppered moth *Biston betularius*, the typical white form with black markings and the melanic form. Above they are shown at rest on a lichen-covered branch: the melanic form is the more conspicuous. Below they are resting on a lichen-free polluted trunk in an industrial area: the pale form is more conspicuous.

a

b

30. (a) Queen honey-bee surrounded by her 'court' of workers; those near her tail end are licking up 'queen substance' from her.

a

(b) Food exchange between worker honey-bees. The bee on the right with outstretched tongue is taking food from the bee on the left.

b

31. (a) Guard bees at the hive entrance have arrested a stranger, detected by her body odours and manner of behaviour; (b) honey-comb showing ordinary worker cells, some of them already closed, and large thimble-shaped queen cells.

a

b

32. Flashlight photograph shortly before dawn showing newly emerged adults of the emperor dragonfly *Anax imperator* still clinging to the larval skins.

a

33. (a) Marching bands of 4th- and 5th-stage 'hoppers' of the desert locust *Schistocerca gregaria* in Tanganyika; (b) part of a large (400 sq. miles) swarm of the desert locust in Ethiopia.

b

a

b

34. (a) Worker honey-bee collecting pollen and nectar from a dandelion flower; (b) pollen gatherer on bluebell. The bee has stopped collecting pollen for a few moments while she combs the pollen from the hairs of her body and packs it into her pollen baskets.

35. (a) The improvement in silkworm cocoons brought about by selective breeding in Japan during the past hundred years. The photographs show four examples of the races available at different periods; (b) commercial silkworm *Bombyx mori* in culture on mulberry leaves.

a

b

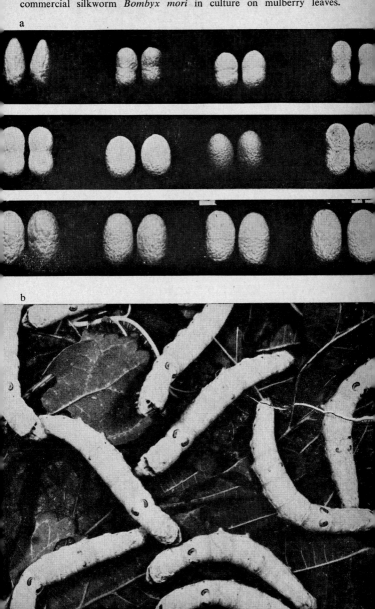

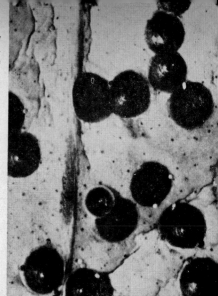

36. (a) Magnified view of the Florida red scale *Chrysomphalus aonidum*. The large discs are mature females. The smaller discs are young larvae. The very small white oval specimens are newly hatched larvae ('crawlers') which have not yet settled down; (b) general view of a small citrus fruit infested by the red scale.

a

b

with other workers (plate 30). This is probably the chief means by which the workers are kept informed of the presence of the queen. If she is removed a change in behaviour among the workers becomes apparent, and within twenty-four hours they begin building large 'queen cells' to rear new queens (plate 31b). At the same time the ovaries of many of the workers ripen and they begin to lay eggs. It may be that absence of the same queen substance, in combination with a special queen scent, is responsible for both these effects.

If the queen is separated from the workers by a gauze screen they recognize her presence and these changes do not appear; but if two gauze partitions are set up so that the workers can no longer touch the queen, they behave as though she were absent (figure 116). Odour alone is insufficient. In the army ants, *Eciton*, etc, the queen is so attractive

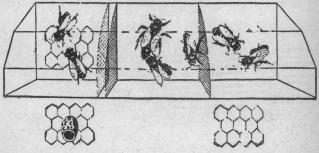

Figure 116.
Diagram of experiment to illustrate the action of the 'queen substance' in the honey-bee. In the middle compartment the queen is attended by workers. In the right hand compartment the workers are separated from the queen by a single gauze screen: they do not build a queen call. In the left hand compartment the workers are separated by a double gauze screen: within forty-eight hours they have built a queen cell (Butler).

to the workers that even when marching she may be completely concealed by a dense covering of agitated workers, licking the surface of her body. Perhaps the same method of communication is in operation here.

This mode of communication in large societies forms a contrast to the state of affairs in a small colony like that of the wasp *Polistes*. *Polistes* build nests of paper like those of the ordinary social wasps, but consisting only of some fifty to eighty cells on a single stalk (figure 117). These little colonies are founded in the spring by fertilized potential queens which have survived the winter. Sometimes several queens unite to build a single nest; and then they form a social hierarchy. One becomes socially dominant and is the true queen, whereas the others, although mated, have small ovaries and shorter lives. In all their contacts and behaviour the subordinate status of these lesser females is apparent. The senior female, or queen, keeps the cells furnished with eggs and thus prevents the stimulus to egg-laying provided by empty cells. If the lesser females do lay eggs these are destroyed by the queen.

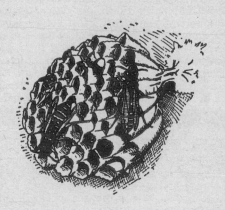

Figure 117.
The nest of the wasp *Polistes gallicus* (Robert).

It is uncertain whether chemical 'pheromones' operate in *Polistes* or whether the influence of the queen is dependent on her domineering behaviour alone; certainly if the dominant female is removed one of the others will take her place. But besides these potential queens there are true *Polistes* workers, which are produced when the temperature is low and nutrition deficient; these workers do not mate and do not survive the winter.

The control of castes by pheromones is most evident among the termites. It has long been recognized that all the eggs laid by the queen termite contain the genetic 'blueprints' for all the castes characteristic of the species. What is uncertain is the method by which the diversion of development in a particular direction is brought about. The most widely held belief is that control is due to 'ectohormones' (pheromones) liberated by each caste and tending to inhibit the development of the same caste; others believe that differences in nutrition are responsible; and yet others hold that a so-called 'group effect' exists, and that the tactile and olfactory stimuli which exist when the colony has a particular composition influence the type of development in the growing larvae. It may be that all these factors are concerned in varying degrees under different circumstances.

The example of 'ectohormonal' control that has been most clearly demonstrated is in the European dry wood termite *Kalotermes*. The caste system in this insect is relatively simple (figure 118). A succession of larval stages end in the full-grown larva or 'pseudergate'. The pseudergate may remain in that state indefinitely; it may proceed to grow into a winged adult (the primary reproductive form which after a mating flight will found a new colony); it may develop into a soldier; or it may turn into a secondary, or 'supplementary reproductive'. In appearance the supplementary reproductives are intermediate between a larva and an adult that has shed its wings; they make their appearance in any colony which has lost the primary reproductive pair.

If the primary reproductives (the queen and her mate) are removed from a colony of *Kalotermes*, several supplementary reproductives develop within a week or ten days. As in the control of queen rearing by the queen substance of the honey-bee, this result does not happen if the queen is merely enclosed in a wire gauze chamber in such a way that the larvae can make contact with her; it does happen if she is enclosed by a double barrier of wire gauze. The pheromone responsible for preventing the development of supplementaries is excreted from the anus of the queen, taken up by the larvae and passed on to other members of the community. This same substance has another effect: if supplementary reproductives are already present it induces the pseudergates to destroy them. Moreover there are two 'pheromones' that are more or less specific for the two sexes: the substance excreted by the male inhibits the formation of male supplementaries, and encourages the selective destruction of any male supplementaries already present. The product of the female has complementary effects.

In the same way the presence of soldiers inhibits the appearance of more soldiers, and if too many soldiers are present in the colony some of them are eliminated. It seems very likely that the soldiers also are producing other pheromones

Figure 118.

Castes of *Kalotermes flavicollis*. After hatching from the egg the insect goes through about seven larval stages, then through a couple of 'nymphal' stages with visible wing lobes, which then become winged adults. Any of these stages, from the fifth stage larva to the 'nymph' may moult to a 'pre-soldier' and then to a soldier (right-hand side). Or any one of them may moult to produce a 'supplementary reproductive' (left-hand side). Finally, the seventh stage larva may remain permanently in that form as a 'pseudergate' or false worker (Lüscher).

which prevent the development of new soldiers, but this has not yet been clearly proved.

In their day-to-day life a large degree of co-operation appears to exist within the communities of all social insects. Their nests, which are of wax in the bees, of paper in the social wasps, of earth in most ants and termites, possess elaborate forms that are characteristic of each species. The termite workers start on their construction by depositing pellets of earth indiscriminately. There is no indication that the builders are operating as a team. But when these pellets begin to form heaps they stimulate the workers to start building columns; and where they are arranged in lines the workers add to them and build blades. The task achieved seems itself to provide the stimulus to further construction. Building continues without a predetermined plan; but the general character of the construction is a built-in part of the inherited pattern of behaviour.

The elaborate structure of the nest, as has been said, is characteristic of the species. Termite species can sometimes be recognized from the form of the termitarium. When such termitaria are cut open, besides the general complex of

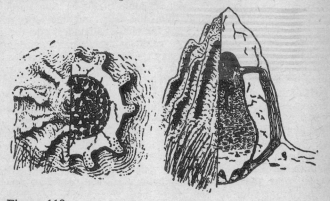

Figure 119.
Giant mound of *Macrotermes,* ten feet high. On the right the mound is shown cut through vertically. The dark spaces in the centre of the nest are the galleries and brood chambers; the large dark cavity below the middle is the royal chamber where the queen is enclosed; the paler cavities are the fungus combs. The nest is ventilated by warm air rising upwards, passing outwards to the ridges of the mound, where it is cooled and freshened by diffusion through the thin walls, and then re-enters the central compartments of the nest. The horizontal section to the left shows the galleries and fungus combs, and numerous small air ducts in the ridges of the mound (Lüscher).

cavities, and fungus chambers, there is a royal cell where the queen and her consort are walled in, and there is a system for ventilation. A large *Macrotermes* mound will house some two million workers with a total weight of about 20 kg. It is estimated that this quantity of insects will require about 240 litres of oxygen, that is, 1,200 litres of fresh air, per day. The nest will contain only about 500 litres; it would last the termites less than twelve hours. The nests are therefore furnished with an elaborate system of ventilation: the air is heated by fermentation in the fungus combs in the centre of the nest and thus rises to a large cavity in the upper part of the mound. In some species the warm air may escape through the thin wall at the top of the mound; or it may circulate downwards through porous channels in the side walls, and in so doing it is freshened by exchanges with the outside air, and then flows into the nest once more and repeats the circulation (figure 119).

The most extensive studies on the methods of co-operation and communication within the society have been made on the honey-bee. During the summer months a worker bee will live about thirty days, and during this time she has been described as performing a set schedule of duties. She starts with the menial task of cleaning the cells, and then does a spell of nursing; for about a week she is a builder, and this is followed by a few days receiving nectar and storing pollen. Around the twentieth day she is standing guard at the entrance of the hive (plate 31a); and from the third week until the end of her life she is foraging in the countryside. Her physiological functions develop in line with these activities: during the nursing period the 'nurse glands' in the head are greatly enlarged to provide the 'royal jelly'; when comb-building begins the nurse glands shrink but the wax glands on the under-surface of the abdomen become active for a short period; in the guard bees and foraging bees both glands have almost disappeared (figure 120).

But when the activities of individual marked bees were followed from hour to hour throughout their entire life in a special type of observation hive, it became evident that the sequence of duties is very much more flexible than had been supposed. The worker bee has a very extensive repertoire of a built-in patterns of behaviour, which can be brought into play by the social needs that she encounters in the hive. She spends much of the time patrolling the comb, cleaning out cells, building comb, feeding the brood, eating pollen, and closing the comb cells which contain mature larvae. A large part of the time she is just resting. But every bee is in a state of alertness, ready to be summoned for any urgent need; and if circumstances demand it, a worker can revert to a duty which she would normally have completed.

It may be that a section of the brood in the centre of the hive is becoming overheated. The bees in that region exude water into the mouth-parts and spread it as a thin film which will cool the air by evaporation. Other workers may increase the effect by fanning with the wings. But they soon run short of water. Any bee bringing in water is immediately surrounded by the agitated hive bees; whereas bees bringing in nectar may have difficulty in finding bees that will accept their burden. The need for water thus becomes communicated to the foraging bees; water collectors dance excitedly and recruit other bees, which suppress their inherent preference for sweet fluid and turn over to the collection of water. Before long the brood is cooled; the demand for water ceases; water collectors have difficulty in finding takers, and they revert once more to the collection of nectar or pollen as the case may be.

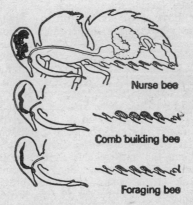

Nurse bee

Comb building bee

Foraging bee

Figure 120.
Diagram of the anatomy of the honey-bee showing the changes that take place in the 'nurse glands' in the head, which are best developed in the young nurse bees, and in the wax glands below the abdomen, which are largest in the comb-building bees (v. Frisch).

This one example illustrates the kind of way in which preformed patterns of behaviour are evoked by the needs of the community, and the way in which the needs are conveyed from one bee to another. If the collection of water or nectar is to be efficient, the workers recruited for the purpose must be instructed where to go. It is here that the dances of bees discovered by Karl von Frisch constitute something like a bee 'language'.

A foraging bee that has found a source of nectar very close to the hive circles repeatedly on the comb in an agitated fashion, performing what is termed a 'round dance' (figure 121). The richer the source of nectar the greater the vigour and duration of the dance; the quality of the nectar is communicated by food exchange. Unemployed bees are excited by the movement; they follow the dancer, noting the scent of the flower which impregnates her coat, and they fly off to discover the collecting ground.

When the source of nectar is more distant from the hive the returning forager performs a figure-of-eight dance (figure 121). Here again the general vigour of the dance conveys information of the richness of the source. But that is not all; during the straight run of the dance between the two circles to left and right, the abdomen is flicked from side to

Figure 121.
To the left, the 'round dance' and, to the right, the 'tail-wagging dance'. Only those bees that are actually following the dancer are indicated, and not the dense crowd of bees surrounding them on the comb (v. Frisch).

side at a rate of about thirteen flicks per second, so that the dance is called the 'tail-wagging dance'. The number of complete flicks of the tail during the straight run, gives a measure of the distance from the hive; one extra flick indicates an increase of some 75 m; and the direction of the run indicates the direction in which the source of nectar lies.

When the bee can dance on a horizontal surface exposed to the sun, it directs the straight run of the tail-wagging dance according to the direction of the sun, or the direction of the pattern of polarized light in the blue sky. Other bees, excited by the dance, follow the dancing bee, and learn the direction by the sun-compass, the distance by the duration of the tail-flicking movements, and the nature of the flower being worked by the clinging scent. Armed with this information they can quickly locate the source.

Foraging bees can convey the same information by dancing on the vertical comb in the darkness of the hive. The degree of agitation and the amount of tail flicking can be appreciated

Figure 122.
When the direction of flight from the hive to the feeding table is in the direct line of the sun the returning bees dance on the upright comb with the straight run of the tail-wagging dance *vertical* (top drawing). When the direction of the feeding table is 40° to the left of the line of the sun the bees dance with the straight run 40° *to the left of the vertical* (bottom drawing) (v. Frisch).

by other bees in close contact with the dancer. But the direction of the straight run is now oriented in relation to gravity. If the source of nectar is directly towards the sun, the straight run is vertically upwards; if away from the sun, it is vertically downwards; and if at an angle from the sun, then at a corresponding angle from the vertical (figure 122).

This same language is used by the honey-bee when deciding upon a new nesting site. It has long been observed by bee keepers that shortly before the hive gives off a swarm, the foragers become lazy and cease to bring in nectar. But some of them will spend their time exploring the countryside for possible sites for a new nest. These are in fact 'scout bees'; and some days later, when the queen leads out the swarm and this settles in some temporary bivouac, the scout bees constitute a committee to advise the emigrants about possible new homes. The individual scouts proceed to dance on the surface of the swarm, each indicating the direction and distance of her preferred site by means of a tail-wagging dance, and her estimate of the quality of the site by the enthusiasm of the dance. Other bees are recruited and visit the site and make their own judgements, which are conveyed to the other members by their dances on their return. Eventually unanimity is achieved and the swarm is led to the chosen site. So precise is the information which the scout bees communicate by their dances, that Martin Lindauer, who first observed them in action, was able to interpret their meaning and then proceed at once to the chosen site to await the subsequent arrival of the bees.

There are many races of honey-bees which have long existed in isolation from one another. It is therefore not surprising that there are small differences in the conduct of their dances which can lead to some confusion when they are brought together in a combined society. The tempo of the dance of Ukrainian bees, for example, is slower than that of Italian bees, and in a mixed colony the Ukrainian bees failed to interpret correctly the dances of the Italian bees, and went to sources too close to the hive. The differing 'dialects' of these races had led to misunderstanding.

One of the most remarkable features about the methods of communication between honey-bees is the evident efficiency of their sensory perceptions. By means of the compound eyes they can judge and remember the angle from the sun with an error of no more than 2–3°. They cannot use this angle, of course, in the tropics when the sun is directly overhead. While the sun is at the zenith they cannot orient themselves and tend to stay in the hive; but this period lasts only about twenty minutes; as soon as the sun is 3° off the zenith they can again steer themselves by it. There is a comparable degree of sensitivity in the 'proprioceptive organs' (p. 208) by which the bee judges its orientation to gravity. The method of perceiving the distance flown is still unexplored.

Other social bees show the same methods of communication in a less perfected form. The primitive dwarf honey-bee *Apis florea* dances only on the horizontal top of the nest, where it indicates the direction of the source of food by the sun-compass. The tiny stingless bees or Meliponini of South America seem to lack the dance language. On finding a good source of food they can alert the other bees by a humming sound which sets up a vibration in the comb, and then lay down a trail of scent leading to the foraging ground. In one respect they are more successful than the domesticated honey-bee for they can lead the novices to a source of nectar high up in the trees—which *Apis mellifera* cannot do.

There are features about the dances of the honey-bee that find their counterparts in other insects. We have seen already that the ability to steer by the sun and by the pattern of polarized light in the blue sky are common to most insects. When the novice follows the dancing bee during the tail-wagging dance, this orientation will become the fixed or preferred orientation. The dance may be described as an 'intention movement' (like the crouch before a spring or the movement of the arm before a stone is thrown, which indicate the direction of the movement that is to follow); the bees that have been following the dance have automatically carried out the intention movements for the ensuing flight.

The use of gravity as a symbol to convey the meaning 'direction of the sun' was a most surprising discovery. But this too has its counterpart in other insects. In ants, also, a point of light, the plane of polarization, and the force of gravity can be interchanged; and the insect will still orient itself at a constant angle to the stimulus even though the nature of the stimulus has changed. Even the ladybird *Coccinella* or the Chrysomelid beetle *Melasoma*, after walking towards a bright light on a horizontal plane, if transferred to a vertical plane in a diffuse light, will then walk upwards. If walking 30° left of the light source, it will walk 30° left of the upward direction.

Even the practice of dancing has been observed in other insects. After imbibing sugar, the blowfly *Phormia* goes through a series of convoluted movements on the ground, with the number of turns per minute increasing with the concentration of the syrup, and the rate of turning falling off after a time. Light and gravity may give some direction to the dance, and dye taken up with the sugar is disgorged and spreads rapidly among neighbouring flies. Perhaps the communication dances of the bees represent a highly evolved form of a primitive pattern of searching behaviour. The tail-wagging dance of the bee may have its counterpart in certain Saturniid moths in North America. On completing a flight these moths perform rhythmic rocking movements, and the number of these movements and the length of time they continue are proportional to the distance that the moth has flown.

Chapter 15

INSECT POPULATIONS, SPECIATION, AND MIGRATION

INSECTS DO not live for themselves alone. Their lives are devoted to the survival of the species whose representatives they are. Apart from the special case of the social insects, all the problems that have formed the subject of earlier chapters in this book, problems of insect physiology and behaviour, have been concerned with the well-being and survival of the individual. We must now stand back and look at the insect as a member of the 'population' or of the 'species' to which it belongs. Indeed, we have now at last reached the heart of the matter—the aim and purpose (so far as we can understand them) of the life of insects.

The size of the population of any one species of insect in a given region represents a balance between births and deaths. It is often pointed out that if the population is to remain steady, then of all the offspring of one female, only two insects, one male and one female, will survive to the point where they are sexually mature and ready to reproduce. If the female lays 200 eggs, this means that 198 of the offspring must perish before they reach maturity.

Two hundred eggs is perhaps an average figure for the females of most insects. But the figure can be far higher than this or far lower. We saw that the tsetse-fly *Glossina* has carried parental care to the point where each egg hatches within the reproductive system of the mother; and the resulting larva is retained and nourished until it is full-grown, and is then deposited in a well selected site just before it is ready to transform into the pupa. As in most animals where parental care is highly developed, the tsetse-fly produces very few young, not more than a dozen during a total adult life of about six months. When the eggs are broadcast they are more numerous; when they are carefully placed on the food of the future larva they are usually fewer. Perhaps the extremes are represented on the one hand by the dwarf females of the woolly aphid *Eriosoma lanigera,* or of the vine *Phylloxera,* which produce a single winter egg that fills their whole body, and which die when the egg is laid; and on the other hand by the queen termites which, assuming a life of ten years, are estimated to lay about a hundred million eggs.

Obviously, when the number of offspring is large the mortality in the young stages must be proportionately greater, if the numbers of the total population are to remain steady. In practice these numbers do not remain steady. They fluctuate from season to season and from year to year. Just how large these fluctuations are is difficult to judge except where careful counts have been made. In general the numbers of insects seem to vary much less when there are many species, and they are living in a mixed woodland, or in a tropical forest, where there are also many kinds of plants, and constant interactions are at work within the whole complex community.

The deaths among insects during their growth are due to many different causes: adverse weather, predaceous hunting insects and birds and other animals, ichneumon flies and other parasites which seek out the larvae and lay their eggs in them, and infectious diseases which spread from one insect to another like an epidemic. Where there are many kinds of insects and plants, and many kinds of enemies and parasites, a tolerably stable balance is set up and the numbers of a given insect do not seem to vary greatly from year to year.

But when there are few sorts of insects and perhaps only a single kind of plant, as in some forests or in deserts, or in the far north, the situation is much less stable. The abundance of the different kinds of moths in the German pine forests was carefully recorded from 1880 to 1940, and fluctuated widely. The pine moth *Panolis* was held fairly steady between 1895 and 1910, although even during this period there were ten-fold differences; but by 1912 it had increased one-hundred-fold and then returned to the former level for five more years. The bordered white moth *Bupalus,* on the other hand, increased more than ten-thousand-fold between 1921, when it was at an exceptionally low level, and 1928 when the outbreak was at its peak.

Even more spectacular increases have been described in the forests of North America. In years when the usual self-regulating system has broken down and the population has got completely out of control, caterpillars have increased to the point where the trees have been completely stripped of foliage and the starving insects have formed a dense moving carpet over the forest floor. Many have become infected with disease, and living and dead have been swept by the rains into the streams and rivers which have become blocked by deep drifts of caterpillars.

It is instructive just to observe with a hand-lens a few twigs on an apple tree in a neglected orchard. They are teeming with life. Predaceous mites are moving up and down in search of smaller mites to prey upon. An Anthocorid bug may be caught in the act of sucking up the contents of a mite egg. Everywhere small parasitic wasps are running feverishly to and fro searching for the caterpillars of the winter moth or the rare clusters of woolly aphids. Hover-flies (Syrphidae) are laying their eggs alongside the colonies of the apple Aphids; Syrphid larvae and the larva of ladybirds may already be raiding these colonies. On neighbouring trees, tits and other birds are diligently searching the branches. And at any time adverse weather may carry off a large proportion of the population.

In few insects do we know exactly how the numbers are controlled. They seem to fluctuate fairly widely for reasons which may be obvious or which may be quite unknown. But when the population of an insect escapes from its restraining factors and builds up excessively, the individuals of that one species begin to compete with one another for food and for living space. It is this competition which sets a final limit to the increase in numbers. And when the numbers do increase in this way, virus and bacterial and fungus diseases usually break out, parasites increase and multiply, and the population crashes once more to a low level.

At the other extreme, when the numbers of an insect are reduced to a very low level (by disease, or by parasitism, or by exceptionally adverse weather—drought or flooding, heat or cold) there are generally a few refuges which provide a retreat where small numbers can survive; and these survivors repopulate the area when conditions again improve.

Thus the population of any insect may be pictured as oscillating, perhaps quite widely, around an average density. This state of affairs may continue for years. The population, whether it fluctuates narrowly or widely, is sometimes said to be in a state of balance. But if this precarious balance is upset in either direction the counterbalancing effects that have just been described come into operation and the 'normal' state of affairs is eventually restored.

There are many sorts of habitat available for insects. Insect evolution has consisted in adaptation to almost every conceivable habit of life. Some are widely distributed and rely for survival upon their powers of rapid multiplication or on individual self-protection of one kind or another. Others have adopted specialized modes of existence and have become ingeniously adapted to life in sheltered surroundings where their generations succeed one another without a hitch.

They pay a high price for this secure existence; for they are so closely adapted that if conditions change the species cannot survive. A sucking louse that is an exclusive parasite of the walrus can survive only so long as walruses continue to exist. The louse *Pediculus humanus* is confined to man; it has already been banished from the cleaner peoples of the earth; if a suitable standard of cleanliness were adopted by all men this insect would die out. The horse bot *Gastrophilus* lays its eggs directly on the hairs of the horse; the eggs hatch when they are licked, and the larvae complete their development in the stomach of the horse. The related bot fly known as the macaw worm *Dermatobia* of Central America uses a mosquito *Psorophora* as an intermediary for the transport of its eggs. These it lays on the body of the mosquito; and while the mosquito sucks the blood of man or some other mammal the young larva escapes from the egg and burrows into the skin, there to complete its development. The caterpillars of the European large blue butterfly *Maculinea arion* have become entirely dependent upon ants as nurses (figure 123). They are carried by the ants into their nests and are there permitted to feed upon the eggs of the ants in return for a sweet secretion which they supply from special glands. Insects that have adopted ingenious specializations of this kind have given hostages to fortune. If anything goes wrong with the other animals on which they have become dependent they can no longer survive.

A puzzling question is how to measure the success of

an insect species. Is a rare insect living a specialized existence, which has enabled it to survive from Permian times, more or less successful than an insect of more recent origin which, under present conditions, is abundant everywhere? It has been pointed out that insects which have developed such good protective coloration that they escape their predators may actually decrease in number because of the increased population of parasites which attack them. It could be argued that the protective coloration is, therefore, of no benefit to the species. Perhaps the answer is that numbers are not the best criterion of success. The important thing is ability of the species to survive.

Besides their struggle with the varied adversities of their environment, and their competition for food and shelter with other members of their own species, insects may be in competition with the members of other species. This will only happen if the two species are in need of the same thing. The sort of living space and the sort of food that is required by different species may be so different that there is no competition between them. They are said to occupy different niches. But if they have some need in common they become competitors.

The outcome of such a struggle between two competitors may vary with the climate. Some years ago the Hymenopterous parasite *Aphytis lingnanensis* was introduced into California from the Orient in an effort to obtain better control of the Californian red scale of citrus, *Aonidiella aurantii*.

Figure 123.
An ant *Myrmica* carrying off to its nest the caterpillar of the large blue butterfly *Maculinea arion* (Frohawk).

The new parasite seemed to be much more successful than the local parasite *Aphytis chrysomphali* and in most of the places where it was introduced the latter insect disappeared almost completely. But after some years it was found that the local parasite was more than holding its own in the coastal regions; and on further investigation it transpired that the newcomer possessed strong biological advantages (particularly in the number of progeny produced) at high temperatures, but at the lower temperatures on the coast the balance of advantage was reversed.

Now insects live in an environment that is liable to change. Not only do conditions change unpredictably from year to year, but they change at the different seasons. An insect that is perfectly suited to one set of conditions may be less well suited to the altered environment. This state of affairs produces a most interesting result. It favours genetic variability within the species.

The twin spot ladybird *Adalia bipunctata* exists in two groups of hereditary forms: red beetles with black spots and black beetles with red spots (figure 124). In the neighbourhood of Berlin the black form enjoys some strong advantage during the summer. It is therefore favoured by selection at that season and increases in frequency. The red form, on the other hand, is at an advantage in winter. What is favoured in such cases is not necessarily the colour pattern; it will often be some associated change produced by some or other of the genes responsible for the colour, and in many instances of this kind the nature of the advantageous change is not known. The genetic make-up of a population

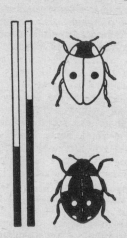

Figure 124.
Charts showing the relative numbers of the two forms of the twin-spot ladybird *Adalia bipunctata*. Left-hand column, in the winter; right-hand column, in the summer. Black columns represent the black form with red spots; white columns the red form with black spots (Timofeéff-Ressovsky).

of insects may thus change in cycles during the course of each year. Or the change may take place over a number of years.

A most interesting feature follows from this kind of observation. Genes have multiple effects. Some of these effects are advantageous, some disadvantageous; and the balance between the good and bad effects will vary with the circumstances. It follows, therefore, that a population of insects living in a particular environment will often be more successful if a given gene and its mutant form (the 'allelomorph' of that gene) are both present; that is, if the individuals are 'heterozygous' for the gene in question, and carry both alternatives.

In this way the population will maintain its genetic variability and can readily change from year to year according to the changing requirements of circumstances. One has a picture of evolutionary change going on all the time within the population—but most of the differences produce so little outward alteration that they will not be noticed by the casual observer. They may be small differences in behaviour, or in the rate of development, or ability to thrive on a particular kind of food; changes which in practice may make all the difference between death or survival.

When populations of insects become split up, each may find itself in slightly different surroundings. Each will therefore be subject to different 'selective pressures' so that different groups of genes will be favoured in the various population groups. This process of isolation, combined with the natural selection of hereditary characters, is the basic idea of the origin of species as pictured by Charles Darwin and Alfred Russel Wallace. From what has just been said a natural population of insects will have a rich and varied selection of genes at its disposal, the entire collection forming a so-called 'gene pool'. Some genes will be carried by some individuals and other genes by other individuals. If a small number of these individuals is separated off and reared in captivity, or manages to colonize an isolated oceanic island, this group will carry only a limited part of the 'gene pool'. As a result, the subsequent fate of each small population isolated in this way may be very different, and each island may give rise to strikingly different species.

That, however, is rather a special state of affairs. As a rule the insects from one population spread outwards and colonize surrounding regions but still retain the chance of mating with members of the original population from which they came. One may picture the insect occupying an area to which it is suited, its numbers being limited in the ways we have already discussed. At the limits of its range one can imagine that only new mutants with specially favourable characters will be able to survive. But the insect is largely prevented from spreading further by the continual arrival of migrants from the central area bringing with them genes that are unsuitable for those individuals that are trying to extend the range of the species into new areas.

Thus there is a conflict between the conservative influence of the original population and the effect of natural selection in the new environment where the species is trying to break new ground. It may happen that the combined effect of natural selection with the appearance of new and favourable mutations may lead to the firm establishment of a new variety in the new environment. An example of this would be the two moths, the clouded brindle *Xylophasia hepatica* and the rosy minor *Miana literosa,* which for a long time were absent from the industrial city area of Sheffield. But within recent years melanic forms have appeared in both these species and they have been able to recolonize the Sheffield area and to form substantial populations there.

In this last instance, the black colouring of the moths is probably itself an important element in their survival; but in addition, as Onslow showed many years ago, these melanic forms are commonly more hardy and capable of living upon polluted foliage. In many instances there are obvious differences in coloration or bodily structure in these new varieties which have no obvious relation to their capacity for survival. The really important new characters they have acquired are of a more subtle kind that has escaped detection.

The separation of new varieties in this way will obviously occur more readily when there is some geographical factor which discourages contact between the parent population and its colony. Further spread may take place from the colony, and a second new variety may appear which is adapted to a more remote environment. The continuation of this process may lead to the occurrence of a succession of varieties each further and further removed from the original population, both geographically and in appearance.

Such a series of forms is commonly called a 'cline'. We saw an example of this in the forms of the moth *Acronycta* in Russia; these are outwardly similar in appearance but they form a 'cline' in regard to the length of day that is needed to prevent diapause (p. 117). Each colony or variety in a series of this kind may merge rather indefinitely into the neighbouring variety and can interbreed readily with this

if occasion allows. But the forms at the extreme ends of the
'cline' may have become so widely separated genetically that
they will no longer interbreed to give fertile offspring. Were
they not connected by the intervening series of varieties
they would be regarded as distinct species; and if the intervening forms were to disappear, two species they would become.

It may happen that the two extreme forms or subspecies
in a 'cline' may come together again to form a 'ring species'
and live side by side in the same locality without interbreeding. For example, the butterfly *Junonia lavinia* appears
to have reached the West Indies from both North and South
America; and where the two lines of migration meet in Cuba
it now behaves as two quite distinct species.

The 'cline' illustrates the way in which new species may
arise without any sharp break between one breeding group
and the next. But probably geographical barriers leading to
the isolation of populations is a more common source of
subspecies, which may eventually become true species no
longer capable of interbreeding when they come together in
the wild state. 'Barriers' can be quite inconspicuous affairs:
colonies of blue butterflies (Lycaenidae) separated by only
a hundred yards or so of long grass or other unsuitable
terrain may diverge to form subspecies.

When discussing the regulation of the numbers of insects
and the natural control of their populations, we assumed
that a given population remained permanently in one area.
But a population threatened with extinction may be well
advised to migrate to new surroundings. On other grounds,
too, it may not be advisable for a population always to
remain in the same place, forming a narrow circle of interbreeding and becoming more and more tied to a single environment. In the interests of the species as a whole it should
disperse and find and colonize new breeding grounds. It
should meet and mate with members of the species from
other localities and thus ensure the spread of all available
mutant genes throughout the population. New combinations
of genes that may be advantageous to the species can thus
be tried out; and the variability within the species will itself be an insurance, increasing the probability that some or
other of its forms will be able to survive sudden adverse
changes in the environment.

These obvious needs are reflected in the behaviour of insects with respect to dispersal and migration. Dispersal is
almost as necessary for insects as reproduction. They must
continually push outwards and colonize new breeding places

before the old ones have become unsuitable. They must avoid overcrowding.

The young or larval stages of an insect are dedicated to feeding and growth. Provided with an adequate supply of food they do not wander but, expending the minimum of energy, they devote their time to feeding, digestion, and growth. Of course there are insects such as the praying mantis or other predaceous forms, such as the larvae of water-beetles, or of Reduviid and blood-sucking bugs, which live much the same kind of life as the adults of their species and must exert themselves to find their prey. But the great majority of insect larvae, feeding on growing plants or on the dead remains of plants and animals, or the helpless larvae of social Hymenoptera fed by their nurses, all lead a more or less sedentary or 'vegetative' life.

But when these vegetative larvae become adult, a great change comes over them. They are now for the most part winged and capable of flight. Even the adults of insects that come from predaceous larvae now have functional wings for the first time. And their mood changes. Almost the first act which the adult performs, as soon as its wings are hardened, is to launch itself into the air and get moving. Corbet has described how the mature larvae or nymphs of the emperor dragonfly, *Anax imperator*, climb out of the water in the evening and clamber up the neighbouring grass stems or tree trunks (plate 32). The adults emerge in the early part of the night and by about an hour before sunrise the wings are sufficiently hardened for them to be capable of flight. Their wings begin to whirr, and this continues for twenty minutes or so; for the air is cold and the flight muscles need warming up before they can work effectively (p. 32). But finally, before the sun rises, they take off in a body and direct their flight away from the pool where they have grown up. They may settle down after a flight of a hundred yards or so; and for some days they keep away from water, hunting their prey and dispersing widely. Only when the reproductive organs are mature does the mood change. The sexes return to the water and mate, and reproduction begins.

This is a very common pattern of behaviour among adult insects. Immediately after the cuticle in these winged adults has hardened and they are capable of flight, they set off on a migration. Since emergence usually takes place in the whole group at the same hour of the day, a large number of insects may start migrating at the same time. The direction of their movement may be decided by the direction of the light at the moment of departure, and the whole group may fly off together. It may be that single insects behave in the same way, but it is only when it happens in large populations that the movement attracts attention.

This habit of making a migratory flight immediately after emergence is an important 'adaptation' which ensures dispersal. It is a 'built-in' pattern of behaviour and not merely the result of crowding or food shortage—although, of course, these may be present. Indeed, in such insects as aphids and locusts, in which the migratory habit is best developed, vast numbers are involved. Enormous losses of individuals occur *en route*, and many never reach a favourable environment; vast swarms of aphids from the pine forests of Northern Europe have been found stranded in Spitzbergen; but these losses the species can afford, and the gain that results in escaping from overcrowding and in colonizing new areas is evident enough.

This migratory behaviour seems to represent a particular 'mood'; the insect is impelled to get moving; and during the period of locomotor activity it is attracted neither by food nor by the opposite sex. Its 'vegetative' reactions are said to be inhibited. Winged aphids are impelled to fly soon after they emerge. They are attracted upwards by the ultra-violet light of the sky. But after a brief flight, it may be of only a few minutes, their reactions change. They turn away from the ultra-violet light and are attracted by green foliage. They settle down and probe the green leaves, and if these prove acceptable in flavour and in the amino acids, sugars, and other nutrients which their sap contains, they remain to feed; they settle down, their flight muscles are dissolved, and the proceeds used to nourish their developing young. The brief period of active adult life is over; the insect has returned to the vegetative existence of mating and producing young.

The Scolytid bark beetle *Trypodendron*, when it first emerges from its burrows as an adult, is strongly attracted to light; this response overcomes all other stimuli and it flies upwards towards the sky. But during flight it swallows air and the pressure of the air bubble in the stomach seems to be a signal which changes its responses; and now it will react to the odour and contact of the pine trunk, and it returns to its breeding grounds.

Aphids which are such remarkable migrants are not strong fliers. But when they take off and fly upwards they get caught in the rising convection currents of air and may be carried up for a mile or more into the sky. On any warm day the air at 1,000 to 5,000 feet up contains vast numbers of insects, not only aphids and small flies of many kinds, but even spiders and mites suspended in the air on threads of silk. Here they may be swept along, perhaps for many miles by strong winds. But in the evening the rising currents subside and the aphids gradually descend; at night the air is almost clear of insects. In this way great numbers of black bean aphids *Aphis fabae* arrive in England in the early summer from the continent of Europe. Many, of course, are forced down into the sea; some are landed on the Alps above the snowline and perish; but those which come down in suitable territory are in no way injured by their journey and as soon as they find a suitable plant they can settle down and reproduce. Every year vast numbers of leafhoppers *Empoasca* which have grown to maturity in the warm Southern States of North America, are carried to the north-east in the early summer and arrive in the cornbelt hundreds of miles to the north.

At the outset of their flights aphids control their own movements: they direct themselves towards the ultra-violet light of the sky. But once they are caught up in the convection currents and wind streams, they are at the mercy of the elements and have no longer any control over the direction of their migration until they are once more dropped to the earth; then they can orient themselves again towards the green plants they require. Locusts have much more control, at least during the early stages of their migratory flights, for they can fly low and orient themselves by the direction of the sun or by conspicuous features in the landscape (p. 238). But when they are well launched upon one of their massive migrations they allow themselves to be lifted by convection, like the aphids. In this way, not only do they avoid obstacles, like mountain ranges, but they pass out of range of the visible ground pattern by which they might be oriented, and they ride the faster-moving upper air. We saw how cohesion is maintained in these swarms by locusts at the edge turning back into the swarm when they tend to become separated; but the swarm as a whole is just bundled across country by the wind.

The desert locust *Schistocerca gregaria* ranges from Northern India to North Africa (figure 125). Great areas of this zone are desert where there is no chance of the locust rearing a brood; breeding is possible only where there is rainfall. But the winds which temporarily converge upon a given region bring the rain. By allowing themselves to be transported by the wind the desert locusts are delivered in the right place at the right time (plate 33).

The phase of restless activity which culminates in migration usually appears in the young adult soon after emergence. But sometimes it becomes apparent at the end of a period of diapause, that is, of arrested reproduction. Indeed, Kennedy has suggested that migratory behaviour itself is an example of diapause; for migrating insects, whether they be aphids, locusts, or beetles, all show a delay in the onset of reproduction, and a reduction in the number of young produced, when compared with non-migrating forms of the same species. Kennedy goes further than this and points out that the

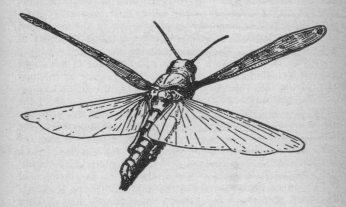

Figure 125.
The desert locust *Schistocerca gregaria* in flight with the legs retracted, the wings beating in turn at about 18 beats per second. The wing span is about 13 cm and the weight about 2 gm; continuous flight at an air-speed of about 10 miles per hour can be maintained for more than twenty hours (Rainey, Anti-Locust Research Centre).

active period, while the insect is migrating, may be regarded as the truly adult state, when the 'vegetative' existence of the larva is for the time being abandoned. But this active condition soon comes to an end and the mature insect reverts once more to a vegetative state, devoting itself to the production of young. As we have already seen (p. 112), the solitary phase of locusts, which lacks the gregarious, energetic, migratory properties of the gregarious phase, and which has a much higher rate of egg production, can be regarded as a more 'juvenile' or 'vegetative' creature.

Restless activity and the urge to fly do not of themselves constitute migration. They could merely lead to the insect moving to and fro in the same locality and effect very little in the way of dispersal. Migration is characterized by what is called a 'straightening out' of the movement. In aphids and in locusts this straightening out is due in some degree to the directed movements of the insects themselves; but for the most part it is brought about by the wind. The migration of butterflies and moths, also, is likely to be influenced by winds; indeed Lepidoptera of various kinds can be found in the upper air being carried along with other insects. But many butterflies and moths fly near the ground and make seasonal migrations in a fixed direction which may be independent of the direction of the wind. For many years these movements were thought to take place in one direction only, so that the butterflies or their offspring never returned to their original home. That was a puzzling observation from the standpoint of evolution; it implied that a pattern of behaviour was being maintained in the population in spite of the fact that all the individuals which showed this behaviour were permanently lost!

But in recent years more and more evidence has been obtained for a return flight. Some of the common butterflies of the British Isles, such as the red admiral *Vanessa atalanta,* the small tortoiseshell *V. urticae,* and the clouded yellow butterflies *Colias croceus* and *C. hyale,* regularly move northwards from the continent of Europe during the spring and move southwards again during the autumn. The painted lady *Pyrameis cardui* and the silver Y moth *Plusia gamma* cannot maintain themselves in Great Britain during the winter at any stage of their life history. They breed in the south of Europe and in North Africa; in the early summer they make the flight across the Mediterranean, across Europe, and the painted lady may even press on to Iceland or Northern Finland, a total distance of about 2,000 miles. In the New World the same butterfly has its winter breeding quarters in Western Mexico and spreads to the north and north-east each spring, when some can even reach to the mouth of the St Lawrence River or to Newfoundland, nearly 3,000 miles from their starting-point.

Actual proof that a particular insect has migrated over these great distances is difficult to obtain. But on 10th March 1960 a specimen of the small Pyralid moth *Nomophila noctuella* captured in England was found to contain a radioactive particle of a type that must have been derived from the atomic bomb exploded in the Sahara on 13th February.

All the evidence available suggested that the particle had been taken up in North Africa and that this small insect had migrated some 1,500 miles.

In some of these cases there is as yet no clear evidence of a southward migration in the autumn. The classic example of a two-way migration is that of the monarch butterfly *Danaus plexippus*. F. A. Urquhart has carried out a very detailed study of this insect extending over many years. The butterflies are to be seen in Canada during the summer months alone. They move southwards in the fall and overwinter in the southern parts of the United States; some hibernate in vast roosts, as in Pacific Grove, on the Californian coast, where they are protected by law as an attraction for tourists; others spend the winter in an active state, as in Mexico and in Florida, where they will breed during the winter months. One of the marked butterflies liberated in Ontario on 18th August 1957 was recovered on 25th January 1958 in Mexico at a distance of 1,870 miles. In the spring some of the same individuals and more of their offspring start to move northwards again, following the sprouting of the milkweed, on which their caterpillars feed, and some of these faded and tattered specimens may find their way right up to Ontario. The maximum distance on the northward flight that has been proved by marking was 600 miles.

The existence of these seasonal migrations in two opposing directions, and observations in nature of butterflies flying consistently in one direction, sometimes for days on end, make it clear that these insects can regulate the direction of flight irrespective of the prevailing wind. This has led to much discussion and speculation on the way in which butterflies can navigate. The question still awaits proof; but since, as we have seen, social bees can navigate by the sun, and by making use of their sense of time can make due allowance for the apparent movements of the sun during the twenty-four hours (p. 246) and since this same capacity for sun navigation is used by Carabid beetles on the sea-shore when alarmed (p. 249) there seems every reason to suppose that this same ability in astronomical navigation is shared by the Lepidoptera—but that still requires testing by experiment.

It may be well to add a few words pointing out once more how the three topics considered in this chapter are linked together. The natural regulation of insect populations is commonly discussed as though these populations were uniform throughout and were confined and insulated within the region under consideration. But, as this chapter has made clear, populations are not uniform. Different forms of adversity will select out for survival different groups of individuals from the population; this process will favour genetic diversity and, when combined with geographical separation, may lead ultimately to the detachment of new subspecies or even new species. The survival of a population of insects is favoured also by their innate tendency to disperse and migrate into new environments; and the need to face the fresh difficulties of these new surroundings will again favour the maintenance of diversity in the gene-pool of the species. The fluctuations in the populations of insects, their migratory habits, and the steps which lead to speciation, are interlocking processes in the life of insects.

Chapter 16

INSECTS AND FLOWERS

THE EVOLUTION of flowers has been the counterpart to the evolution of insects. The earliest flowering plants were doubtless fertilized by wind-borne pollen. As soon as the pollen capsules opened, the grains were carried away by the wind and were of little value as a food for insects. The first step towards the utilization of insects for the transport of pollen was the provision of a sticky coat to the pollen grains. They became covered with an oily liquid secreted by the anthers, which did not evaporate and was long persistent. These adherent pollen grains became a valuable insect food; they also clung to the body of the insect; and when the styles of the female flowers secreted small amounts of sweet fluid, the way was prepared for insects to play an ever-increasing part in the transfer of pollen.

Alongside these changes, the anthers and the pollen grains themselves acquired a strong attractive scent, perhaps related in its origin to the adhesive oil. Later the flower petals could take over the production of scent, until insect-pollinated flowers acquired scents characteristic of each species. At the same time the visual characters of flowers changed. They acquired colours and shapes which made them stand out conspicuously from the green of the main plant so that they became attractive from a distance. But these changes could be effective only because there was a parallel evolution in the senses of insects, their perception of scents and colours, their memory and association of experiences. Many flowers developed organs which secreted excess sugars in the form of nectar, which provided an additional, and sometimes the sole attraction for insects.

The use of insects for pollen transfer encouraged also the combination of the two sexes in a single flower; for this would obviously increase greatly the chances that an insect covered with pollen would come into contact with the female organ. Moreover, pollen is attractive only to biting insects; but insects collecting only nectar, may pick up pollen incidentally and then bring this into contact with the pistils of the flowers at their later stage of maturity.

Another way of getting round this difficulty of pollination in plants with flowers of two sexes, was for both sexes to secrete nectar. Both these changes have encouraged more and more insects to lose their biting mouth-parts, to give up feeding upon pollen, but to visit flowers for their nectar and in so doing to assist in pollination. Finally, nectar-secreting flowers with combined sexes may have the organs of the one sex diminished or completely suppressed, and thus revert to flowers of male or female sex only, sometimes growing on separate plants. That is the case in the willows and sallows where both male and female flowers have active nectaries, so that both sexes are visited by the same insects. Sometimes the flowers with one sex suppressed may exist side by side on the same plant with bisexual flowers; and in some Compositae, such as the cornflower *Centaurea,* completely sexless florets around the outside of the bloom serve merely to provide a visual attraction.

There are also flowers which offer their visitors no nectar but only abundant pollen. These 'pollen flowers' of the new style are no longer green but white or brightly coloured to stand out conspicuously, and are also scented. Such flowers as field poppies, wild roses, peonies, etc, depend particularly on pollen-eating beetles which become coated with the sticky pollen as they feed. This pollen is produced in great excess. But certain of these 'pollen flowers' do secrete nectar—indeed there are all stages of transition between 'pollen flowers' and 'nectar flowers'.

In some plants, species of *Cassia* for example, only a proportion of the anthers produce genuine, fertile pollen. Others have become modified to produce a pollen-like powder which is quite sterile but furnishes an excellent food for pollinating insects. Orchids do not provide nectar, and their pollen is enclosed in 'pollinia' (p. 297) and is not available as food. Some orchid species provide instead a rich mixture of sugar and protein which can be sucked up or bitten off with the jaws. Other orchids are furnished with 'food hairs' rich in fat which can be nibbled off by insects.

Nectar is formed in many different parts of the flower in

different plants, and commonly in places adapted to the needs of the chief pollinator on which the plant in question has come to depend. The common 'nasturtium' of our gardens *Tropaeolum majus* is a native of Peru. It secretes its nectar in the long spur behind the flower; and here it is readily accessible to the humming-birds which are their chief pollinators. In Europe, where we have no humming-birds, the *Tropaeolum* is attractive particularly to bumble-bees. But the short-tongued bumble-bees cannot reach the nectar by the normal route; they bite into the wall of the spur and rob the nectar from outside without effecting pollination. Indeed the short-tongued bees have learned to rob many flowers in this way. We have already had occasion to mention the conspicuous visual 'honey guides' and the associated 'scent guides' which serve to lead the insect to the sites of nectar secretion.

Many factors will determine the efficiency of insects as carriers of pollen. Obviously the pollen must cling to the insect; insects that fly rapidly from flower to flower will be more useful; and insects such as the social bees, which visit flowers not only for their own nourishment but repeatedly, to feed their brood, will be the most valuable of all.

It is not necessary to repeat that insect senses have been evolved in parallel with the blooms of flowering plants; the sense of smell, of taste, of form and colour vision, have largely been adapted to finding and utilizing flowers as a source of food. It is well to remember that the chemical sense of smell may operate not only at a distance but in immediate and close contact with the sense organs.

Many of the peculiarities of insect senses have been discussed in earlier chapters. We have reviewed the ways in which the colour vision of insects differs from our own. We saw how the bees, the most important of flower-visiting insects, do not perceive pure spectral red, but are highly sensitive to ultra-violet. The native flowers of Europe are mostly blue or purple red, and deep red flowers, like those of the field poppy, are visible to the bee because they reflect a large amount of ultra-violet. This is in striking contrast to flowers that are pollinated by birds, such as the cultivated *Saliva splendens* of a pure brilliant red, which is a native of Brazil and is normally fertilized by humming-birds.

There are all degrees of mutual adaptation between plant and pollinating insect. In the most extreme examples the relation between the two amounts to a complete 'symbiosis' in which plant and insect are wholly dependent upon one another and their season life cycles have become fitted in together. The most famous example of this kind is that of the yucca moth (*Pronuba yuccasella* and related species) which has become as necessary to the yucca plant in the southern parts of North America, in ensuring the fertilization of the seed, as the yucca plant is essential for the growth and multiplication of the yucca moth.

The yucca moth is little more than a centimetre in length. It becomes active at night and, after mating, the female visits the hanging flowers of the yucca to collect pollen. The moth's proboscis has become modified so that it can feed neither on nectar nor on pollen. It has taken on the form of a pair of curved tentacles, and with the help of these it collects the sticky pollen from the open anthers and works

Figure 126.
The yucca moth *Pronuba*, about 1 cm in length, applying its packet of pollen to the pistil of the yucca flower (Riley).

this into a ball that may be several millimetres across. Supporting this pollen ball between the tentacles, the head, and the fore-legs it flies off to another flower of the same species and lays its eggs in the seed buds. It then wanders up the pistil to the stigma where it applies some of its pollen (figure 126). Repeating this deliberate process of egg-laying and pollination in a number of flowers, it provides its larvae with a rich store of ripening seeds. Indeed there are far more seeds than the caterpillars require; and the excess can ripen after the full-grown larvae have left to burrow in the soil. Next year when the yucca is again in flower the moths are ready to repeat the process of pollination.

Flower visitors are to be found among most of the higher

orders of insects, and these show varying degrees of modification and specialization for the purpose. Perhaps the beetles have been the least modified. They were probably already
well established as scavengers, with their mouth-parts of the
standard form (p. 64) before the flowering plants came into
existence. For the most part those which visit flowers show
little change in their anatomy. They can collect pollen with
their mandibles and lick up nectar with their other mouth-
parts, provided it is easily accessible. But in tropical America
there is one flower-visiting genus of beetles, *Nemognatha*,
belonging to the family of oil beetles, or Meloidae, whose
mouth-parts have become modified for sucking up nectar
from deep recesses. The mandibles are of the usual kind, but

Figure 127.
Head of the flower-visiting beetle *Nemognatha* showing how the
maxillae are elongated and grooved to form a sucking-tube like that
of a butterfly (Knoll).

the maxillae have become drawn out and linked together by
hairs so as to form a sucking tube that may be as long as
the rest of the body (figure 127). This tube cannot be coiled
like the proboscis of the butterflies and moths, but in other
respects the two structures are closely similar.

Many beetles are more or less destructive for the flowers
they visit and some, such as the chafer-beetles (the rose
beetle *Cetonia*, the may bugs, etc) may devour the entire
contents of the flowers. Chafer-beetles (Scarabaeidae) are
largely responsible for the pollination of the giant lily of
the Amazon, *Victoria regia*. These flowers open in the eve-

ning and the beetles are strongly attracted by their heavy scent. Then the flowers close until the following evening. During their time of imprisonment the beetles feed on the interior of the lily, but they also pollinate the female parts. When the flower opens again they leave, carrying pollen to other newly opened blossoms.

Among the Lepidoptera, the most primitive forms such as *Micropteryx calthella* still have functional mandibles with which they can collect and eat pollen. Evidently the earliest flower-visiting Lepidoptera were pollen feeders, which incidentally took up nectar, before they had developed true sucking organs. But all other flower-visiting butterflies and moths have lost their mandibles, and the maxillae have been converted into a coiled sucking tube adapted solely to collecting nectar (p. 68); pollen is no longer an article of diet. The coiled proboscis may be no more than a centimetre long; but in the largest flower-visiting hawk-moths of the tropics it may be as much as 25 cm in length. When the tube is unrolled a distinct kink is visible part way along it; this joint helps the introduction into the flower.

A typical example of a 'butterfly flower' is the purple-red flower of *Dianthus*, with a long tubular calyx which contains both pistil and anthers, and with the source of nectar at the bottom. The long proboscis is well suited to transfer pollen in such a structure. In this process a certain element of 'learning' on the part of the moth or butterfly is involved. It may require several attempts before the insect becomes adept at inserting the proboscis in a particular kind of flower, and learns to associate the scent and pattern of that flower with the presence of nectar.

Other flowers, such as *Saponaria officinalis* and tobacco, have such an elongated calyx that the nectar is accessible only to insects with a very long proboscis; they have become dependent on the humming-bird hawk-moth *Macroglossa* and other Sphingids for their pollination. The rapid movements of these moths as they flit in the sunlight or in the dusk from flower to flower, collecting the nectar as they hover in mid-air, represents one of the most elegant modes of insect pollination (figure 128). The humming-bird hawk-moth has been used extensively for experiments with flowers. It has been shown, for example, that it will be attracted to the yellow flowers of toad-flax (*Linaria vulgaris*) even when these are enclosed between glass plates so that the scent is excluded. Moreover the proboscis is extended directly towards the deep yellow 'honey guide' on the flower, which likewise is located by vision alone. Other hawk-moths, such as the convolvulus hawk (*Protoparce convolvuli*), which feed after dark, when trained to visit white flowers will also visit small, odourless, porcelain containers of the same size; and they can continue to find blue or violet flowers when there is so little light that these appear black and colourless to us. Nevertheless the scent may well be important in putting these insects in the mood to search for nectar—just as incidental properties of food will evoke 'appetite' in ourselves.

Diptera are apt to visit flowers with freely exposed nectar, such as the flowers of ivy, along with wasps and other insects. Many species also eat pollen and appear along with many sorts of beetles on the flower heads of Umbelliferae and Compositae. The hover-flies and drone-flies of the family

Figure 128.
The humming-bird hawk-moth *Macroglossa stellatarum* collecting nectar during flight from the flowers of the crane's-bill *Geranium pratense*.

Syrphidae are the most frequent. In order to deal with pollen these flies collect the grains between the two grooved lobes of the labium (p. 75) which can be rubbed against one another and the collected pollen pressed backwards into the main groove of the labium which leads to the mouth.

On the other hand the bee-flies (*Bombylius*), which can be seen in the spring visiting the grape hyacinths (*Muscari*) and other flowers, have a long projecting labium adapted solely to take up nectar. They probably make no use of the pollen.

One of the most remarkable methods of insect pollination is that evolved by the cuckoo pint or Aaron's rod (*Arum maculatum*). When the protective spath of this wild lily unfolds, a club-shaped process is revealed which gives off an evil smell that is attractive to insects which breed in putre-fying matter. The surface of the club is smooth and moist and the insects fall to the base of it. Here the larger flies escape but small beetles and small flies, particularly 'moth flies' of the genus *Psychoda* fall down into a thimble-shaped trap below. This cavity is guarded above by a ring of stiff processes with downwardly directed spines which prevent the flies from getting out again (figure 129). Below this ob-struction is the male part of the flower which will later pro-duce the pollen. Then follows another obstruction of the same type as before, and lastly the female part of the flower

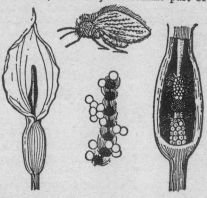

Figure 129.
Pollination of the cuckoo pint *Arum maculatum;* explanation in the text. In the middle is the moth-fly *Psychoda* (about 1.5 mm long) and detail of a part of the antenna showing adherent pollen grains (Knoll).

with droplets of attractive juice on the stigmas. Here the flies remain trapped for the night and any pollen they have brought in is smeared on the stigmas. The walls of the cham-ber are smooth and moist and the flies cannot climb up. But by the next morning the flowers are beginning to shrivel. The walls can be climbed; the obstructing rings of spines have become limp; the male parts of the flower have rip-ened and showers of pollen grains are liberated and adhere to the flies as they make their escape. But no sooner have they regained their liberty than they are drawn to another newly opened lily and trapped once more to ensure the cross-fertilization of the second plant. *Aristolochia clematis* is another plant which makes use of a similar device to se-cure fertilization by small Diptera.

The gall-wasps (Cynipidae) are known mainly as the pro-

ducers of the abnormal plant growths termed 'galls', which
furnish both shelter and nourishment for their larvae. In the
tropics the gall-wasps play a most important role as pollinators, for they are the sole means of fertilization in the many
hundreds of species of wild figs. The same is true of the
cultivated fig of Southern Europe. Even in Ancient Greece

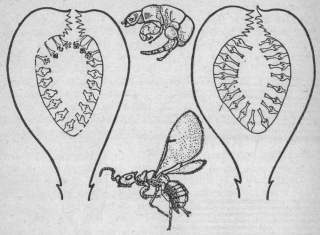

Figure 130.
The wingless male of the fig insect, the gall-wasp *Blastophaga
psenes,* above, and the winged female, below. On the left, a schematic
figure of the inedible 'goat fig' in longitudinal section; it shows the
short-necked female flowers where the galls are formed, lining the
cavity below, and the male flowers above, round the entrance to the
cavity. On the right, a section through the edible fig which contains only long-necked female flowers (Knoll).

the part played by the tiny fig gall-wasps (*Blastophaga
psenes*) was correctly understood and applied to practical
use.

By continued vegetative propagation purely female strains
of the edible fig were obtained, probably in Asia, and later
introduced into Greece and Italy. These female figs will not
set seed and ripen unless they are pollinated, and the only
way in which pollination can take place is through the
agency of the fig insects coming from what the Romans
called 'goat figs' (*caprificus*). Presumably these also were derived by vegetative propagation from the ancestral stock.
They never produce ripe fruit but the flask-like interior of
the hard figs they do produce carry female flowers which
serve as the sites of egg-laying and gall formation by the

Blastophaga wasps (figure 130). The curious wingless males settle on these ripe galls, bite a hole in their wall, and mate with the female within. Then the females make their way out and escape through the mouth of the fig, becoming coated with pollen from the male flowers in the process, and migrate to the young female fruits of the edible fig. Here they find that the flowers lining the cavity of the fig are too long in the neck for use in egg-laying and gall formation; but not until they have roamed around and pollinated all these flowers do they leave the young fruit.

When Smyrna figs were introduced into California they remained unfruitful for years, until the ancient practice was adopted and the appropriate goat figs together with their gall-wasp were also imported and grown alongside, or their galled fruits suspended among the branches of the edible figs. Meanwhile excellent edible figs have been produced which form fruit in the absence of gall-wasps. But these are seedless varieties unsuitable for drying and export.

The most important pollinators in temperate latitudes are the social bees which gather pollen and nectar throughout the summer to feed their brood (plate 34). They have developed sundry modifications to assist in the collection of pollen. Certain of the mining bees of the genus *Dasypoda*, called by the Germans 'breeches bees', have the hind-legs furnished with abundant hairs which accumulate so much pollen that it may amount to half the total weight of the insect. The mason bees (*Osmia* species) and the leaf-cutting bees (*Megachile*) (figure 110) have a dense coat of hairs on the lower surface of the abdomen which serves the same purpose. But the most elaborate arrangement is that of the bumble-bees and particularly the honey-bee (figure 131). The equipment here consists of the broad tibia of the hind pair of legs which on its outer surface is smooth and hollowed out and surrounded by a fringe of long curved hairs. This is the 'pollen basket'. At the inside of the tibia at its broad lower end is a row of spines which form the 'comb'. Below the tibia comes the first segment of the tarsus which also is very broad and flat and carries a dense 'brush' of hairs on its inner surface. Finally, at the upper end of this broad tarsal segment, just opposite the comb, is a stout 'spur' with bristles. The pollen is collected by the brush; it is mixed with a little nectar to render it sticky and is then combed out by the comb of the opposite leg; it is moved upwards and pressed into the pollen basket by means of the spur and this dexterous procedure continues until the pollen baskets are bulging with the sticky mass.

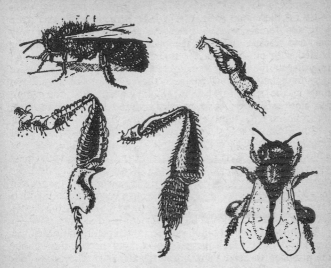

Figure 131.
Pollen-collecting apparatus of the honey-bee. Top left, worker bee showing the concave tibia and the broad first segment of the tarsus on the hind-leg. Below, the detailed structure of the hind-leg from the outside (left) and inside. The outer view shows the hollow in the tibia surrounded by curved hairs (the 'pollen basket') and the 'spur' of bristles on the tarsus just below the pollen basket. The inner view shows the row of spines on the tibia forming the 'comb' and the dense 'brush' on the tarsus. Top right, a small ball of pollen in the basket; and below, a bee with the pollen baskets fully laden (v. Frisch).

The whole economy of the social bees is centred upon the collection of nectar and pollen. Their sensory perceptions, their capacity for finding their way about and communicating to other members of the hive the latest information on the best collecting grounds, their memory for time, and for colour and scent, have all been evolved in parallel with the flowering plants. The systematic fashion in which they will work a single crop or species of flower until the nectar is exhausted, makes them the most efficient of all pollinators. The ability of the bee to recognize the time of day has its counterpart in the habit of many flowers which secrete their nectar at a particular hour only, and it is to this hour that the bees confine their visits.

Bees will collect nectar from a great variety of flowers, but the most characteristic 'bee-flowers' are those of 'labiate' or

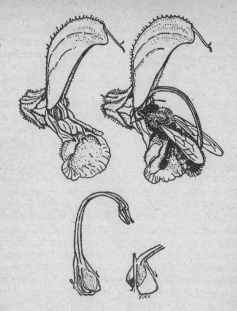

Figure 132.
A bee entering the flower of the garden sage *Salvia officinalis* causes the stamens to swing downwards so that the anthers touch the back of the bee and smear it with pollen. The forked stigma in this young flower remains clear of the bee. The hinged attachment of the stamens is shown below (Robert).

'snap-dragon' type with an upper and lower lip. In some of these the nectar is accessible to other insects as well; butter-flies may reach it with their slender proboscis; in others the nectar can be got only by the bees, and in all of them the bee is by far the most efficient pollinating agent. A typical example is the common sage (*Salvia officinalis*) and related species (figure 132). Here the two pollen-bearing anthers are concealed below the upper lip. But they are hinged below to a flap which obstructs the way to the nectar at the base of the calyx. The strongly built bumble-bee can press against this flap and force its tongue down into the calyx. The pressure on the flap brings down the anthers which smear the back of the bee with pollen. These youngest flowers are in the male phase with the formed stigma projecting horizontally and not obstructing the entry to the flower. But if the bee, now coated with pollen, enters an older flower in the female phase, the stigma is hanging down at the entry and it picks up the pollen as the bee forces its way in.

In many of the orchids the entry to the spur, where the sugary tissue that is sought by the bees is to be found, is guarded by a ring of club-shaped 'pollinaria', or packets of pollen. These have a sticky disk at the lower end, and one or more of them will adhere to the head of the bee as it presses into the opening (figure 133). The roof of the passage leading to the sweet supplies also bears the sticky concavity of the stigma, and when the bee subsequently visits an orchid in the female phase the pollen packet adheres to this area and is left behind.

In certain orchids of tropical South America, belonging to the genus *Catasetum*, the pollen packet is held in a spring, and as the bee, the long-tongued bee *Euglossa*, seeks the sweet content in the male flower, the catch is triggered and the adhesive pollen packet is shot out and sticks to its body, later to be carried to the female flower.

In most of these mechanisms for pollen transfer the flower plays a passive role. But the flower of the barberry, *Berberis vulgaris*, takes a more active part in planting its pollen on the visiting bee. The lemon yellow flowers have six shell-like petals each of which carries a single anther, whose pollen capsule opens with two lids held widely part. In the base of the flower is a ring of dark orange nectaries, and as the tongue of the bee is extended to the nectar it touches the stalk of one or other of the anthers. At once the anther bends quickly over towards the pistil in the centre of the flower; the pollen-covered lids of the anthers are thus brought into contact with the bee's tongue, which is smeared with pollen ready for pollinating the pistil of the next flower visited. The anther then uncurves again in readiness for the next bee.

In considering the methods of self-defence employed by insects we discussed at some length the type of 'mimicry' in which an insect, without defensive aids, may acquire the outward appearance of another species that is armed with venoms or other undesirable qualities which are advertised by a suitable 'warning coloration'. Some plants have evolved a 'mimicry' of a different sort which lures the insect to convey their pollen.

This is most highly developed in the bee and fly orchids of the genus *Ophrys*. The 'labellum', or lip, of the flower in these orchids mimics in both form and colour the appearance of some particular species of bee or wasp (figure 133).

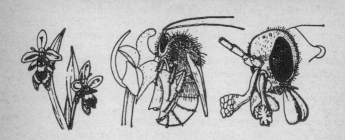

Figure 133.
To the left, the flowers of the bee-like orchid *Ophrys insectifera*.
In the centre, the long-horned bee *Eucera* attempting copulation with
the flower of *Ophrys bombyliformis*. To the right, the head of the
male bee *Gorytes campestris* with the pollinia of two species of
orchids, *Ophrys insectifera* (left) and *Listera ovata* (right)
(Kullenberg).

In Southern Europe where this relation has been studied in
most detail each species of orchid is said to attract only the
males of those species whose females are mimicked by the
labellum.

But, for attracting the male insect, their form and colour
are of far less importance than their scents. These scents
mimic the sexual attractant scents given off by the females
of the species concerned. The males are attracted from a distance by the scents, and on alighting in the flower they become highly excited and attempt to mate with it (figure 133).
The flower has been described as a 'copulation dummy', and
the effect is enhanced by suitably disposed hairs on the lip
of the flower, which are arranged like the hairs on the
back of the female, and cause the male insect to remain and
persist in his attempts until he has dislodged and picked up
the pollinia. Accessible nectar is absent in these flowers, for
that might serve to distract the visiting male, but sham nectaries may be present.

Chapter 17

INSECTS AND MAN

THIS BOOK concerns the life of insects, not the life of Man. But Man regards himself as the 'lord of creation'; and since this title is not conceded by the insects, man and insect are frequently in conflict.

In a small way man has made use of insects. Primitive peoples who live by 'food gathering', such as the aborigines of Australia, collect honey from wild bees, raid the nests of termites to obtain the egg-filled queens, and take advantage of locust swarms to supplement the protein in their diet. The huge maggot of the palm weevil is a familiar delicacy in the markets of West Africa; and African boys join with the lizards and geckos in feasting on the swarms of winged termites that collect around the lamps when a flight is in progress. The dried excrement of scale insects is still gathered as manna from the desert floor in Sinai.

Settled communities of man make more systematic use of insects. The honey-bee has long been domesticated and used as a source of honey, of wax and, perhaps even more important in modern times, as an agent for pollinating agricultural crops; while the 'royal jelly' of the nurse bees has furnished a most profitable field for the operation of the charlatan.

In addition to beeswax, some of the more important waxes of commerce, Chinese insect wax, lac wax, cochineal wax, etc, are insect products; and shellac is a resinous and waxy substance of a very special kind, the product of various lac insects *Tachardia,* etc, which even now has not been wholly displaced by synthetic plastics. Dyes also came from insects in the past: the Aztecs dyed their cloth with 'cochineal', or 'carmine', extracted from the scale insect *Dactylopius* that occurs in profusion on cacti in Mexico. The crimson dye 'kermes' that was widely used in Ancient Greece and Rome came from another scale insect *Lecanium* (figure 154) that feeds on Mediterranean oaks. But as articles of commerce, which held their own for some thousands of years, these have now been largely superseded by synthetic dyes based on coal tar.

Insects occasionally find a use in medicine. The South American Indians will clip together the margins of a gaping wound by allowing driver ants to hold the apposed edges in their powerful jaws; the ants are then decapitated and the jaws remain clamped in position. Aphrodisiacs have continually been sought among insect products. The beetle *Diamphidia* is used as a source of arrow poison by the bushmen in the Kalahari desert; and it is certain that there are plenty of other good insect poisons to be found. The 'cantharidin' extracted from the 'Spanish fly', a Meloid, or 'blister beetle', *Lytta vesicatoria,* still figures in the pharmacopoeia as a blistering agent.

It is not uncommon for flies that breed in the decaying carcasses of animals to lay their eggs in infected wounds. Indeed there are some flies, such as the notorious screwworm fly *Cochliomyia* of Central America and the Southern United States, which specialize in this mode of life and develop solely in this manner, causing much damage to cattle on the ranges; and certain of the sheep blowflies have gone some way in that direction. It was observed by the great French surgeon of the sixteenth century, Ambroise Paré, that the rate of healing of gun-shot wounds was greatly improved when they were invaded by maggots. The same discovery was made by W. S. Baer during World War I, and he did much to popularize the use of maggots in the treatment of long-standing ulcers or chronic infections of bone (osteomyelitis). There was no doubt about the effectiveness of this treatment—although never popular with doctors, nurses, or patients. Welcome claims were made that the beneficial action resulted merely from the excretory product allantoin discharged by the larvae, and this chemical was advocated as a substitute for living maggots. Whatever the basis of these claims may be, the whole subject has been pushed into the background by the development of modern antibiotics.

The insects with the longest history of domestication are the silkworms. There are a number of large Saturniids, species of *Antherea, Philosamia,* or *Telea,* both wild and semidomesticated, which serve as sources of the coarser types of silk (Shantung, tussore, etc). But the domestic mulberry silkworm *Bombyx mori,* whose origin is lost in the antiquity of Chinese culture, is unknown in the wild state. It is a highly artificial product of selective breeding, with a great variety of strains and races which differ in the colour and quality of their silk, the size and shape of the cocoon, the number of generations a year, and so forth. The modern cocoons, the product of genetical research, are so large and tough that the moths cannot get out of them unaided (plate 35). The silk industry of China and Japan and of Southern Europe is not what it was; but it still holds its own in competition with synthetic fibres.

It is of interest to note that most synthetic fibres, such as nylon, which resemble silk quite closely in their properties, are totally unrelated chemically. But in recent years something more like a genuine synthetic silk has been produced. This is a polymer of the amino acid alanine. Natural silk is very largely a linear polymer of alanine, but it also contains some tyrosine, and it is this amino acid which is responsible for the slow browning of natural silk. It may be claimed that the man-made copy is an improvement, for being free of tyrosine it does not have this defect.

The silkworms as a source of fabrics, and the scale insects as a source of dyes, have contributed to the arts of man. The wing cases of beetles have figured in the ornamentation of ancient temples in the East, and the iridescent wings of *Morpho* butterflies from South America have a recurring vogue for the preparation of jewellery. The singing of crickets is much appreciated in China and Japan, where they are kept in little hanging cages or in suitable containers concealed inside the clothing; and fighting crickets are a favourite medium for sport and betting. In Western Europe the chirping of the cricket on the hearth survives in poetry, but the domestic cricket itself has largely been banished to the refuse dumps.

Most of these are small matters. In the world at large the impact of insects on human affairs is on an altogether different scale. It must not be thought that the relation between man and insect always takes the form of a direct clash of interests. Far from it. The web of life on this planet is infinitely complex, and the balance between advantage and disadvantage for a particular species may be finely drawn.

It may be distressing from the human standpoint when wounds of man or of his stock become invaded by the maggots of flies, or when these flies get at the meat which he had reserved for his own use. But the great company of flesh-flies play an invaluable part in the economy of nature in rapidly dispersing the carcases of dead animals. Such carcases are colonized by a succession of insects according to the progress of decomposition. Among the late-comers are the Dermestid beetles (*Anthrenus,* etc) and the various Tineid moths which have discovered how to deal with the keratin of hair and feathers, and they also are playing a useful part in restoring the elements of these substances to the circulation of life. But man does not take it kindly when these same 'carpet beetles' and 'clothes moths' turn their attention to the fur pelts and woollen fabrics with which he has surrounded himself in his home.

The vast majority of insects feed on plants, and when these plants are being grown by man for his own use, he finds himself in direct competition with those insects that feed upon them, and he designates such insects as 'pests'. But even here the insects in question are not wholly noxious. The raspberry beetle *Byturus tomentosus,* which grubs are so troublesome in the ripening fruit of blackberries and raspberries, is one among the army of pollinators which play such an essential part in ensuring the set of apples and other fruit in the spring. And when the control of insects for agricultural purposes by means of insecticides has been pressed to excess, farmers have run into trouble through lack of pollinators, and special arrangements may have to be made for the importation of colonies of honey-bees—which themselves may fall victims to the insect poisons.

We saw in an earlier chapter how populations of insects are limited by a multiplicity of factors: adverse weather, enemies in the form of predators or parasites, and virus, bacterial or fungal diseases. From the point of view of man and his crops it is the outcome of this many-sided battle that is important. An insect species may increase in numbers until it becomes a 'pest'; but how this has come about is commonly unknown. It is agreed that a multiplicity of controlling factors makes for stability. But the development of agriculture during the past century has had the opposite effect, for it has encouraged the planting of larger and larger areas under single crops. That in itself favours the insects which attack those crops and creates a situation where great outbreaks of insect pests are liable to occur. This situation has been met in recent years by the development of ever more potent synthetic insecticides and their use on an ever-increasing scale.

Broadly speaking this policy has been successful. But it has often been carried out without any real appreciation of the facts of life. We tend to think only of the insect pest by which we are troubled and not at all of the other insects by which its numbers are being kept in check; with the result that the thoughtless use of insecticides has sometimes led to the outbreak of new pests which were previously held to be of small account. When DDT was first used on a large scale in orchards, in Pennsylvania and elsewhere, for the purpose of controlling the codling moth, it led to prodigious outbreaks of the woolly aphis which until then had been held in check by its parasitic wasp *Aphelinus mali*—which proved to be much more sensitive to DDT than the woolly aphis itself. Aphids were not considered to be of any great importance as pests of cotton in the Southern States. But when growers changed over from calcium arsenate to the extensive use of DDT for the control of caterpillars, heavy infestations of mites and aphids developed for the first time. That was traced to the elimination by the insecticide of ladybirds, predaceous bugs, and other insects. Until that happened neither the potential danger from mites and aphids, nor the helpful activities of the 'beneficial insects' had been appreciated.

Even in the citrus groves of California, where there have been so many successful examples of so-called 'biological control' of insect pests, the barriers have been giving way under the pressure of modern insecticides. Very familiar is the story of the fluted or cottony-cushion scale *Icerya purchasi*, which had been unwittingly introduced into California with citrus plants, and which in 1886 was appearing in such numbers as to threaten the very survival of the industry; and how A. Koebele brought in the ladybird beetle *Vedalia cardinalis*, a predator from Australia which specializes during both larval and adult stages on this one prey. Within a year or two the citrus industry had been saved and the fluted scale had virtually disappeared. The same success has been repeated in every citrus-growing country where the scale insect had managed to become established without its predators. But the ladybird has proved more susceptible to modern insecticides than the scale insect itself, and now insecticidal treatments are being devised to cope with the renewed outbreaks of the fluted scale!

A similar example of small dimensions has been observable

in England during recent years. The use of insecticides applied to the soil has been highly successful in dealing with the cabbage root fly *Eriorischia* (*Chortophila*) *brassicae*. But this success has been gained at the expense of largely eliminating the Carabid beetles and other predators which had helped to keep this fly in check. Indeed it has been observed on some occasions that small doses of insecticides may actually increase the numbers of cabbage root flies because the predators suffer more than the pest.

These examples do not detract from the importance of insecticides in the control of insect pests. At the present time there is no known substitute for their use. The examples are intended merely to illustrate some of the complexities of biological relationships. The problem for man is to try to intervene and upset these relationships, to disturb the 'balance of nature' in an intelligent fashion so as to produce results that are in his long-term interests. What he should do is not to waste time arguing about the relative theoretical merits of chemical control and biological control, but to try to understand the situation, and then to introduce such changes, in cultivation, or chemical treatments, or biological control of one sort or another, as will permanently tip the balance against the pest and in favour of the crop.

It has to be admitted that these situations are so complex and many-sided that they are seldom completely understood; and in the most successful achievements there has often been an element of good fortune. In the early nineteen forties there was a tremendous outbreak of the European spruce saw-fly *Gilpinia hercyniae* in Eastern Canada, and a campaign was got under way to bring in certain of the chief parasites of this insect from Europe, to breed them up in large numbers and to liberate them in the forests. The results were amazingly successful; the outbreak just melted away. This would have been claimed as a great success for biological control by the use of parasites, had it not been that the result was achieved just a little *too* quickly. Indeed, on looking closely into the matter, it was found that the collapse of the saw-fly population was being brought about by a virus disease. Perhaps this had been unwittingly introduced from Europe. Certainly the experience has given encouragement to the delibrate search for insect diseases that can be used for purposes of control. The more usual belief has been that these diseases are commonly latent and smouldering in the insect population all the time. It is only when the numbers of insects have got out of hand, and they are becoming overcrowded, that the disease breaks out in epidemic form and decimates the population.

In the last chapter we saw examples of the intensive and persistent action of natural selection. This operates also in the field of insect control. The exposure of insect populations to modern insecticides is just about as intensive a form of selection as can be imagined. Any insect which by reason of some small difference in behaviour, in structure, or in physiology, can escape the fatal action of the insecticide, will survive. And if the difference in question is inherited, it will quickly spread throughout the population. In this way strains of insects more or less resistant to insecticides are rapidly built up, and some of them are so resistant that the insecticide ceases to be of value for their control.

This unavoidable biological phenomenon has been known for many years, ever since the citrus scale, *Aonidiella*, in California became resistant to cyanide gas some fifty years ago. But the intensity of selection with modern insecticides is such that resistance is apt to build up very rapidly to a high level. This again has underlined the need to approach the artificial regulation of insect populations in an intelligent manner and not to try and bludgeon the insects into subjection.

It is sometimes argued that we make a mistake in trying to get one hundred per cent control of insect pests in growing crops; that we should aim only at a moderate level of control, and leave a fair population of the potential pest, so that there will always be reserves of the appropriate predators and parasites standing by as a line of defence against a sudden increase in its numbers. This idea of dealing gently with the pests has been put into practice with some success in the orchards of Nova Scotia. But once again, no single method is suitable for universal application.

These same considerations apply equally to insects as pests of growing crops, as pests of stored products of every kind, as pests of forests and of harvested timber, and as pests of livestock, and carriers of disease among domestic animals and man himself. But in some of these groups we should certainly not be prepared to tolerate anything less than one hundred per cent control. We care nothing about a nice balance of populations among the fleas and bed-bugs in our houses, or among the sucking lice upon our persons; we expect all these to be completely banished. We aim reasonably enough at the same insect-free standards in stored products and in timber. The farmer may well wonder why we should expect him to be content with anything less. The only answer is to point to the complexity of the environment in growing crops. Where insects are moving in from the wild grasses to cereal crops, or from the hawthorns in the hedgerows to the fruit trees in the orchard, man does not yet have the power to eradicate the insects completely.

Local migrations of this sort always add to the problems of the farmer. But invasions by some pests may come in from hundreds of miles away. There is little doubt that many of the aphids appearing in England in the early summer have come in from the mainland of Europe. The leafhoppers that attack the potato in the Midwestern States of America have migrated northwards from the Southern States. At infrequent intervals the diamond back moth *Plutella maculipennis* appears suddenly in England as a serious pest of cruciferous crops. These invading swarms come from Eastern Europe.

The most notorious of migrant pests are the locusts. Ecologically these fall into two groups sometimes classed respectively as 'grasshoppers' and 'locusts'. Grasshoppers are always present, feeding and multiplying, and often a continuous source of loss in crops of many kinds. Locusts are grasshoppers which appear in dual form (p. 112). In their 'solitary phase' they live like other grasshoppers and may do so little damage as not to qualify as pests. But when their numbers increase above a certain level they go over to the 'gregarious phase', and form huge bands which migrate on foot as 'hoppers' or in the adult state as winged swarms. These vast swarms, which may increase until they are hundreds of square miles in extent, having bred up in some distant locality, may suddenly descend upon a farmer's crops and in a few hours eliminate every green leaf.

The locust has no respect for national boundaries. It can be countered only on an international footing. In an effort to compete successfully with it, international organizations have been set up with the joint aims of learning more about the movements of locusts and the build-up of their populations, of providing early warning of the approach of swarms so that counter-measures can be prepared in advance, and of keeping an eye on the 'solitary' forms in their native haunts, so as to detect the early signs of an increase in the population and the change over to the 'gregarious' phase, so that control measures may be undertaken at the points of origin. This last procedure has met with considerable success in dealing with the migratory locust *Locusta migratoria* and with the red-locust *Nomadacris septemfasciata* which have fairly well defined 'outbreak areas' (figure 134). Early application of insecticides in these areas have probably served to avert

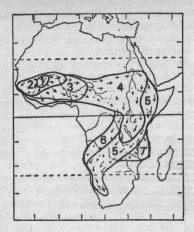

Figure 134.
Map of Africa showing the approximate rate of spread of the migratory locust *Locusta migratoria* during seven years following an outbreak on the middle Niger (1) about 1928 (Uvarov).

outward migrations of the dangerous gregarious phase. Unfortunately, the desert locust *Schistocerca gregaria* ranges over such a vast extent of territory, from Northern India to Morocco, that it has not proved possible to contain it by these means. The locust has been with us since the dawn of history, but it can still bring famine to a whole community. Only improvement in communications and the development of food storage enables the importation of food to soften the blow.

Improved communications have had another, less favourable, influence, for they have helped in the dissemination of insect pests. This great change was heralded in the 1860's when the settlers moving westwards across the United States reached the eastern slopes of the Rocky Mountains. At this time the harmless colorado beetle *Leptinotarsa*, which had hitherto subsisted on the buffalo burr of the deserts, changed its diet to the potato and became a major pest of agriculture, sweeping across the American continent to the Atlantic seaboard and, today, across Europe. The production of Paris green and lead arsenate as agricultural insecticides was the answer. That was the beginning of agricultural entomology as we know it today. The hundred years that have passed since these events have been characterized by the continued spread and introduction of pests from one country to another, and by the progressive elaboration of insecticides and other methods of control.

The recognition of the importance of insects in human and veterinary medicine likewise dates from the middle of the last century. Starting with the work of Patrick Manson, who showed in 1878 that mosquitoes are concerned in carrying the filaria worms that cause elephantiasis, there followed a period of twenty-five or thirty years (sometimes called the 'golden age' of tropical medicine) during which insects and related arthropods were shown to be responsible for the transmission to man of nearly all the great epidemic fevers of the tropics: yellow fever, dengue, and malaria by mosquitoes; the relapsing fevers and typhus in all its varieties by ticks, mites, and lice; bubonic plague by fleas; five-day fever, kala azar, and Oriental sore by sand-flies (*Phlebotomus*); sleeping sickness by tsetse-flies (*Glossina*), etc, etc. The same proved true of many diseases of livestock: trypanosomiasis by the tsetse-flies in Africa; the fevers of cattle by ticks in Africa, the United States, and elsewhere, and many more.

In all these examples an infective organism (a virus, bacterium, protozoon, or parasitic worm, as the case may be) is carried by the insect and injected into the animal or man, usually during the act of feeding. A comparable state of affairs exists in agricultural crops where plants are infected with virus diseases that are carried by aphids, leafhoppers, and the like.

Micro-organisms seem to have found a favourable environment in the insect. Often they seem to cause no ill effect, but they utilize the insect as a vehicle to carry them to new breeding grounds. Flies feeding on human excrement may become contaminated with the bacteria of typhoid, dysentery, or cholera; and later when they settle on human food they may smear this with these same micro-organisms and thus can play a considerable part in the carriage of these and other intestinal infections from one man to another.

Blood-sucking insects will pick up the micro-organisms that are circulating in the blood of their host. Some of these organisms are tolerated and cause no ill effect in insect or in mammal. But others may cause serious outbreaks of disease among the rodents or other mammals into which they are introduced. A state of affairs is reached in which the continued existence of the disease is dependent on the blood-sucking insects that have become adapted to carrying it. And then from time to time the infected animals will die off and their blood-sucking parasites are left without a source of food. Under these circumstances they may turn to man as a source of blood and the disease spills over into the human population.

Bubonic plague is a disease of rodents, above all of the domestic rats. But in many parts of the world it has spread from the rats to the wild rodents of the countryside: the ground squirrels of California, the cavies of the Andes, the marmots of Siberia and Mongolia, or the gerbilles of South Africa. Trappers who take these animals for fur may pick up the disease. If there is a big outbreak of plague among the wild rodents these may die off in large numbers; their hungry fleas may carry the infection to the domestic rodents of man; and when these begin to die of plague the scene is set for an outbreak of bubonic plague in the human population—a disease which in the middle of the fourteenth century, under the name of the Black Death, is credited with destroying twenty-four million souls in Europe, a quarter of the total population.

This same pattern is to be found in many human diseases. Yellow fever in Central and South America is largely a disease of the jungle, maintained in monkeys and transmitted from one to another by the mosquitoes of the forest. Men who make clearings in the jungle may occasionally be bitten by infected mosquitoes and pick up the disease. They may then return to the towns and infect the domestic yellow fever mosquito *Aedes aegypti* and a sudden devastating epidemic of yellow fever is the result. Leishmaniasis in the form of Oriental sore or of kala azar in many parts of the East is primarily a protozoal disease of hamsters and other mammals and only occasionally spreads to man. 'Scrub typhus', which became so prominent among troops operating in the jungles of Burma and Malaya, is again a disease of rodents, carried by mites. It is only when men pick up these mites that they contract the disease.

But other micro-organisms can become specialized human parasites. Many mammals (foxes, rodents, etc) harbour spirochaetes which are carried from one to another by blood-sucking ticks. Occasionally men may be bitten by these infected ticks and develop a severe relapsing fever. That happened often in North Africa and Palestine during World War II when soldiers, against instructions, slept in caves. Certain of these spirochaetes find the human louse a suitable host in which to develop, and may then begin to spread from man to man. And finally, some spirochaetes have become wholly adapted to the louse and now produce an exclusively human disease, epidemic relapsing fever.

A parallel line of evolution is to be found among the

typhus diseases that are caused by minute bacteria known as *Rickettsia*. Some are diseases of rodents or other animals only occasionally spread to man through the agency of ticks or mites. Others have become adapted to develop in the louse and are the cause of the fatal epidemic typhus, or 'gaol fever', which has been such a major cause of death through the ages during times of war and famine.

Malaria, perhaps the most important of all human diseases, is caused by several species of protozoa of the genus *Plasmodium*, which are not shared with other mammals. They undergo an elaborate cycle of development in the blood of man and an equally elaborate cycle in the body of the *Anopheles* mosquito. The existence and transmission of the disease is wholly dependent on the mosquito. There are indeed between one and two hundred kinds of *Anopheles* mosquito in the world, but only a few of these are concerned in carrying the disease. For it must be a species that breeds near human habitations, which enters houses and feeds for preference on man. The relations between man and mosquito are complex, and different in every locality. In many parts of the world malaria is a man-made disease. By cutting down trees and exposing the streams to the sun he provides breeding grounds for some of the most dangerous carriers. Nomads in the Middle East settle in the summer months along the dried-up river beds where the relict pools harbour another dangerous species. Engineers building roads and railways commonly dig 'borrowpits' along the route to provide earth for their embankments. These pits soon fill with water and furnish breeding places for *Anopheles* mosquitoes. It is not surprising that engineers have acquired an evil reputation as creators of malaria.

The earlier method for dealing with these malaria problems was to aim at understanding the habits of the species of mosquito concerned and then to try to modify the way of life of the human population so as to break the contact between *Anopheles* and man. All this needed much thought and study. But when DDT and other new insecticides became available, all this painfully acquired knowledge was jettisoned, and the control of malaria was achieved by thorough spraying of the inside of the houses so as to leave a poisonous residue everywhere that killed off the settling mosquitoes. The results were quite outstanding. Malaria has been virtually banished from many countries, and the consequent fall in infant mortality has led to an explosive rise in the human population, which is producing sociological problems of the greatest difficulty. So generous and widespread has been the use of these insecticides that more and more mosquitoes are becoming resistant to them. And today there is a tendency to look again at the methods of the past, to see if these cannot usefully be combined with the killing of mosquitoes by insecticides, and with the treatment of malaria with modern drugs.

The tsetse-fly is not a world-wide problem like the *Anopheles* mosquito. But it is important enough to man, in many parts of Africa, as a carrier of protozoa (trypanosomes) that cause diseases of stock animals, grouped together under the name 'nagana', as well as several types of human sleeping sickness. As with *Anopheles* mosquitoes there are many species of tsetse-fly (*Glossina*) and the relation between insect and disease in man and animal is closely bound up with the habits of each species. But it is true to say that large tracts of tropical Africa are still sealed off from settlement by man because they are occupied by the tsetse-fly.

The tsetse-fly is an insect little larger than a house-fly which breeds slowly and produces no more than a dozen offspring during its six months of life (p. 133). To hold man at bay in this fashion would make one regard it as a formidable enemy. But there are those who consider the tsetse-fly to be the one great saviour of the African soil. By ignorant procedures, or by ruthless exploitation for short-term gains, so much of the soil surface of this planet has been squandered, and vast areas of Africa reduced to semi-desert, that it is possible to regard any insect which bars the way, and conserves the soil for the more enlightened cultivators of the future, as a true friend of man.

Appendix

A CATALOGUE OF INSECTS

THE ORDER of insects, as represented in the phylogenetic tree on p. 16, fall into groups. The first four orders containing the bristletails and springtails, Thysanura, Diplura, Protura, and Collembola, are quite separate from the rest in that they are all wingless and have clearly come from wingless ancestors. They have certain other primitive features, and some authorities would exclude some or all of them from the insects altogether. But they do have three pairs of legs, and a head, thorax, and abdomen. It seems best to retain them with the insects but to put them into a subclass, the Apterygota—apterous, or wingless, insects.

The remaining orders are the true winged insects, the subclass Pterygota, some of which have in fact become secondarily wingless.

The Pterygota fall into two main divisions. Orders 5–19 form *Division I*. These are called *Exopterygota* because in their young stages the rudiments of wings are visible as small projections on the outside. Alternatively they may be called *Hemimetabola,* a name which refers to the fact that the general structure of the body during the young stages is not so very different from that of the adult insect; that is, they undergo a comparatively mild metamorphosis when they pass from the larval stage to the adult. These young larval stages, which commonly live a life like that of the mature insect, are often termed 'nymphs'; but in this book we have usually referred to them simply as larvae.

Orders 20–28 form *Division II*. These are the *Endopterygota,* so named because the wings develop internally: they are quite invisible during the larval stages. The other name for this division is the *Holometabola,* which refers to the fact that the young stages commonly differ greatly from the adults in habits and in structure. For this reason they always undergo a complex metamorphosis, and an intermediate

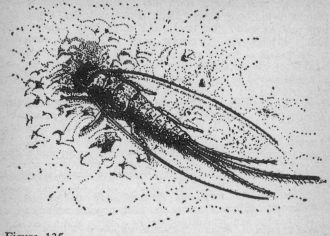

Figure 135.
Thysanura: the fire-brat *Thermobia domestica* (about 1.5 cm long) (Borror and Delong).

stage or pupa is interposed between the larva and the adult. It is at the pupal stage that the wings make their appearance on the outside for the first time.

Subclass: APTERYGOTA

The four orders of this group are put together for convenience; they are not thought to be closely related to one another.

Order 1: THYSANURA (Bristletails)

These are the only members of the Apterygota that are at all closely related to the winged insects (Pterygota). They include the most primitive of all known insects; about three hundred and fifty species have been named; fossil forms have been found in early Mesozoic strata. The most familiar examples today are the silver-fish *Lepisma saccharina* which is common in kitchens, and the fire-brat *Thermobia domestica* (figure 135) which sometimes swarms in warm bakehouses. Most of the wild species live concealed in the soil or in rotting wood, or in decaying leaves in the forest floor, though *Petrobius maritimus* is to be found on the rocky coasts of Europe, close to the edge of the sea.

In their characteristic form they are smooth tapering insects with the body covered with glistening scales, a pair of long antennae on the head, and three long slender tail feelers behind. An interesting point about their anatomy is the presence of rudimentary appendages along the lower surface of the abdomen. These are regarded as the vestiges of limbs and as being a survival from the time when the ancestors of incests had limbs on all the segments of the body. The young stages closely resemble the full-grown adults. As in other insects they grow by shedding their cuticle or 'moulting' at intervals. But they are most exceptional in becoming sexually mature before they are fully grown, and then continuing alternately to moult and to reproduce throughout their life; whereas all other insects grow and moult no more once they have reached the adult stage.

Order 2: DIPLURA

These are similar to the Thysanura and used to be included with them. They likewise live under fallen logs and stones, among decaying leaves, or in the soil. About four hundred species are known. The most familiar genus is *Campodea* (figure 136), slender white eyeless insects, about a quarter of

Figure 136.
Diplura: the two pronged bristletail *Campodea* (about 7 mm long) (Sedlag).

an inch in length, to be seen hurrying for shelter if decaying logs are quickly rolled over, or stones lying on humid leaf soil are lifted. They have long slender antennae and cerci. In *Japyx*, a somewhat larger insect which occurs in Australia and elsewhere, the cerci have become modified to form hard pincers, rather like those of the earwig, which they use in catching their prey. The Diplura were separated from the Thysanura chiefly because the mouth-parts lie in a deep pouch (that is, they are 'entognathous') whereas in the Thysanura and other typical insects the mouth-parts are exposed ('ectognathous').

Order 3: PROTURA

These are very minute white creatures little more than a sixteenth of an inch in length. They live in much the same situation as the Diplura. They are peculiar among insects in having no antennae. When they walk they hold the fore-legs upwards in front of them as tactile organs (figure 137). That gives a hint of how the antennae of insects presumably arose by the modification of an existing pair of limbs.

Figure 137.
Protura: *Acerentomon* (about 1 mm long) (Berlese).

Order 4: COLLEMBOLA (Springtails)

The earliest fossil insects known, discovered in Devonian shales in Scotland, are almost certainly members of this order. They have many features which distinguish them from typical insects and they have two structures which are nearly always present. The first is a fork-shaped organ which is attached to the hind-end of the abdomen and is folded forwards and held below a catch, or 'hamula'. By extending this fork so that it is suddenly released from its catch, the springtails can project themselves for several inches. The other organ is the 'ventral tube', a sucker-like object projecting downwards from the front end of the abdomen. At one time it was supposed that this acts as an adhesive organ used in climbing up vegetation, and it was this idea that gave the order its name of Collembola, which refers to this supposedly 'gluey peg'.

The springtails are not conspicuous; they are seldom more than a fifth of an inch long, but some two thousand species are known and they are, in fact, among the most abundant of all insects. It has been estimated that there may be nearly 250 million springtails in an acre of English meadow land, and one of the commonest species present, the little glob-ular green *Sminthurus viridis* (figure 138) has become a serious pest of pastures in Australia, where it is known as the 'lucerne flea'. Collembola can exist only under humid conditions, either in the moist depths of the vegetation or in the soil. Many species are found under the decaying bark of fallen trees. A few species frequent the nests of ants and termites; there are some that live much of their lives on the surface of water (figure 14) where their aggregations may form quite large grey patches; several are littoral or marine. *Anurida maritima* is common along the coasts of Europe, on the sand or on the surface of rock pools. It is one of the few marine insects and is daily submerged by the tides.

Figure 138.
Collembola: the lucerne flea *Smithurus viridis* (about 2 mm long) (Sedlag).

Subclass: PTERYGOTA

Among the earliest winged insects of which fossil remains have been found (from the late Carboniferous and Permian times) many had their wings permanently extended on each side of the body, or held erect above the thorax. They were unable to fold the wings back over the abdomen when at rest. This whole group of insects are called Palaeoptera to distinguish them from the greater number of present-day insects which do possess such a wing-flexing mechanism and which are called Neoptera. (In a few instances, such as butterflies, the wing-flexing mechanism has been lost again and the wings are held erect.)

There are only two surviving orders that belong to the Palaeoptera: the dragonflies and the may-flies.

Division I: EXOPTERYGOTA (HEMIMETABOLA)

Order 5: ODONATA (Dragonflies)

Dragonflies like those in existence today were plentiful in Permian times, and the closely related 'Protodonata', which have since become extinct, go back much further and were thriving in the swamps and forests of the Carboniferous pe-

Figure 139.
Odonata; Zygoptera: the damsel-fly *Platycnemis* (about 3.5 cm long) (Robert).

riod. Fossil remains of one of these species, the giant *Meganeura*, show that they attained a wing span of more than two feet and must have had larvae at least twelve inches long. One of the existing dragonflies, *Megaloprepus*, measures seven and a half inches from wing tip to wing tip.

Some five thousand species of dragonflies are known today. Throughout their long existence they have remained remarkably uniform in structure. They either hold their wings extended laterally when at rest, as in the heavily built 'dragonflies' (Anisoptera), or fold them together above the back, as in the slender 'damsel-flies' (Zygoptera) (figure 139). All have a long narrow abdomen; the antennae are reduced to tiny threads, and they depend for their appreciation of the outside world chiefly on their enormous eyes. The thorax is curiously modified in shape so that the upper part, which carries the wings, has grown backwards and the lower part which carries the legs, has grown forwards towards the mouth (figure 140). This arrangement is related to their manner of feeding. They hunt on the wing, preying on all kinds of flying insects. These are caught between the spiny outspread legs as in a cage and carried to the mouth.

Another curious feature of the dragonflies is their unique method of mating. They can often be seen flying 'in tandem' with the male in front holding the female by the neck with clasping organs at the tip of the abdomen (figure 140). The actual copulatory structures of the male are not at the end of the abdomen as in most insects, but in a pouch below the second and third segments and it is here the penis is developed. Before seizing the female in the way described the male has already discharged the sperm into this pouch; and during the flight in tandem the female curls her abdomen forward, inserts the tip into the pouch, and receives the sperm.

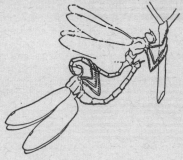

Figure 140.
Odonata; Anisoptera: the dragonfly *Aeschna* mating; male above, female below. Note the long spiny legs set well forward (Calvert).

The larvae of dragonflies are aquatic and predaceous. They too are uniform in structure and, like the adult, depend for their hunting on their eyes. They have chewing mouth-parts like the adult; but in addition they have a peculiar structure termed the 'mask'. This is the lower lip or labium (p. 78) which has become enormously developed and hides the rest of the mouth-parts. But it can be unfolded and shot forwards well in front of the head. Instead of carrying just sense organs, the tip of the labium has a pair of sharp hooks between which the prey is seized and held while it is being chewed up by the mandibles (figures 41, 88).

Order 6: EPHEMEROPTERA (May-flies)

The may-flies were a far more prominent group of insects in Permian times than they are today; but even now some

1,500 species are known to be in existence. Their nymphs, or larvae, are aquatic, with various sorts of gills which enable them to breathe in water (figure 19). This growing period may be prolonged up to three years; but when their growth is complete they rise to the surface, cast their larval skin and emerge as the fully winged form. In the winged state their life is short indeed; their mouth-parts are vestigial, they cannot feed, and often die within the day. It is from this ephemeral existence that the order gets its name.

The emergence of the winged may-flies is often more or less simultaneous over a wide area. They are attracted to strong lights and great mounds of these insects may collect around the arc lamps in Chicago or in the cities on the borders of the Swiss lakes. May-flies show one most unusual feature. The insect that emerges from the full grown nymph has perfect wings, but these have a dull appearance and the power of flight is weak; it is called by anglers a 'dun' and by entomologists a 'subimago'. Within a few minutes or a few hours the skin is cast again and the may-fly now appears in its final form with crisp glittering wings and normal colouring (figure 141). It is now a 'perfect insect' or 'imago'. The wings are always held erect above the back. The forewings are much larger than the hind-wings; in some species the hind-wings are absent altogether.

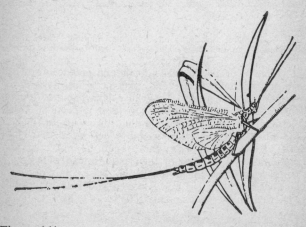

Figure 141.
Ephemeroptera: the may-fly *Ephemera* (about 2 cm long, without the tails).

Order 7: DICTYOPTERA (Cockroaches and Mantids)

This is the first of the neopterous orders, in which the wings are folded neatly back and rest on the abdomen. The fore-wings are more or less thickened and leathery in texture and form a protection for the delicate hind-wings, but they are still used in flight. The hind-wings have an enormous expanse when they are unfolded; when at rest they are pleated like a fan beneath the fore-wings.

The Dictyoptera fall into two well-defined groups, the cockroaches (suborder Blattaria) and the Mantids (suborder Mantodea). The cockroaches were abundant in the coal mea-sure forests of the Carboniferous and even at that time they were so diverse in structure and so widely spread throughout the world that they must have had already a very long past. The order must have been in existence altogether for some four hundred million years.

The cockroaches today contain between three and four thousand named species; they are most plentiful in tropical and subtropical regions, but certain species, *Blatta orientalis* (known in England as the 'black-beetle'), *Periplaneta ameri-cana* (the American roach), *Blattella germanica* (the German cockroach) (figure 48) and some others, have become domes-ticated and carried around the world by commerce. Cock-

Figure 142.
Dictyoptera; Mantidae: the praying mantis, *Mantis religiosa* (about 5.5 cm long) (Robert).

roaches are omnivorous terrestrial insects; many of the species seldom fly and in some the wings have become reduced or absent, particularly in the female, as in the common *Blatta orientalis*. Unlike the Odonata they depend more on their antennae than their eyes; the antennae are as long or longer than the body and are almost continuously in movement, sensing the surroundings. The cerci are quite short cigar-shaped structures. In present-day cockroaches the eggs are laid in a varnished packet (the ootheca) and the young stages are like the adult in general form, the wing pads developing gradually on the exterior as growth proceeds.

The Mantids are classified with the cockroaches because of many similarities in general structure, but they form a very well defined group of about 1,800 species easily recognizable by the peculiar form of the front legs. These 'praying mantids' (figure 142) have a row of sharp spines along the opposed margins of the femur and tibia of the forelegs. They sit motionless with these powerful raptorial legs raised together as in an attitude of prayer. When small insects venture within range the legs are shot forward and retracted again within a twentieth of a second and the prey is impaled between the rows of spines. The group is mostly confined to the tropics and subtropics; some of the large South American species will attack even small birds, lizards, and frogs.

Figure 143.
Plecoptera: the stone-fly *Perla* (about 3 cm long) (Pesson).

Order 8: PLECOPTERA (Stone-flies)

The stone-flies are another archaic group of insects which occur as fossils as far back at least as the Permian. Some 1,500 species have been described. They have a rather characteristic appearance, somewhat flattened, with a broad square head carrying long antennae, clear wings folded back over the abdomen, and long tapering cerci (figure 143). They are weak fliers and do not wander far from water, where they are commonly found resting on stones or tree trunks near the water's edge. The larvae are aquatic and resemble the adults except that they are wingless, and have gills for breathing under water. The stone-flies are typically found in rapidly flowing streams with a stony bed.

Order 9: ISOPTERA (Termites or White Ants)

The termites, of which around 1,700 species are known in the tropics and warm temperate countries, have been found as fossils only in Tertiary strata; but related forms certainly existed far earlier. In their fully developed mature form they have two similar pairs of wings, rather fragile and primitive in structure. The winged state is short-lived, for after a brief mating flight, and shortly before the two sexes pair, the wings of both are detached along a preformed breaking line near their base and are shed (figure 51). The pair then seeks out a suitable retreat and founds a colony.

The habitations or nests of termite colonies vary with the species. The simplest consist merely of series of galleries excavated in damp decaying wood. Others will settle in the dry wood of furniture, or the structural timbers of buildings. Many live in the earth but make covered ways, or tubes of earth, leading to wooden structures above the ground. Other species construct great mounds of earth (termitaria) on the surface of the ground (figure 119). Termitaria built by certain termites in Australia may be 20 feet in height and 12 feet in diameter at the base. Others again produce only small mounds on the surface and live in great subterranean colonies whence they emerge to raid the surrounding vegetation, causing much damage to crops.

In some species the colonies are quite small, with at most a few hundred members; but in the cavities and galleries of the huge termitaria there will be hundreds of thousands. A striking characteristic of termite colonies is the diversity of 'castes' which make up the society (figure 118). The original founders, male and female, occupy a royal cell; the female becomes prodigiously distended like a soft white sausage which may be several inches long in a large species (figure 51). The construction and provisioning of the nest, and the care of the eggs, is the duty of the 'workers'. In some species there is a permanently wingless sterile caste of soft white workers; other species make use solely of child labour, and all the workers will in time grow up to become sexual forms or, alternatively, will become 'soldiers'. The soldiers form another sterile wingless caste concerned in the defence of the colony. In some species they are heavily armoured with large heads and powerful mandibles (figure 144); in others the mandibles are vestigial but the tip of the head is drawn out to a point (nasute soldiers) from which a protective fluid is discharged at the enemy (figure 80).

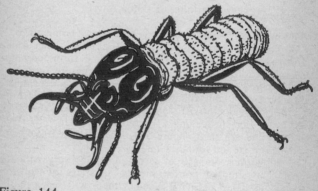

Figure 144.
Isoptera: soldier of the common Indian termite *Odontotermes obesus* (about 1 cm long) (Shell Chemicals Limited).

There is little accurate information about the length of life of termites, but it may be very great. The reproductive forms of large termites may perhaps live for fifteen to fifty years. Termitaria have been known to persist as active colonies for a hundred years; but in these the original sexual pair may well have been replaced.

Order 10: EMBIOPTERA

These are uncommon insects which live under stones or under bark, chiefly in tropical countries. I have come across them in nature on one occasion only, and then they were living in silken galleries in the bark of rubber trees in the Niger delta. They are small creatures, seldom more than half an inch in length, wingless in the female (figure 145), with smoky grey wings in the male. The first segment of the tarsus of the fore-leg is conspicuously dilated; it contains the silk glands which this insect uses in weaving its silken tunnels.

Figure 145.
Embioptera: *Embia sabulosa* (about 7 mm long) (Enderlein).

Order 11: DERMAPTERA (Earwigs)

The earwigs are known as fossils as far back as the Jurassic; about 1,100 present-day species have been named. They have a characteristic and familiar appearance, with an elongated body bearing a pair of curved forceps at the hind-end (figure 146) which are regularly used in defence, and for

Figure 146.
Dermaptera: the earwig *Forficula auricularia* with wings folded and wings extended (A. Smith).

folding the wings in those species which fly. The fore-wings of earwigs are short leathery structures (tegmina) serving only as a protection for the delicate hind-wings. The hind-wings themselves are beautiful objects, quite unlike the wings of any other insect. They are semicircular and can be pleated like a fan, and then folded across twice and stowed away under the tegmina. Although the common earwig of gardens in Europe *Forficula auricularia* has well formed wings of this kind, it seldom, if ever, flies; but there are smaller species that are not uncommonly seen on the wing. Earwigs are omnivorous and live mainly on animal food, but they may also feed from time to time on the petals of flowers. The female lays her eggs in a batch in the soil and broods over them like a hen until they hatch, and even then the young stages, which resemble the adult in general form, remain with her until they can fend for themselves.

A few of the Dermaptera have become parasitic. The best known of these is *Hermimerus* which lives in the fur of African rats (*Cricetomys*). Superficially they look like small parasitic cockroaches, and have also some of the characters of crickets (Gryllidae).

Order 12: NOTOPTERA (or GRYLLOBLATTODEA)

This is a small group of six wingless species scattered through the cold mountainous regions of North America, Japan, and Russia. The first to be discovered was *Grylloblatta campodeiformis,* in the Canadian Rockies in 1914. As its name implies it combines some of the characters of cockroaches and crickets with an appearance like the primitive *Campodea* (p. 315). The chief interest of this group lies in the fact that they provide what used to be called a 'missing link'. It is possible to regard them as the surviving remnants of a primitive stock from which both Dictyoptera and Orthoptera evolved.

Order 13: PHASMIDA (Stick-insects and Leaf-insects)

A group of some two thousand species, particularly evident in the tropics of the oriental region, the Phasmida are remarkable for their close resemblance to the twigs and foliage upon which they rest and feed. They stand motionless during the day and move and feed only after dark. Most are twig-like 'stick-insects', exceedingly elongated, some as much as ten inches in length, with knobs and excrescences or thorn-like spines, and shades of coloration which accord in the utmost detail with the twigs of the plant on which they rest. Many are wingless or have reduced wings; but others have leathery tegmina which conceal beautiful fan-shaped hind-wings which may be highly coloured. The eggs, which often bear a striking resemblance to seeds, and sometimes are almost indistinguishable from the actual seeds of the host plant on which they feed, are scattered singly.

The other type has the body depressed and broad with flattened expansions of the legs and of the abdomen. These are the 'leaf-insects' (figure 147), in which the thin flat outgrowths of the limbs and the fore-wings themselves represent in astonishing detail of form and coloration the leaves of their host plant.

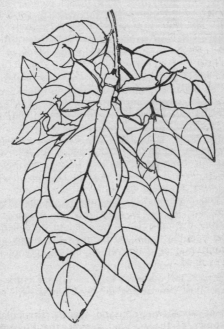

Figure 147.
Phasmida: the leaf-insect *Phyllium bioculatum* (about 10 cm long).

Order 14: ORTHOPTERA (Grasshoppers, Locusts, and Crickets)

The Orthoptera embrace more than ten thousand described species and have representatives among the fossil insects of the Carboniferous. They are mostly insects of moderate or large size. Characteristically the hind pair of legs are modified for jumping, with an enlarged femur containing powerful muscles to extend the tibia. Indeed this order of jumping insects is sometimes called the 'Saltatoria'. They show a relatively slight degree of metamorphosis; the large hindlegs and other features are already evident when they hatch from the egg (figure 55). Many of the Orthoptera have sound-producing, or stridulatory organs, and auditory organs to match, which play an important role in mating.

The order falls into two main groups, those with the antennae as long or longer than the body (Tettigoniids or long-horned grasshoppers, katydids (figure 100), and Gryllids or crickets) and those with short antennae (Acridiids or short-horned grasshoppers and locusts) (figure 7).

The females of Tettigoniids usually have a conspicuous sword-like egg-laying structure, or 'ovipositor', by means of which the eggs are inserted into the soil or, more commonly, into the leaves or stems of plants, where they are often arranged in neat rows, partially exposed. As in the cockroaches and Phasmids, the hind-wings are fan-like and the fore-wings leathery, often with leaf-like markings (figure 77). It is these leathery tegmina which provide the sound-producing organs. The right wing has a circular area or 'mirror' with a thickened ridge (a modified wing vein) beside it. The corresponding vein on the left wing bears a row of teeth and forms the 'file'; and when the two wings are rubbed together the file scrapes the edge of the right tegmen, which is set in vibration, the mirror acting as a resonator.

The crickets stridulate in a similar fashion but the tegmina are even more strongly modified for the purpose. The house cricket *Acheta domestica* and the field cricket *Gryllus campestris* are familiar members of the group whose songs are well known. But some of the larger species of the tropics produce a more powerful music. *Brachytrypes megacephalus,* which used to be known in West Africa as the 'cry baby', produces a most penetrating din which it is hard to credit to an insect.

The mole crickets (*Gryllotalpa* and its allies) are members of this group which have become adapted to a subterranean mode of life (figure 148). They have lost the jumping hindlegs, and the fore-legs have become modified for digging in the soil and bear a strange resemblance to the fore-feet of the mole. The femur and particularly the tibia have become greatly expanded and furnished with a row of stout teeth along one side, like the stout fingers of a mole.

The Acridiids, or short-horned grasshoppers, form the largest family of the Orthoptera and alone embrace about five thousand species; they include the common small grasshoppers of temperate lands, but members of the group are

Figure 148.
Orthoptera: the mole cricket *Gryllotalpa vulgaris* (about 4 cm long).

far more plentiful in hotter countries, where they include the species that are liable to build up destructive swarms and are called locusts. The locust exists in two forms or 'phases'. At times when their numbers are few they assume a 'solitary phase' with a characteristic form and colour and behaviour. At times, when the number of locusts is greatly increased, their form and colour become changed, often

Figure 149.
Psocoptera: a winged Psocid *Ectopsocus parvulus* with the egg cocoon (about 2.5 mm) (Weber).

very strikingly; they now assume a 'gregarious phase'. It is the presence of great numbers of these gregarious locusts and their tendency to gather together in vast aggregations, or swarms, which turn a harmless solitary insect into one of the most feared and destructive of agricultural pests.

Order 15: PSOCOPTERA (Psocids or Book-lice)

These are minute soft-bodied insects of which some 1,100 species are known. The most familiar is the common book-louse *Liposcelis divinatorius* which is common among books and papers kept in slightly damp conditions, so that the moulds on which this insect feeds can grow on the paste and bindings. This and other Psocids can work havoc among collections of dried insects. These common domestic forms are wingless but the majority of species are found on tree trunks and under bark; many of them are winged (figure 149).

Order 16: MALLOPHAGA (Bird-lice or Biting-lice)

Some 2,600 species of Mallophaga have been named. They are external parasites living among the feathers of birds and a few in the fur of mammals; they soon die when separated from their hosts. They have chewing mouth-parts, and nibble the feathers and scaly surface of the skin, and a few species are said regularly to bite through the soft base of the feather and obtain blood. *Columbicula columbae* is a

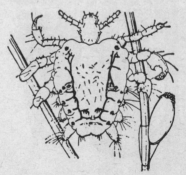

Figure 150.
Anoplura: the crab louse *Phthirus pubis* with egg attached to a hair (about 2 mm long) (Weber).

familiar elongated louse almost always to be found among the feathers of pigeons. *Menopon pallidum,* the common chicken-louse, can be a very troublesome pest.

All are small, some less than 1/32 inch long and most not exceeding 1/8 inch. They are flattened and wingless with poorly developed eyes, and all stages are much alike. They are strictly tied, each species to its own host, and in some cases the bird hosts seem to have evolved and changed more extensively than their parasites. Thus the Mallophaga of the flamingoes are similar to those of the ducks, which gives added support to the belief that the flamingoes and ducks are related.

Order 17: ANOPLURA (Sucking-lice)

Only some 230 species of sucking-lice have been described but there are doubtless many more to be discovered. They have the same general appearance as the biting-lice, wingless and flattened with a tough leathery integument (figure 150). But they are all parasites of mammals and have the mouth-parts highly modified to form slender stylets that pierce the skin to reach the blood vessels. They feed solely on blood and cannot survive away from their hosts. Their adaptation to the mammalian host is seen also in the way in which the large terminal claw of the leg closes against a thumb-like

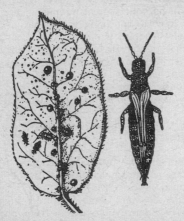

Figure 151.
Thysanoptera: the glasshouse thrips *Heliothrips haemorrhoidalis* enlarged, and on a small leaf of apple with the characteristic brown droplets of excrement (about 2 mm long) (Bovien and Thomsen).

expansion of the single tarsal segment to grip a single hair, and in the way in which the eggs, or 'nits', are each cemented firmly to a hair close to the skin.

Geologically speaking the Anoplura are a recent group which has evolved along with the mammals on which they live. As in the bird-lice, the genera of sucking-lice run parallel with their hosts: *Enderleinellus* is restricted to squirrels, *Pedicinus* to the Cynomorph monkeys, *Pediculus* is shared between man and the chimpanzee. The *Pediculus humanus* of man affords an example of the tendency of insect species to form 'biological races' which often differ in habits without showing any very definite structural differences. In this case there is the head-louse, race *capitis*, which lives in the hair of the scalp, and the body-louse, race *corporis,* which lives on the clothes in contact with the skin. Here is a line of evolution which must have gone forward since man took to covering his body with garments. The body-louse is the carrier of some of the worst epidemic fevers of man, relapsing fever and gaol fever, or epidemic typhus.

Order 18: THYSANOPTERA (Thrips)

Each wing of these tiny insects consists of a narrow strip with a broad fringe of fine hairs on either side. About three thousand species are known. All are small, many not more than 1/50 inch. Almost any flower head, notably of the dandelion, will harbour a great number of these minute elongated black insects, but it is impossible to make out the details of their structure without a microscope. On hot days in summer they migrate in vast numbers; they are popularly called 'thunder flies' and cause annoying tickling of the exposed skin on hands and face. A few are pests of crops, notably the onion thrips (*Thrips tabaci*) and the glasshouse thrips (*Heliothrips haemorrhoidalis*) (figure 151).

Order 19: HEMIPTERA (Plant-bugs, Cicadas, Aphids, or Greenfly, Scale insects, etc)

The Hemiptera are the order called 'bugs' by the entomologist. They are an enormous group with more than fifty-five thousand named species. Many of these interfere seriously with the affairs of man; some by direct injury to growing plants, others by conveying viruses from one plant to another; a few may transmit diseases from man to man.

The Hemiptera have one feature in common which unites them all: the mouth-parts are modified for piercing and for sucking up fluids. The labium has become elongated to form a long tapering beak, or 'rostrum' (figure 35). This is not in fact the structure that pierces, but it provides a deep groove, or sheath, to enclose the mandibles and maxillae which now take the form of slender stylets. Most feed on the sap of plants, but a few (Reduviidae, etc) prey upon other insects or (Triatomidae and Cimicidae, or bed-bugs and their allies) suck the blood of mammals and birds.

The Hemiptera fall into two suborders: Heteroptera and Homoptera, distinguished by the nature of their wings. In Heteroptera one half or more of the fore-wing is leathery and forms a protective covering for the hind-wings; only the tip is more or less soft and membranous. In Homoptera both pairs of wings are clear and glassy.

The families which make up the Heteroptera can be conveniently grouped into the land-bugs and water-bugs. The former contain such well known insects as the shield-bugs (Pentatomidae) (figure 75), Capsid bugs and many more which feed on plants; the Nabids and Reduviids, or 'assassin bugs', with curved beaks through which they feed on the blood of other insects; the closely related Triatomid bugs and the Cimicidae, or bed-bugs, which suck the blood of man and other warm-blooded animals. The most familiar water-bugs are the water-skaters (Gerridae) (figure 15) and the true water-bugs such as the water-boatmen (Corixidae), the water scorpions (Nepidae) (figure 24) and the backswimmers or water-boatmen (Notonectidae) (figure 16). Most of these are predaceous insects, plunging their stout rostrum into small fish or tadpoles and into other insects. The giant water-bugs (Belostomatidae) have the fore-legs modified like a pair of wide pincers for seizing prey (figure 152); the family includes *Lethocerus grandis,* one of the largest of known insects, exceeding 4 inches in length, which preys on frogs and small fish as well as insects.

Figure 152.
Hemiptera-Heteroptera; Belastomatidae: *Hydrocyrius columbiae* male carrying eggs deposited by the female on the folded wings (Pesson).

The Homoptera include an equally wide variety of insect families: the cicadas (Cicadidae), large species of which may be several inches long with beautiful reticulated glassy wings (figure 101); the cuckoo-spit insects (Cercopidae); the tree-hoppers (Membracidae) (figure 153), many of which have grotesque outgrowths from the front of the thorax; the leaf-hoppers (Jassidae) with many species that damage agricultural crops; the lantern-flies (Fulgoridae), a tropical family, many of them very large, with a huge hollow projection from the front of the head like a grotesque nose, at one time erroneously believed to be luminous. Other families are the jumping plant-lice (Psyllidae), small insects in which the legs are modified for jumping; the tiny

Figure 153.
Hemiptera-Homoptera; Membracidae: *Centrotus* (about 1 cm long) (Robert).

white flies (Aleyrodidae) (figure 46); the greenfly or plant-lice (Aphididae) (figures 36, 67), which have a most elaborate series of alternative generations; the closely related Phylloxeridae with the notorious vine *Phylloxera;* the scale insects or Coccidae and related families, which not only include many serious pests but also the lac insects and cochineal insects of commerce. It is the adult female scale insect that is commonly seen, and she is hardly recognizable as an insect at all (figure 154). A few little dark round spots can generally be seen on any orange. These are the few remaining specimens of the red scale *Aonidiella aurantii* which have escaped the cleaning and polishing operations to which the fruit is subjected (plate 36). What is seen is the mixture of wax and cast skins which provides a tough shield for the degenerate female and her brood of eggs beneath.

In most Hemiptera the young stages live in much the same way as the adults and their general form is similar. One exception is the cicada, where the larva is adapted to life in the soil and has enormously enlarged fore-legs suited for burrowing. In the Coccids, where the female is a flat-

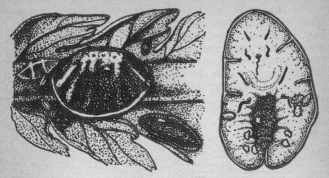

Figure 154.
Hemiptera-Homoptera; Coccidae: to the left, *Lecanium hemis-phaericum* mature female (about 3 mm long) surrounded by larvae at different stages of growth. To the right, mature female of *Lecanium hesperidum* (about 4.3 mm long) viewed from below. The small antennae and legs and the wavy stylet bundle can be seen. In the back half of the insect is the large egg chamber; some empty egg shells are visible and several newly hatched larvae (Bovien and Thomsen).

tened, wingless, scale-like object (as are the young stages) the adult male is a delicate flying insect with a single pair of fragile wings.

Division II: ENDOPTERYGOTA (HOLOMETABOLA)

Order 20: NEUROPTERA (Alder flies, Lacewings, Ant-lions, etc)

This is the first of the 'endopterygote' orders or Holometabola, with a distinct pupal stage between the larva and the

Figure 155.
Neuroptera: the alder fly *Sialis lutaria* female (about 1 cm long) with a batch of eggs, and the snake-fly *Rhaphidia* (about 14 mm long) (Pesson).

adult. Nearly five thousand species are known. The adults have gauzy net-like wings and rather feeble powers of flight. Perhaps the most familiar example is the lacewing *(Chrysopa)* with golden eyes and delicate green wings (figure 156). The alder fly *(Sialis)* (figure 155) which is to be seen in abundance resting on the vegetation at the margin of ponds and slowly flowing streams, the wings folded roof-wise over the back, is another common insect; the snake-fly *(Rhaphida)*

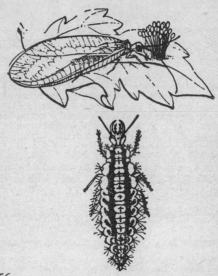

Figure 156.
Neuroptera: the green lacewing-fly *Chrysopa perla* (about 2.5 cm long) with its eggs and its larva.

is more rare (figure 155). Others are the ant-lion flies (Myrmeleonidae) which can resemble dragonflies in their general appearance; and the Mantispidae, which have the front legs modified like those of the praying mantis for capturing other insects.

The larvae of all Neuroptera are carnivorous. Many of them have long curved mandibles for seizing their prey. The larvae of the lacewings creep about on plants in search of their victims; the ant-lions dig conical pits in the sandy soil of dry countries and lie in wait at the base of the cone for any insect that may fall in (figure 33).

Order 21: MECOPTERA (Scorpion-flies)

This order, with about 350 species, is of great interest to entomologists because it provides a connecting link in evolution. The Mecoptera first appear as fossils in the Lower Permian—before any of the Lepidoptera (butterflies and moths), Trichoptera (caddis flies) or Diptera (two-winged flies) are to be found. All these orders, together with the Neuroptera,

Figure 157.
Mecoptera: female scorpion-fly *Panorpa* (about 1.75 cm long).

are believed to have arisen from some primitive stock of Mecoptera. They are often grouped together as the 'Panorpoid complex'.

The most familiar example of the group is the scorpion-fly (*Panorpa*) (figure 157). This is readily recognized by its speckled wings, the beak-like prolongation of the head and, in the male, the upturned tip of the abdomen, which bears a striking resemblance to the sting of the scorpion. The larva, which lives in the soil, is very like a caterpillar.

Order 22: TRICHOPTERA (Caddis Flies)

Between four and five thousand caddis flies are known. They are moth-like insects and can easily be mistaken for Lepidoptera; but the wings are clothed with fine hairs and not with broad scales. The mouth-parts are poorly developed and many of them take no food at all in the adult stage (figure 158).

The larvae are the familiar 'caddis worms'. All these are aquatic and most of them construct cases of leaf fragments, grains of sand, pieces of stalk, shells of small molluscs—each species using its chosen material. They creep about dragging their case behind them; the greater part of the body protected by the case is soft and white; only the ex-

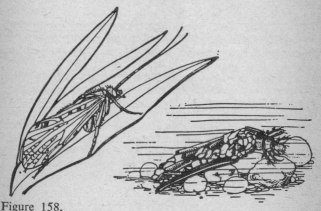

Figure 158.
Trichoptera: adult caddis fly *Rhyacophila* (about 1.2 cm long) (Robert), and caddis fly larva in its case (A. Smith).

posed head and thorax are armoured. Other caddis larvae are carnivorous and weave silken nets in flowing water to catch their prey.

Order 23: LEPIDOPTERA (Butterflies and Moths)

Already 200,000 species of butterflies and moths have been named and there are certainly many more to be discovered. As the name of the order implies, they have the wings covered with scales.

If the flower-head of a buttercup is examined in the early summer it will often be found to harbour a number of tiny little moths. These are *Micropteryx calthella,* the most primitive of all Lepidoptera; indeed they are more primitive in structure than the Trichoptera, and some authors class them as forming a separate order of insects. These Micropterygidae have biting mouth-parts of the same general type as the cockroach, but in all other Lepidoptera the mandibles have practically disappeared and the maxillae have become enormously elongated to form a sucking 'proboscis', adapted for securing the nectar of flowers, which when not in use is coiled below the thorax (p. 68).

The Lepidoptera are one of the most recently evolved groups of insects. No fossil forms have been found earlier than Tertiary times. Indeed they developed along with the flowering plants: flowers and Lepidoptera have evolved side by side. The larvae have become caterpillars, almost all of which feed on the leaves or stems or roots of flowering plants, while the adults are adapted to feed in the flowers. The pupa bridges the gap between the two. The rudiments of the wings are now visible on the surface but, along with the rudiments of antennae and legs, they are cemented down to form a compact structure in which only their outlines can be detected.

The Lepidoptera are grouped in some eighty families, six of which are popularly called 'butterflies' while all the remaining families are called 'moths'. The diurnal habits and conspicuous colours of the butterflies put them among the most familiar insects, remarkable as much for the beauty of their appearance as for the interest of their natural history. The 'moths' range in size from the tiny *Nepticula*, whose larvae develop between the upper and lower walls of a single leaf, with a wing-span of only 1/8 inch, to the giant atlas moth (*Attacus atlas*), which measures about 10 inches from wing-tip to wing-tip. They include many species that are harmful to growing plants of use in agriculture and forestry, species that attack stored products such as flour or dried fruit, and species that destroy furs and woollen goods, as well as the domesticated silkworm which produces most of the raw silk of commerce.

Order 24: DIPTERA (Two-winged Flies)

The true flies or Diptera are another order of comparatively recent origin. The earliest known fossils go back to the Jurassic, some 150 million years ago. Their great expansion took place along with the mammals and the flowering plants; most of them are flower lovers and feed on nectar, but some prey on other insects and not a few have taken to sucking the blood of man and other animals. Altogether some 85,000 existing species are known.

As the name of the order implies they retain only the first pair of wings; the second pair is reduced to little knob-like sense organs named 'halteres'. The more primitive Diptera are slenderly built insects which form the suborder Nematocera or midges, including the large crane-flies or daddy-long-legs. These include also the mosquitoes (Culicidae) and other blood-sucking forms in which the mouthparts are adapted for piercing the skin. A second suborder is named Brachycera and includes the heavily built blood-sucking horse-flies and clegs (Tabanidae). The great majority of flies belong to a third suborder, the Cyclorrhapha, which are all compactly built: house-flies (figure 52), bluebottles, hover-flies, dung-flies, fruit-flies (figure 91), etc. The mouth-parts of these are adapted for sucking up exposed fluids; the biting and piercing mandibles and maxillae have been lost. But this group includes the blood-sucking stablefly (*Stomoxys*) and the tsetse-fly (*Glossina*) in which an entirely new mechanism for piercing the skin has been evolved (p. 76).

The life of larval Diptera is extremely varied. Perhaps the commonest type of food is the decaying remains of plants and animals, or the dung of mammals. They play a most important role in the economy of nature by rapidly removing such remains from the surface of the earth. But many feed on growing plants and others are predaceous. There are larvae living in the soil and in water. They show, therefore, an extraordinary variety of form and structure. The headless maggots of the Cyclorrhapha are among the most specialized of all insect larvae.

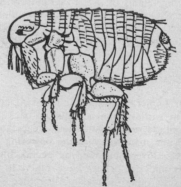

Figure 159.
Siphonaptera: the human flea *Pulex irritans* (about 1.5 mm long) (Terzi).

Order 25: SIPHONAPTERA (Fleas)

About 1,100 sorts of fleas have been named. They are a distinctive group of insects, compressed from side to side in a most unusual fashion and adapted in many ways to their parasitic existence in the fur and feathers of their hosts. They are wingless, and the mouth-parts are modified for piercing the skin and obtaining blood (figure 159). Among the existing orders they seem to come closest to the Diptera, and that is borne out by their life history: the larva and pupa have much in common with the Diptera-Nematocera. The larva feeds on debris in the nest or lair of their host.

Order 26: HYMENOPTERA (Ants, Bees, Wasps, Ichneumon-flies, etc)

The present number of known species of Hymenoptera, something like 100,000, must represent only a small part of the species in existence. They are among the most highly evolved insects, whose elaborate specializations of structure almost equal those of the Diptera. They have clear membranous wings linked together by a row of hooks so that the fore- and hind-wings function as a single organ (figure 160). The mouth-parts have the usual biting components, but in some species, such as the bees, they have an alternative method of feeding. The labium is drawn out to form a soft

Figure 160.
Hymenoptera: the method of linking the wings by a row of hooks on the hind-wing and a fold on the fore-wing (Grenier).

flexible tongue or 'glossa' and its sides are curled downwards so as to form a deep groove that amounts almost to a closed tube up which fluids such as nectar can be sucked (figure 31).

The Hymenoptera fall into two main groups, the Symphyta and the Apocrita.

The Symphyta are the saw-flies (figure 161) and wood-wasps, the former so named because the females have a delicate saw-like ovipositor by means of which they insert their eggs into the stems or leaves of plants. The Symphyta are distinguished by the fact that the thorax joins on to the abdomen without an obvious 'waist'; whereas in the Apocrita there is a narrow constriction between the two. All the saw-flies feed on plants; their larvae resemble the caterpillars of Lepidoptera in having a series of fleshy 'prolegs' or false legs on the abdomen in addition to the three pairs of true in the thorax (figure 161).

The Apocrita again fall into two groups: the parasitic fam-

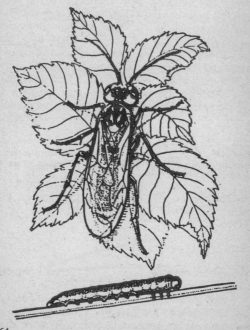

Figure 161.
Hymenoptera-Symphyta: the green saw-fly *Rhogogaster viridis* (about 1.3 cm) (Robert); and a saw-fly larva (Pesson).

ilies (Parasitica) and the sting-bearing families (Aculeata).
The Parasitica lay their eggs in the larvae or sometimes in
the eggs of other insects (figure 162); they include the ichneumon-flies and the minute Chalcids; also the gall-wasps
(Cynipoidea), parasites of plants, the larvae of which provoke the plant to produce characteristic swellings or 'galls'.

The Aculeata are the bees, wasps, and ants; most sorts of
bees and wasps are solitary but all provide food for their
helpless grub-like larvae, which are supplied with pollen and
honey by the different sorts of bees, and with insect prey by
wasps. It is the egg-laying organ, or 'ovipositor', of the female which has been modified to inject poison and has become the sting. Some bees and wasps and all ants have developed a highly organised social life, with a differentiation

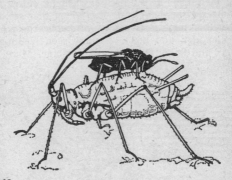

Figure 162.
Hymenoptera-Apocrita: a parasitic wasp *Zarhopalus inquisitor* (Fam.
Encyrtidae) feeding at the puncture it has made in an aphid during
egg-laying (Griswold).

of the members of the community into 'castes' with differing
structure and duties, providing constant care for their brood
of larvae.

Order 27: COLEOPTERA (Beetles)

The beetles are a vast group of animals containing some
275,000 known species distributed among well over a hundred separate families. The smallest are about 1/32 inch in
length; the largest, the hercules beetle (*Dynastes hercules*),
if the horn on its head is included, is more than 6 inches
long (figure 8). The solid, heavily built goliath beetle
(*Goliathus regius*), though little more than 4 inches in length,

has about eight million times the bulk of the smallest kinds of beetles.

Fossil beetles have been found as far back as the Permian, but their earlier ancestry is unknown. Indeed they are a compact group without obvious relationship to other insects. They are easily recognized by the fact that the forewings have been modified to form hard sheaths, or 'elytra', to cover the hind-wings which are folded beneath and are alone used in flight. The upper surface of the abdomen is soft and delicate, but when the elytra are folded back in their normal position there is hardly a weak spot in the armour of the beetle; they are the hardest and horniest of all insects. Most live in the soil, under stones, or under bark or vegetable refuse, and do not force themselves on our attention. Indeed many of them have lost the power of flight; either the muscles which operate the wings, or the wings themselves, are degenerate. But there are plenty of beetles which are conspicuous enough and are commonly seen feeding on plants or flowers and flying freely in the sunshine. Many others are aquatic.

Figure 163.
Coleoptera: the stag beetle *Lucanus cervus* (about 6.5 cm long) (Albrecht Dürer, 1505).

The beetle larva varies in appearance with its way of life. It may be a legless grub which leads a sheltered existence in the roots of plants; but free-living beetle larvae which prey on other insects have well-formed legs and powerful jaws;

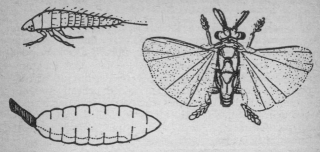

Figure 164.
Strepsiptera: *Stylops* male (right) (about 5 mm long); female left, below; and 'triungulin' larva top left (Weber).

and when they feed exposed on the leaves of plants they may show some resemblance to the caterpillars of Lepidoptera.

Order 28: STREPSIPTERA

The last order of insects is a puzzling group whose larvae are parasites of Homoptera and Hymenoptera. The female never leaves the body of the host and is little more than a sac of developing eggs. The male is a strange winged insect. The hind-wings alone have been retained; the fore-wings are reduced to knobbed structures like the 'halteres' of Diptera. The natural relationships of these insects, of which the best known belong to the genus *Stylops* (figure 164), are uncertain, but they are usually placed near the Coleoptera and sometimes actually included among them.

BIBLIOGRAPHY

The purpose of this Bibliography is to enable the reader to follow up in greater detail any topic that has been mentioned in the text. Where comprehensive textbooks on a subject are available, selected examples of these are given; under chapter I, for example, a number of general textbooks of entomology are listed. Otherwise, reference is made to review articles, or to original publications, in scientific journals. The titles of such journals are abbreviated in accordance with the *World List of Scientific Periodicals*. After the reference to a journal, a short statement is given in brackets; this will tell the reader what the article in question is about—the language of the original will depend, of course, upon the language of the journal. Separate lists are given for each chapter and the topics in each list have been arranged in the same sequence as in the text.

Chapter 1:

Introduction

WILLIAMS, C. B. (1960) *Amer. Nat.* **94**: 137–51 (the numbers of insects)

IMMS, A. D. (1936) *Trans. Soc. Brit. Ent.* **3**: 1–32 (ancestry of insects)

JEANNEL, R. (1951) *Traité de Zoologie* (P. P. Grassé Ed.) **9**: 3–110 Masson: Paris (fossil history of insects)

MARTYNOVA, O. (1961) *Ann. Rev. Ent.* **6**: 285–94 (palaeoentomology)

SNODGRASS, R. E. (1935) *Principles of insect morphology* McGraw-Hill: New York

FORD, E. B. (1960) *Mendelism and evolution* 7th Ed. Methuen: London

IMMS, A. D. (revision by O. W. RICHARDS and R. G. DAVIES) (1957) *A general text-book of entomology* Methuen: London

WEBER, H. (1954) *Grundriss der Insektenkunde* 3rd. Ed. Fischer: Stuttgart

WIGGLESWORTH, V. B. (1957) *Insect physiology* Methuen's Monographs: London

GILMOUR, D. (1961) *The biochemistry of insects* Academic Press: London

Chapter 2:

The Insect as a Terrestrial Animal

EDNEY, E. B. (1956) *The water relations of terrestrial arthropods* University Press: Cambridge

RICHARDS, A. G. (1951) *The integument of arthropods* University Minnesota Press: Minneapolis

WIGGLESWORTH, V. B. (1948, 1957) *Biol. Rev.* **23**: 408–51; *Ann. Rev. Ent.* **2**: 37–54 (reviews on the insect cuticle)

——. (1945) *J. exp. Biol.* **21**: 97–114 (transpiration through the cuticle)

BEAMENT, J. W. L. (1961) *Biol. Rev.* **36**: 381–420 (the permeability of insect cuticle)

WIGGLESWORTH, V. B. (1931) *Biol. Rev.* **6**: 181–220 (review of insect respiration)

BUCK, J. (1962) *Ann. Rev. Ent.* **7**: 27–56 (review of insect respiration)

SCHNEIDERMAN, H. A. (1956) *Nature* **177**: 1169–71 (cyclical respiration in insect pupae)

FRAENKEL, G. & BLEWETT, M. (1944) *Bull. ent. Res.* **35**: 127–39 ('metabolic water')

CRAIG, R. (1960) *Ann. Rev. Ent.* **5**: 53–68 (excretion in insects)

CHURCH, N. S. (1960) *J. exp. Biol.* **37**: 171–212 (control of the body temperature in flying insects)

FRAENKEL, G. (1929) *Biol. Zentralbl.* **49**: 657–80 (locusts controlling their temperature by their position in the sun)

UVAROV, B. P. (1931) *Trans. ent. Soc. Lond.* **79**: 1–246 (review of insects and climate)

MESSENGER, P. S. (1959) *Ann. Rev. Ent.* **4**: 183–206 (insects and climate)

MELLANBY, K. (1939, 1940) *Proc. Roy. Soc. Lond.* (B) **127**:

473–87; *J. Animal Ecol.* **9**: 296–301 (acclimatization of insects to low temperatures)

HINTON, H. E. (1960) *Nature* **188**: 336–7; *J. ins. Physiol.* **5**: 286–300, survival of *Polypedilum* larvae in a desiccated state)

SALT, R. W. (1961) *Ann. Rev. Ent.* **6**: 55–74 (resistance of insects to freezing)

WIGGLESWORTH, V. B. (1953) *The principles of insect physiology* Methuen: London (survey of the physiology of the integument, respiration, excretion, water and temperature relations etc)

Chapter 3:

The Movements of Insects on Land, in Water, and in the Air

BARTH, R. (1937) *Zool. Jahrb., Anat.* **62**: 507–66 (mechanism of crawling in caterpillars)

HUGHES, G. M. (1952) *J. exp. Biol.* **29**: 267–84 (walking movements of insects)

GILLETT, J. D. & WIGGLESWORTH, V. B. (1932) *Proc. Roy. Soc.* (B) **3**: 364–75 (adhesive or climbing organ in the bug *Rhodnius*)

BROCHER, F. (1909) *Ann. Biol. lac.* **4**: 89–138 (surface forces and aquatic insects)

BAUDOIN, R. (1955) *Bull. Biol. Fr. Belg.* **89**: 16–164 (surface forces and aquatic insects)

WESENBERG-LUND, C. (1943) *Biologie der Süsswasserinsekten* Springer: Berlin (swimming, respiration etc of aquatic insects)

KEILIN, D. (1944) *Parasitology* **36**: 1–66 (respiration of larvae and pupae of Diptera)

EGE, R. (1915) *Z. allg. Physiol.* **17**: 81–124 (air stores of aquatic insects as physical gills)

THORPE, W. H. (1950) *Biol. Rev.* **25**: 344–90 (plastron respiration in aquatic insects)

DAMANT, G. C. C. (1924) *J. Physiol.* **59**: 345–56 (regulation of buoyancy in the phantom larva *Corethra*)

PRINGLE, J. W. S. (1957) *Insect flight* University Press: Cambridge

WIGGLESWORTH, V. B. (1963) *Nature* **197**: 97–8 (origin of wings in insects)

WEIS-FOGH, T. (1956) *Phil. Trans. Roy. Soc.* (B) **239**: 415–584 (biology and physics of locust flight)

BOETTIGER, E. G. (1960) *Ann. Rev. Ent.* **5**: 53–68 (working of insect flight muscles)

Chapter 4:

The Dietary of Insects

BRUES, C. T. (1946) *Insect dietary: an account of the food habits of insects* Harvard University Press: Cambridge, Mass.

WEBER, H. (1933) *Lehrbuch der Entomologie* Fischer: Jena (mouth-parts of insects etc)

CHRISTOPHERS, S. R. & PURI, I. M. (1929) *Trans. Far Eastern Assoc. trop. Med.* (7th congr.) **2**: 736–8 (feeding of mosquito larvae)

EASTHAM, L. E. S. & EASSA, Y. E. E. (1955) *Phil. Trans. Roy. Soc.* (B) **239**: 1–43 (feeding mechanism in a butterfly)

KEMPER, H. (1932) *Z. Morph. Oekol. Tiere* **24**: 491–518 (feeding mechanism in the bed-bug *Cimex*)

PATTON, W. S. & CRAGG, F. W. (1913) *A text book of medical entomology* (Christian Literature Society for India: Calcutta; mouth-parts of blood-sucking flies etc)

ROBINSON, G. G. (1939) *Parasitology* **31**: 212–42 (action of mouth-parts of female mosquito)

LAVOIPIERRE, M. M. J., DICKERSON, G. & GORDON, R. M. (1959) *Ann. trop. Med. Parasit.* **53**: 235–45, 347–57, 465–72 (method of feeding of blood-sucking insects)

JOBLING, B. (1933) *Parasitology* **24**: 449–90 (mouth-parts of the tsetse-fly)

WEBER, H. (1930) *Biologie der Hemipteren* Springer: Berlin (feeding, excretion etc in Hemiptera)

WATERHOUSE, D. & DAY, M. F. (1953) *Insect physiology* (Roeder, K. D., Ed.), 273–349 Wiley: New York (digestion in insects)

WIGGLESWORTH, V. B. (1929) *Bull. ent. Res.* **20**: 403–6 (extra-intestinal digestion in the larvae of tiger beetles, Cicindelidae)

LIPKE, H. & FRAENKEL, G. (1956) *Ann. Rev. Ent.* **1**: 17–44 (insect nutrition)

WIGGLESWORTH, V. B. (1949) *J. exp. Biol.* **26**: 150–63 (fuel consumption during flight in *Drosophila*)

———. (1938) *J. exp. Biol.* **15**: 235–47 (salt uptake by mosquito larvae)

WEIS-FOGH, T. (1952) *Trans. 9th Int. Cong. Ent.* (*Amsterdam*) **1**: 341–7; *Phil. Trans. Roy. Soc.* (B) **237**: 1–36 (fuel and weight economy in flying locusts)

ZEBE, E. (1954) *Z. vergl. Physiol.* **36**: 290–317 (fuel for flight in butterflies)

GILMOUR, D. (1961) *The biochemistry of insects* Academic Press: London (vitamin requirements etc of insects)

WIGGLESWORTH, V. B. (1952) *Tdsch. Entom.* **95**: 63–9 (symbionts supplying vitamins in blood-sucking insects)

BUCHNER, P. (1953) *Endosymbiose der Tiere mit pflanzlichen Mikroorganismen* Birkhäuser: Stuttgart

Chapter 5:
The Eggs of Insects

WIGGLESWORTH, V. B. (1953) *The principles of insect physiology*, 3rd Ed. Methuen, London (1–6; egg-shell, absorption of water, desiccated eggs etc)

WEBER, H. (1931) *Z. Morph. Oekol. Tiere* **23**: 575–753 (absorption of water from plants by eggs of white-flies)

WIGGLESWORTH, V. B. & BEAMENT, J. W. L. (1950) *Quart. J. micr. Sci.* **91**: 429–52 (respiration of insect eggs)

HINTON, H. E. (1962) *Science Progress* **50**: 96–113 (plastron respiration in insect eggs)

SIKES, E. K. & WIGGLESWORTH, V. B. (1931) *Quart. J. micr. Sci.* **74**: 165–92 (hatching of insect eggs)

SLIFER, E. H. (1938) *J. Morph.* **63**: 181–205 (digestion of egg-shell in grasshopper by secretion of the pleuropodia)

WIGGLESWORTH, V. B. (1938, 1953) *J. exp. Biol.* **15**: 248–54; *Quart. J. micr. Sci.* **94**: 507–22 (filling of the tracheal system with air)

BUCK, J. & KEISTER, M. (1955) *J. exp. Biol.* **32**: 681–91 (filling of the closed tracheal system with air)

Chapter 6:
The Growth and Metamorphosis of Insects

SHAROV, A. G. (1957) *Rev. Ent. U.R.S.S.* **36**: 569–76 (types of insect metamorphosis)

WIGGLESWORTH, V. B. (1954) *The physiology of insect metamorphosis* Cambridge University Press: London

——. (1956) *Quart. J. micr. Sci.* **97**: 465–80 (abdominal muscles and moulting)

COTTRELL, C. B. (1962) *J. exp. Biol.* **39**: 395–458 (emergence of adult blowflies and the hardening of the cuticle)

SWEETMAN, H. L. (1952) *Proc. 9th int. Congr. Ent. (Amsterdam)* **1**: 411–15 (growth, moulting and reproduction in Thysanura)

HINTON, H. E. (1948) *Trans. R. ent. Soc. Lond.* **99**: 395–409 (origin of the pupal stage)

WILLIAMS, C. M. (1956, 1959) *Nature* **178**: 212; **183**: 405 (extraction of juvenile hormone)

WIGGLESWORTH, V. B. (1959) *The control of growth and form* Cornell University Press: Ithaca, N. Y.

——. (1961) *Insect polymorphism* (J. S. Kennedy, Ed.), Symposium of Roy. ent. Soc. London 103–13 (survey of insect polymorphism)

KENNEDY, J. S. (1956) *Biol. Rev.* **31**: 349–70 (change of 'phase' in locusts)

——. (1961) *Insect polymorphism*, Symposium of Roy. ent. Soc. London 80–90 (change of 'phase' in locusts)

SALT, G. (1927, 1931) *J. exp. Zool.* **48**: 223–331; **59**: 133–66 (*Stylops* and sex reversal in Hymenoptera)

LEES, A. D. (1961) *Insect polymorphism* (J. S. Kennedy, Ed.), Symposium of Roy. ent. Soc. London 68–79 (polymorphism in Aphids)

WODSEDALEK, J. E. (1917) *Science* **46**: 366–77 (moulting in the beetle larva *Trogoderma* during five years' starvation)

LEES, A. D. (1955) *The physiology of diapause in arthropods* Cambridge University Press: London

DANILIEVSKY, A. S. (1961)*Photoperiodicity and seasonal development in insects* (in Russian, Leningrad University, 243)

DE WILDE, J. (1962) *Ann. Rev. Ent.* **7**: 1–26 (photoperiodism in insects)

CORBET, P. S. (1956) *J. exp. Biol.* **33**: 1–14 (diapause in the emperor dragonfly *Anax imperator*)

MÜLLER, H. J. (1955) *Naturwissenschaften* **42**: 134–5 (length of day controlling seasonal dimorphism and diapause in *Araschnia levana*)

Chapter 7:

Mating and Reproduction

DAVEY, K. G. (1960) *Proc. R. ent. Soc. London* (A) **35**: 107–13 (evolution of spermatophores in insects)

KHALIFA, A. (1949–1950) *Trans. R. ent. Soc. Lond.* **100**: 449–71; *Quart. J. micr. Sci.* **90**: 281–92; *Proc. R. ent. Soc. Lond.* (A) **25**: 33–42, 53–61; *Parasitology* **40**: 283–9 (spermatophores in insects)

MAGNUS, D. B. E. (1958) *Z. Tierpsychol.* **4**: 397–426 (vision and mating in the butterfly *Argynnis*)

KETTLEWELL, H. B. D. (1946) *Entomologist* **79**: 8–14 (assembling scents in Lepidoptera)

BUTENANDT, A. (1955) *Naturw. Rdsch.* **12**: 457–64 (sexual attractant in the female silkmoth etc)

FREILING, H. H. (1909) *Z. wiss. Zool.* **92**: 210–90 (scent organs in male and female Lepidoptera)

BARTH, R. (1937, 1944) *Zool. Jahrb., Physiol.* **58**: 257–329; *Z. wiss. Zool.* **150**: 1–32; *Zool. Jahrb., Anat.* **68**: 331–62 (scent glands and mating in Lepidoptera)

TINBERGEN, N. *et al.* (1942) *Z. Tierpsychol.* **5**: 183–226 (scent scales and courtship in the grayling butterfly *Satyrus*)

DOWNES, J. A. (1955) *Trans. R. ent. Soc. Lond.* **106**: 213–26 (swarming and mating in the midge *Culicoides*)

BUCK, J. B. (1948) *Ann. N.Y. Acad. Sci.* **49**: 397–482 (light organs and mating in insects)

ROTH, L. M. (1948) *Amer. Midl. Nat.* **40**: 265–352 (hearing and mating in mosquitoes)

BUSNEL, R. G., DUMORTIER, B. & BUSNEL, M. C. (1956) *Bull. biol. Fr. Belg.* **90**: 219–86 (hearing and mating in grasshoppers)

WIGGLESWORTH, V. B. (1960) *Proc. Nutr. Soc.* **19**: 18–23 (nutrition and reproduction in insects)

DE WILDE, J. & DE BOER, J. A. (1961) *J. ins. Physiol.* **6**: 152–61 (diapause in the adult Colorado beetle)

SUOMALAINEN, E. (1962) *Ann. Rev. Ent.* **7**: 349–66 (parthenogenesis in insects)

HAGAN, H. R. (1951) *Embryology in the viviparous insects* Ronald Press Co.: New York

LEES, A. D. (1959) *J. ins. Physiol.* **3**: 92–117 (day-length and parthenogenesis in Aphids)

HUGHES-SCHRADER, S. (1930) *J. Morph.* **50**: 475–95; *Ann. ent. Soc. Amer.* **23**: 359–80 (hermaphroditism in the scale insect *Icerya purchasi*)

WIGGLESWORTH, V. B. (1953) *The principles of insect physiology* 67–70 Methuen: London (gynandromorphs and intersexes); 482–90 (parthenogenesis, paedogenesis etc)

Chapter 8:

Luminous Insects

HARVEY, E. N. (1952) *Bioluminescence* Academic Press: New York

RICHARDS, A. M. (1960) *Trans. R. Soc. N.Z.* **88**: 559–76 (New Zealand glow-worm *Arachnocampa* (*Bolitophila*)

GILMOUR, D. (1961) *The biochemistry of insects* 167–71 Academic Press: London (chemistry of light production)

BUCK, J. & CASE, J. F. (1961) *Biol. Bull. Woods Hole* **121**: 234–56 (control of flashing in fire-flies)

WIGGLESWORTH, V. B. (1953) *The principles of insect physiology* 297–300 Methuen: London (light-producing organs of insects)

Chapter 9:

The Colours of Insects

GILMOUR, D. (1961) *The biochemistry of insects* Academic Press: London

FOX, H. MUNRO & VEVERS, G. (1960) *The nature of animal colours* Sidgwick and Jackson: London

MASON, C. W. (1926, 1927) *J. Phys. Chem.* **30**: 383–95; **31**: 321–54, 1856–72 (structural colours in insects)

LIPPERT, W. & GENTIL, K. (1959) *Z. Morph. Oekol. Tiere.* **48**: 115–22 (thin plates producing metallic colours of butterfly scales)

CROMARTIE, R. I. T. (1959) *Ann. Rev. Ent.* **4**: 59–76 (insect pigments)

WALSHE, B. M. (1950, 1951) *J. exp. Biol.* **27**: 73–85; **28**: 57–61 (use of haemoglobin in Chironomid larvae)

KNIGHT, H. H. (1924) *Ann. ent. Soc. Amer.* **17**: 258–72 (effect of temperature on melanin and carotene pigments of the bug *Perillus*)

LONG, D. B. (1953) *Trans. R. ent. Soc. Lond.* **104**: 541–91 (crowding and colour change in caterpillars)

GOODWIN, T. W. (1952) *Biol. Rev.* **27**: 439–60 (biochemistry of locust pigmentation)

BÜCKMANN, D. (1959) *J. ins. Physiol.* **3**: 159–89 (colour change in full-grown larva of *Cerura* (*Dicranura*) *vinula*)

DUPONT-RAABE, M. (1957) *Arch. Zool. exp. gén.* **94**: 61–262 (colour change in the stick insect *Dixippus* and other insects)

Chapter 10:

Defence and Offence

KETTLEWELL, H. B. D. (1959) *Endeavour* **18**: 200–10 (protective adaptations in Brazilian insects)

Cott, H. B. (1940) *Adaptive coloration in animals* Methuen: London

Blest, A. D. (1957) *Behaviour* 11: 209–55 (uses of eye-spot patterns on wings of Lepidoptera)

Süffert, F. (1932) *Z. Morph. Oekol. Tiere.* 26: 147–316 ('countershading' etc in Lepidoptera)

Kettlewell, H. B. D. (1961) *Ann. Rev. Ent.* 6: 245–62 (industrial melanism in Lepidoptera)

Faure, J. C. (1932) *Bull. ent. Res.* 23: 293–405 (locusts adapting to background colour)

Brecher, L. (1938) *Biol. generalis* 14: 212–37 (adaptive coloration in pupae of *Pieris* etc)

Poulton, E. B. (1892, 1903) *Trans. ent. Soc. Lond.* 1892: 298–487; 1903: 311–68 (caterpillars assuming the colours of their surroundings)

Ernst, E. (1959) *Rev. suisse Zool.* 66: 289–95 (protective spraying by nasute termites)

Rothschild, M. (1961) *Proc. R. ent. Soc. Lond.* (C) 26: 22 (hydrocyanic acid produced by burnet moths *Zygaena* etc)

Bisset, G. W. *et al.* (1960) *Proc. R. Soc. Lond.* (B) 152: 255–62 (poisons in the tiger moth *Arctia caja* and related insects)

Edwards, J. S. (1961) *J. exp. Biol.* 38: 61–77 (the toxic saliva of the assassin bug *Platymeris*)

Beard, R. L. (1952) *Bull. Connecticut Agr. Exp. Sta.* 562: 26 (venom of the parasite *Habrobracon*)

Hodgson, N. B. (1955) *Bee World* 36: 217–22 (bee venom)

Stumper, R. (1960) *Naturwissenschaften* 47: 457–63 (ant poisons)

Pavan, M. (1959) *Fourth int. Congr. Biochem.* 12, *Biochemistry of insects* 15–36 Pergamon Press: Oxford (insect poisons)

Roth, L. M. & Eisner, T. (1962) *Ann. Rev. Ent.* 7: 107–36 (chemical defences of insects)

Schildknecht, H. & Holoubek, K. (1961) *Angew. Chem.* 73: 1–7 (explosive equipment of the bombardier beetle *Brachinus*)

Windecker, W. (1939) *Z. Morph. Oekol. Tiere.* 35: 84–138 (warning coloration of the cinnabar caterpillar *Hippocrita jacobaeae*)

Brower, J. van Z. (1960) *Amer. Nat.* 94: 271–82 (experimental study of mimicry with the starling)

Sheppard, P. M. (1959, 1961) *Cold Spr. Harb. Symp. Quant. Biol.* 24: 131–40; *Insect polymorphism* (J. S. Kennedy Ed.), Symposium of R. ent. Soc. Lond. 20–9 (evolution and genetics of mimicry)

ROTHSCHILD, M. (1961) *Trans. R. ent. Soc. Lond.* **113**: 101–21 (Müllerian mimicry of odours among insects)

Chapter 11:

Insect Vision

WIGGLESWORTH, V. B. (1953) *The principles of insect physiology* 134–59 Methuen: London (insect vision)

DETHIER, V. G. (1953) *Insect physiology* (K. G. Roeder Ed.) 488–522 Wiley: New York (insect vision)

FRIEDERICHS, H. F. (1931) *Z. Morph. Oekol. Tiere* **21**: 1–172 (vision in tiger-beetle larvae, Cicindelidae)

DETHIER, V. G. (1942, 1943) *J. cell. comp. Physiol.* **19**: 301–13; **22**: 116–26 (vision in caterpillars)

EXNER, S. (1891) *Die Physiologie der facettierten Augen von Krebsen und Insekten* Leipzig

BURTT, E. T. & CATTON, W. T. (1961) *J. Physiol.* **159**: 52P, 64–6P (visual acuity of the compound eye)

AUTRUM, H. (1953) *Klin. Wochenschr.* **31**: 241–5 (acuteness of vision in flying insects)

WALLACE, G. K. (1956) *J. exp. Biol.* **36**: 512–25 (visual scanning by locusts)

BARLOW, H. B. (1952) *J. exp. Biol.* **29**: 675–84 (relative efficiency of compound eye and vertebrate eye)

BURTT, E. T. & CATTON, W. T. (1962) *Proc. Roy. Soc.* (B) **157**: 53–82 (new theory of insect vision)

BALDUS, K. (1926) *Z. vergl. Physiol.* **3**: 475–505 (perception of distance by dragonfly larva)

HERTZ, M. (1935) *Naturwissenschaften* **23**: 619–24 (perception of shapes by the honey-bee)

GOLDSMITH, T. H. (1961) *Light and Life* (W. D. McElroy and Bentley Glass Ed.) 771–94 Johns Hopkins Press: Baltimore (colour vision of insects)

LUTZ, F. E. (1924) *Ann. N.Y. Acad. Sci.* **27**: 181–283 (ultraviolet reflection of flowers and insect behaviour)

FRISCH, K. v. (1961) *Aus dem Leben der Bienen,* Edn. 6 Springer: Berlin (vision of bees)

DAUMER, K. (1956) *Z. vergl. Physiol.* **38**: 413–78 (colour sense in the honey-bee)

——. (1958) *Z. vergl. Physiol.* **41**: 49–110 (flowers as seen by bees)

MAZOKIN-PERSHNIAKOV, G. A. (1956) *Biofizika* **2**: 352–62 (ultra-violet reflection from the wings of butterflies)

KNOLL, F. (1925) *Z. vergl. Physiol.* **2**: 329–80 (colour vision and visiting of flowers by the hawk-moth *Deilephila*)

MOERICKE, V. (1952) *Z. Naturforsch.* **7**b: 304–9 (attraction of Aphids to yellow)

STOCKHAMMER, K. (1956) *Z. vergl. Physiol.* **38**: 30–8 (perception of the plane of polarized light by insects)

MÜLLER, E. (1931) *Z. vergl. Physiol.* **14**: 348–84 (ocelli in bees and ants as 'stimulatory organs')

Chapter 12:

Hearing, Smell, and other Senses

DETHIER, V. G. (1963) *The physiology of insect senses* Methuen: London

SLIFER, E. H. (1961) *Int. Rev. Cytol.* **11**: 125–59 (fine structure of insect sense organs)

WEIS-FOGH, T. (1949) *Nature* **164**: 873 (tactile organs on the head stimulating locust flight)

PUMPHREY, R. J. (1940) *Biol. Rev.* **15**: 107–32 (hearing in insects)

PRINGLE, J. W. S. (1961) *The cell and the organism* (J. A. Ramsay and V. B. Wigglesworth Ed.) 256–82 Cambridge University Press: London (proprioception in insects)

LINDAUER, M. & NEDEL, J. O. (1959) *Z. vergl. Physiol.* **42**: 334–64 (tactile hairs and sense of gravity in the honey-bee)

FINLAYSON, L. H. & LOWENSTEIN, O. (1958) *Proc. Roy. Soc. Lond.* (B) **148**: 433–49 (stretch receptors in insects)

THORPE, W. H. & CRISP, D. J. (1947) *J. exp. Biol.* **24**: 310–28 (pressure receptors in aquatic bugs, *Nepa, Aphelocheirus*)

PRINGLE, J. W. S. (1948) *Phil. Trans. Roy. Soc.* (B) **233**: 347–84 (the halteres and control of equilibrium during flight)

RISLER, H. (1953) *Zool. Jahrb., Anat.* **73**: 165–86 (Johnston's organ in *Anopheles*)

ROTH, L. M. (1948) *Amer. Midl. Nat.* **40**: 265–352 (hearing and mating in mosquitoes)

FRINGS, H. & FRINGS, M. (1958) *Ann. Rev. Ent.* **3**: 87–106 (sound production and hearing in insects)

AUTRUM, H. (1940) *Z. vergl. Physiol.* **28**: 326–52 (hearing in grasshoppers; location of sounds)

BUSNEL, R. G., PASQUINELLY, F. & DUMORTIER, B. (1955) *Bull. Soc. Zool. Fr.* **80**: 18–22 (communication by vibrations in *Ephippiger*)

——. (1953) *Ann. Epiphyt.* **1953**: 333–421 (songs of Orthoptera)

HASKELL, P. T. (1961) *Insect sounds* Witherby: London

PRINGLE, J. W. S. (1954) *J. exp. Biol.* **31**: 525–60 (songs of cicadas)

BUSNEL, R. G., BUSNEL, M. C. & DUMORTIER, B. (1956) *Ann. Epiphyt.* **1956**: 451–69 (response of *Ephippiger* to the songs of different species)

ROEDER, K. D. & TREAT, A. E. (1957) *J. exp. Zool.* **34**: 127–58 (hearing of ultrasonic waves by moths and their escape from bats)

WIGGLESWORTH, V. B. & GILLETT, J. D. (1934) *J. exp. Biol.* **11**: 129–39, 408 (location of the host by warmth and smell in the blood-sucking bug *Rhodnius*)

——. (1941) *Parasitology* **33**: 67–109 (sense organs and behaviour in the louse *Pediculus*)

DETHIER, V. G. (1955) *Quart. Rev. Biol.* **30**: 348–71 (chemoreceptors of the blowfly)

THORSTEINSON, A. J. (1960) *Ann. Rev. Ent.* **5**: 193–218 (taste and choice of foodplant by insects)

FISCHER, W. (1957) *Z. vergl. Physiol.* **39**: 634–59 (smell in man and bee compared)

HODGSON, E. S. (1958) *Ann. Rev. Ent.* **3**: 19–36 (chemical senses of insects)

Chapter 13:

The Wisdom of the Insect

ROEDER, K. D. (1959) *Smithsonian misc. Coll.* **137**: 287–306 (the mantis and its prey: the efficiency of the insect nervous system)

LOEB, J. (1918) *Forced movements, tropisms and animal conduct* Philadelphia

FRAENKEL, G. & GUNN, D. L. (1962) *The orientation of animals* Constable: London

KÜHN, A. (1919) *Die Orientierung der Tiere im Raum* Fischer: Jena

CARTHY, J. D. (1958) *An introduction to the behaviour of invertebrates* Allen & Unwin, London

WIGGLESWORTH, V. B. (1941) *Parasitology* **33**: 67–109 (mechanisms of orientation in the louse *Pediculus*)

BUDDENBROCK, W. v. (1932, 1953) *Vergleichende Physiologie* **1** & **2** Birkhäuser: Basel (sensory and nervous physiology)

KENNEDY, J. S. (1939) *Proc. Zool. Soc. Lond.* (A) **109**: 221–42 (visual responses of flying mosquitoes)

——. (1945) *Trans. R. ent. Soc. Lond.* **95**: 247–62 (visual orientation of locusts; menotaxis)

TINBERGEN, N. (1932, 1935) *Z. vergl. Physiol.* **16**: 305–35; **21**: 699–716 (succession of responses in the bee-hunting wasp *Philanthus*)

VAN DER KLOOT, W. G. & WILLIAMS, C. M. (1953, 1954) *Behaviour* **5**: 141–74; **6**, 233–55 (sequence of behaviour in cocoon spinning by the cecropia silkworm)

BAERENDS, G. P. (1941) *Tijdschr. Ent.* **84**: 64–275 (nest-building behaviour in the solitary wasp *Ammophila*)

——. (1959) *Ann. Rev. Ent.* **4**: 207–34 (complex acts or sequences of behaviour in insects)

THORPE, W. H. (1963) *Learning and instinct in animals* Methuen: London

V. FRISCH, K. & LINDAUER, M. (1956) *Ann. Rev. Ent.* **1**: 45–58 ('language' and orientation of the honey-bee)

WEISS, K. (1953, 1954) *Z. Tierpsychol.* **10**: 29–44; *Z. vergl. Physiol.* **36**: 9–20; 531–42 (learning experiments with bees and wasps in a labyrinth)

LINDAUER, M. (1961) *Communication among social bees* Harvard University Press: Cambridge, Mass.

HARKER, J. (1958) *Biol. Rev.* **33**: 1–52; *Ann. Ent. Rev.* **6**: 131–45 (diurnal rhythms in insects)

Chapter 14:

The Organization of Insect Societies

MICHENER, C. D. (1961) *Insect polymorphism* (J. S. Kennedy Ed.), Symposium of Roy. Ent. Soc. London 43–56 (social polymorphism in Hymenoptera)

FOREL, A. (1928) *The social world of ants.* 2 vols. Putnam: London

WHEELER, W. M. (1910) *Ants: their structure, development and behaviour* Columbia University Press: New York

——. (1922) *Social life among the insects* Constable, London

SCHNIERLA, T. C. (1953) *Insect physiology* (K. D. Roeder Ed.), 656–779 Wiley: New York (insect behaviour)

GRASSÉ, P. P. (1949) *Traité de Zoologie* **9**: 408–544 (termites)

LIGHT, S. F. (1942, 1943) *Quart. Rev. Biol.* **17**: 312–26; **18**: 46–63 (production of castes in social insects)

RIBBANDS, C. R. (1953) *The behaviour and social life of honey-bees* Bee Research Assoc.: London

BUTLER, C. G. (1954) *The world of the honey-bee* Collins: London

———. (1959) *Bee World* **40**: 269–75 (queen substance)

KARLSON, P. & BUTENANDT, A. (1959) *Ann. Rev. Ent.* **4**: 39–58 ('pheromones' or 'ectohormones')

DELEURANCE, E. P. (1955) *Insectes Sociaux* **2**: 285–302 (social behaviour of the wasp *Polistes*)

PARDI, L. (1948) *Physiol. Zool.* **21**: 1–13 (dominance order in *Polistes* wasps)

LÜSCHER, M. (1961) *Insect polymorphism* (J. S. Kennedy Ed.), 57–67 Symposium of Roy. ent. Soc. Lond. (social control of polymorphism in termites)

GRASSÉ, P. P. (1959) *Insectes Sociaux* **6**: 41–84 (co-operative building of termites)

LÜSCHER, M. (1955) *Acta tropica* **12**: 289–307 (ventilation system of termite nests)

LINDAUER, M. (1962) *Ann. Rev. Psychol.* **13**: 35–70 (communication among social insects)

v. FRISCH, K. (1950) *Bees, their vision, chemical senses and language* Cornell University Press: Ithaca, N. Y.

DETHIER, V. G. (1957) *Science* **125**: 331–6 (dancing as a means of communication in many insects)

Chapter 15:

Insect Populations, Speciation, and Migration

SCHWERDTFEGER, F. (1942) *Z. angew. Ent.* **28**: 254–303 (fluctuations in the populations of forest pests in Germany)

SHEPPARD, P. M. (1959) *Natural selection and heredity* Hutchinsons: London

———. (1961) *Advances in Genetics* **10**: 165–216 (population genetics of Lepidoptera)

DE BACH, P. & SISOJEVIĆ, P. (1960) *Ecology* **41**: 153–60 (temperature and competition between parasites of the California red scale)

DOBZHANSKY, T. (1961) *Insect polymorphism* (J. S. Kennedy Ed.), 30–42 Symposium of R. ent. Soc. London (chromosomal polymorphism in *Drosophila*)

KETTLEWELL, H. B. D. (1961) *Ann. Rev. Ent.* **6**: 245–62 (industrial melanism)

VALLINS, F. T. (1959) *Proc. South London Ent. Nat. Hist. Soc.* **1959**: 61–72 (species formation in insects)

HUXLEY, J. S. (1955) *Heredity* **9**: 1–52 (morphism and evolution)

TIMOFÉEFF-RESSOVSKY, N. W. (1940) *The new systematics* (J. S. Huxley, Ed.), 73–136 Oxford University Press: London (seasonal changes in genetic races of the ladybird *Adalia bipunctata*)

JOHNSON, C. G. (1954) *Biol. Rev.* **29**: 87–118 (migration of Aphids)

———. (1960) *Nature* **186**: 348–50 (migration and dispersal of emerging insects)

RICHARDS, O. W. (1961) *Ann. Rev. Ent.* **6**: 147–62 (control of insect populations)

WATT, K. E. F. (1962) *Ann. Rev. Ent.* **7**: 243–60 (control of insect populations)

CORBET, P. S. (1957) *J. Anim. Ecol.* **26**: 1–69 (life history and dispersal of the emperor dragonfly *Anax imperator*)

KENNEDY, J. S. (1961) *Nature* **189**: 785–91 (modern study of insect migration)

RAINEY, R. C. (1960) *Symp. Soc. exp. Biol.* **14**: 122–39 (carriage of locusts by the wind)

WILLIAMS, C. B. (1957) *Ann. Rev. Ent.* **2**: 103–80 (insect migration)

———. (1958) *Insect migration* Collins: London

SCHNEIDER, F. (1962) *Ann. Rev. Ent.* **7**: 223–42 (insect dispersal and migration)

KETTLEWELL, H. B. D. (1961) *Nature* **189**: 671 (migration of *Nomophila* from North Africa to England)

URQUHART, F. A. (1960) *The Monarch Butterfly* University Press: Toronto

BROWER, J. VAN Z. (1961) *Ecology* **42**: 76–83 (migration and overwintering of the monarch butterfly)

FORD, E. B. (1945) *Butterflies* Collins: London (including dispersal, genetics, and evolution)

Chapter 16:

Insects and Flowers

KNOLL, F. (1956) *Die Biologie der Blüte* Springer: Berlin

GRANDI, G. (1929) *Boll. Lab. ent. Bologna* **2**: 1–147 (biology of the fig insect *Blastophaga psenes*)

KULLENBERG, B. (1961) *Zool. Bidrag, Uppsala* **34**: 1–340 (bees and *Ophrys* pollination)

Chapter 17:

Insects and Man

BUCK, F. & PIGORINI, L. (1938) *Die Seidenspinner, ihre Zoologie, Biologie und Zucht* Springer: Berlin

HINMAN, H. (1953) *J. Trop. Med. Hyg.* **36**: 128–34 (the use of insects in medicine)

MILNE, A. (1962) *J. theoret. Biol.* **3**: 19–50 (natural control of insect populations)

METCALFE, C. L. & FLINT, W. P. (1962) *Destructive and useful insects,* Edn. 4 (revised by R. L. Metcalf) McGraw-Hill: New York

SWEETMAN, H. L. (1958) *The principles of biological control* Brown: Dubuque, Iowa

BROWN, A. W. A. (1958) *Insecticide resistance in arthropods* World Health Organization Monograph Series No. 38: Geneva

UVAROV, B. P. (1928) *Locusts and grasshoppers* Imperial Bureau of Entomology: London (new edition in preparation)

GORDON, R. M. & LAVOIPIERRE, M. M. J. (1962) *Entomology for students of medicine* Blackwell: Oxford

SYMES, C. B., THOMPSON, R. C. & BUSVINE, J. R. (1962) *Insect control and public health* Elsevier: Amsterdam

BUXTON, P. A. (1955) *The natural history of tsetse flies* Lewis: London

Appendix:

A Catalogue of Insects

BRUES, C. T., MELANDER, A. L. & CARPENTER, F. M. (1954) *Classification of insects* Harvard University Press: Cambridge, Mass.

TUXEN, S. L. (1959) *Smithsonian misc. Coll.* **137**: 379–416 (phylogeny of Apterygota)

PACLT, J. (1956) *Biologie der primär flügellosen Insekten* Fischer: Jena

IMMS, A. D. (revision by O. W. RICHARDS and R. G. DAVIES) (1957) *A general textbook of entomology* Methuen: London (a general account of all orders)

GRASSÉ, P. P. (1951) *Traité de Zoologie* **9** & **10** Masson: Paris (detailed accounts of all orders by specialist authors)

HINTON, H. E. (1958) *Ann. Rev. Ent.* **3**: 181–206 (phylogeny of the panorpoid orders)

GLOSSARY

Abdomen—The hindmost of the three parts of the body, made up of at most eleven segments.

Algae — Primitive plants growing in water and damp situations, many of them single-celled.

Allelomorph — One of any pair of alternative hereditary characters; 'gene' which can occupy the same position (locus) as another gene in a particular 'chromosome'.

Allometry—The growth of a part of the body at a rate that is greater or less than that of the body as a whole.

Amino acid — Organic compound containing both basic amino (NH_2) and acidic carboxyl (COOH) groups. There are twenty kinds of amino acid; hundreds of these compounds combine to form a protein.

Amniotic fluid — The fluid in which the developing embryo is suspended in the egg.

Anal papillae — Thin-walled projections from the anus of various aquatic larvae of Diptera, notably mosquito larvae.

Androconia — Scent-producing scales and hairs on the wings, etc, of male butterflies and moths.

Antenna — Segmented 'appendage' on the head carrying sense organs ('sensilla') of various kinds.

Antibiotic — Substance (like penicillin) produced by some fungus, bacterium, etc, which prevents the growth of other micro-organisms.

Anus—The posterior opening of the gut or alimentary canal.

Appendage — A projection from the body, such as the antennae, mouth-parts, limbs, etc.

Apterous—Without wings.

Apterygote—Belonging to the subclass Apterygota, primarily wingless insects.

Arthropoda — The largest major group or phylum of

363

the animal kingdom which includes crabs, spiders, centipedes, and insects.

Axon — The long filament from a nerve cell which carries the electrical message, or 'impulse', from one part of the body to another.

Biological control—The control of pests by the use of other living animals, usually parasitic or predaceous insects.

Bolus — The mass of food prepared in the mouth for swallowing.

Campaniform organ — Sense organ in which the nerve ends in a disc or dome of thin cuticle which is sensitive to bending.

Cellulose — Complex carbohydrate ('polysaccharide') formed by the combination of many glucose molecules to give the fibrous material which is the fundamental constituent of the cell wall in plants.

Cerci — Paired appendages, usually carrying sense organs, at the hind-end of the abdomen.

Chemoreceptor—A chemical sense organ perceiving taste or smell.

Chitin — A 'polysaccharide' resembling 'cellulose' but containing nitrogen, normally combined with protein.

Chordotonal organ—An elongated sense organ attached at both ends to the body wall and sensitive to stretching.

Chorion—The tough protein membrane which forms the shell of the insect egg as laid down by the mother.

Chromosomes — The threadlike bodies in the nuclei of all cells, which carry the hereditary 'genes'.

Chrysalis—The 'pupa' of butterfly or moth.

Cline — Continuous gradation in the form of a species throughout its geographical distribution.

Conditioned reflex — A 'reflex' modified by experience; notably a response given to a particular 'stimulus' because the animal has learned to associate that stimulus with some particular experience; e.g. the sound of a bell with the presence of food.

Conidia—The fruiting bodies of certain fungi.

Cornea — The transparent lens-like thickening of the cuticle overlying a simple eye or a single facet of the compound eye.

Corpus allatum — A small gland of internal secretion situated behind the brain, the source of the juvenile hormone.

Corpus cardiacum — Small organ of nervous origin behind the brain, believed to discharge into the blood the hormone from the 'neurosecretory cells' of the brain.

Countershading — The presence of a pale area in that part of the body that is normally shaded, which serves to counteract the apparent roundness.

Coxa—The first (basal) segment of the leg, which is attached to the thorax.

Crypsis or cryptic coloration — Colour and pattern which simulate the background on which the insect rests.

Crystalline cone—The transparent lens-like structure which lies below the 'cornea' in each 'ommatidium' of the compound eye.

Cuticle—The outer non-cellular layer of the body laid down by the 'epidermis'.

Diapause—A state of dormancy with arrested growth and development, associated with a very low rate of 'metabolism', that may supervene at any stage in the life history.

Ectoderm — The outermost layer of the embryo, developing into 'epidermis' including tracheae, and also the nervous system, etc.

Elytron (plur. *Elytra*)—The front-wing of beetles (Coleoptera) modified to form a horny protective sheath for the hind-wings.

Embryonic cuticle—A thin cuticle formed by the larva in the late stages of development within the egg and cast off at the time of hatching.

Endopterygote—Belonging to the subclass Endopterygota in which the developing wings do not appear externally until the 'pupa' stage.

Enzyme—A protein which acts as a ferment, or catalyst, and leads to the rapid break-down or build-up of other substances, e.g. digestive enzymes cause the break-down of foodstuffs before they are absorbed from the gut.

Epicuticle—The most superficial layer of the 'cuticle'; commonly contains waxes needed for waterproofing.

Epidermis—The single layer of cells which lays down the 'cuticle'.

Exopterygote — Belonging to the subclass Exopterygota in which the developing wings are visible throughout the young stages.

Extensor — A muscle that straightens out part of the body.

Fat-body—A diffuse 'tissue' below the 'epidermis' and around the gut, etc, which serves as a store for fat, 'glycogen', and protein, and plays an active part in 'metabolism'.

Femur—The long stout segment of the leg, above the 'knee-joint'.

Flagellum — The whip-like part of the antenna, beyond the second segment.

Flexor—A muscle that bends a part of the body.

Fore-gut—That part of the gut connected with the mouth (including the 'pharynx', crop, and gizzard) which is lined by cuticle.

Gall—Abnormal growth on a plant caused by chemicals introduced by an insect.

Ganglion—A central mass of nerve cells and their fibres giving out and receiving nerves.

Gene—A unit of inheritance. Nowadays a very short piece of a 'chromosome', believed to control the chemical changes necessary for a particular hereditary trait, is regarded as a gene.

Genetics—The study of heredity and variation.

Glossa—A small lobe one on each side of the 'labium'; these become enlarged to form the tongue of the bee.

Glycogen — A 'polysaccharide' similar to starch; carbohydrate is stored mainly in this form.

Gynandromorph — Insect of mixed sex, some parts genetically and structurally male, others female.

Haemoglobin—The red oxygen-carrying pigment that occurs in the red blood cells of vertebrates.

Haltere—The modified hindwing of two-winged flies (Diptera); club-shaped organ with sensory function.

Hemicellulose—A group of carbohydrates related to 'cellulose' but more easily digested; may serve as a food reserve in the seeds of plants.

Hermaphrodite — An insect producing both male and female sex-cells (spermatozoa and ova).

Heterozygous — Having both the normal gene and the mutated gene (the two alternatives or 'alleles') present in the 'chromosomes'.

Hind-gut—That part of the gut connected with the 'anus' which is lined by cuticle.

Hormone—A substance produced in small quantity in one part of the body (usually in a gland of internal secretion) and transported to other parts where it exerts its action.

Hydropyle—A special region on the surface of the egg concerned in the regulated absorption of water.

Hydrostatic — Concerned in mechanical balance or equilibrium in water.

Hypermetamorphosis—A series of changes in form beyond the usual 'larva', 'pupa', and 'imago'.

Hypopharynx—A tongue-like lobe in the floor of the mouth, the site of discharge of the saliva; greatly elongated in blood-sucking flies.

Imago—Adult sexually mature insect.

Impulse—The electrical disturbance, or 'message', that is carried along the nerve fibre or 'axon'.

Intersex—An insect which is genetically of one sex throughout, but in which parts of the body have developed the characteristics of the opposite sex.

Juvenile hormone — 'Hormone' secreted by the 'corpus allatum' which controls metamorphosis in the young stages and yolk formation in the adult female.

Keratin—The tough fibrous protein, containing sulphur, which occurs in the skin, hair, horn, claws, and feathers of vertebrates.

Labella—The pair of soft expansions at the lower end of the 'labium' in flies.

Labium — The lower lip, which consists of the paired mouth-parts of one segment fused together in the mid-line.

Labrum—The upper lip, a cuticular flap hinged to the head above the mouth.

Lignin — A complex compound which is added to cellulose by woody plants to give hardness; it forms about 30 per cent of the wood.

Lipid—Fat-like substance.

Luciferase—The 'enzyme' in

luminous organs necessary for light production.

Luciferin—The substance on which 'luciferase' acts to produce light.

Mandibles—The first pair of mouth-parts.

Maxillae — The second pair of mouth-parts.

Meconium—The contents of the 'rectum' of the adult insect d i s c h a r g e d on emerging from the pupa.

Metabolism — Comprises all the chemical processes occurring within the living body.

Metamorphosis — The transformation from the young or larval form to the adult or 'imago'.

Metathetely — The appearance of an abnormal monster resulting from an adult insect retaining some characteristics of the larva or pupa.

Micron—One thousandth of a millimetre.

Micropyle—Pore in the egg membranes through which the spermatozoa enter and fertilize the egg.

Mimicry — Protective similarity in the appearance of one species of insect to another.

Mitochondria — Minute bodies present in every living cell, the site of many 'enzymes' notably those concerned in oxidation.

Morphology—The study of form and structure.

Moulting — (1) The whole

cycle of growth which leads up to the formation of a new and larger 'cuticle' and the shedding of the old cuticle; or (2) the final act of shedding the remains of the old cuticle.

Moulting fluid—The fluid between the old and the new cuticle which digests and dissolves the inner layers of the old cuticle.

Moulting suture—Line in the cuticle along which the substance is not 'sclerotized', and therefore splits after digestion by the 'moulting fluid'.

Mucus—The slimy secretion of the nose and gut of vertebrates; contains compounds of polysaccharide with protein.

Mutation—A permanent alteration in a gene which changes the effects it produces and is transmitted to the offspring. The changed gene is 'allelomorphic' to the old.

Mycetome—A group of cells which regularly contains 'symbiotic' bacteria or fungi.

Natural selection—The preferential survival of certain varieties (or 'mutants') which according to Darwin's theory is the principal mechanism of evolutionary change.

Neoteny—Persistence of the larval form in a full-grown insect.

Neurosecretory cells—Nerve cells which themselves secrete hormones.

Neurotoxin—A poison which acts on the nervous system.

Nymph — A term applied sometimes to the larva of an 'exopterygote' insect (e.g. a cockroach or bug), sometimes to the last larval stage of such an insect when the wing lobes are prominent, occasionally (as by the French) as a synonym for the pupa.

Ommatidium — The separate element of the compound eye, with lens, light-sensitive cells, etc.

Ootheca—A packet of eggs bound together by secretion from the glands of the female genital ducts.

Order—The animal kingdom is divided into phyla (e.g. Arthropoda), the phyla into classes (e.g. Insecta), the classes into orders (e.g. Lepidoptera, see Appendix), the orders into families (e.g. Bombycidae), the orders into Genera (e.g. *Bombyx*) and the genera into species (e.g. *Bombyx mori* the silkworm).

Osmeterium — An eversible scent-producing o r g a n, notably in caterpillars of s w a l l o w t a i l butterflies (Papilionidae).

Ovipositor — Modification of the hind-end of the abdomen of the female through which the eggs are laid.

Paedogenesis — Reproduction in the larval stage.

Palps—Sensory 'appendages' attached to the 'maxillae' and 'labium'.

Parthenogenesis — Development of the ovum, or egg, without fertilization.

Peritrophic membrane — A loose, thin sheath of chitin enclosing the food in the gut.

Pharynx—The first part of the 'fore-gut' behind the mouth, concerned in swallowing the food.

Phase—The term used to describe the forms of a single species of locust, which differ in coloration and in their migratory habits.

Pheromone—A general term for chemicals secreted by animals and used to influence or convey information to other animals.

Phloem—The system of vessels which carry food substances throughout a plant.

Phylogeny — Evolutionary history.

Physiology — The study of the processes which go on in the living animal.

Plastron—A film of air on the surface of an aquatic insect, continuous with the tracheal system and so held that it cannot be displaced by water.

Pleuropodia — Vestiges of former abdominal limbs converted to other uses in present-day insects.

Poikilothermic — Varying body temperature, more or less following that of the surroundings.

Polymorphism — The occurrence of several different forms in the same species.

Polysaccharide — Carbohydrate produced by the combination of many molecules of a simple sugar or similar substance.

Prestomal teeth—'Sclerotized' teeth developing on the 'labella' of higher flies.

Proboscis — The elongated mouth-parts of some insects.

Prolegs — Stumpy appendages without joints on the abdomen of caterpillars and saw-fly larvae.

Proprioceptors — Sense organs which give information about the parts of the body itself, notably about their position.

Proteins — Highly complex organic compounds made up of hundreds of 'amino acid' molecules.

Prothetely — The appearance of an abnormal monster resulting from a larva or pupa developing some of the characteristics of the pupa or adult.

Pseudotracheal membrane— The surface of the 'labella' in house-flies, etc, carrying split tubes which superficially resemble 'tracheae'.

Ptilinum — An eversible sac on the front of the head in the higher flies, used for rupturing the 'puparium'.

Pulvilli—A pair of lobes or pads on the last segment of the 'tarsus' below the claws.

Pupa—The non-feeding stage between larva and adult in 'endopterygote' insects.

Puparium—The 'sclerotized' larval cuticle in the house-fly, etc, which encloses the delicate pupa.

Rectal glands—Pads of enlarged cells in the 'rectum' which absorb water and salts.

Rectum—The last portion of the 'hind-gut' before the 'anus'.

Reflex—The simplest type of behaviour in which a certain 'stimulus' evokes at once one specific kind of simple response.

Releaser — Stimulus which sets off an instinctive act.

Respiration — (1) The conveyance of oxygen from air or water to the living tissues (via tracheae, gills, etc), and the escape of carbon dioxide. (2) The chemical reactions by which the animal uses oxygen to obtain energy from its food-stuffs.

Retina — The light-sensitive apparatus of the eye.

Retinal rod or *rhabdom* — The rod-like structure formed from the united sensory borders of the retinal cells.

Rostrum — The beak-like mouth parts of the bugs (Hemiptera).

Royal jelly — The secretion of the head glands (pharyngeal glands) of the young honey-bee.

Saprophytic—Feeding on organic matter from dead and decaying tissues of plants or animals.

Scale—A modified hair, arising from a socket, which has become broad and flattened.

Sclerotin—The horny substance of cuticle formed by the tanning of protein.

Sensillum (plur. *sensilla*)—A small simple sense organ.

Serosal cuticle — An inner egg-shell formed by the outer membrane of the embryo (the serosa).

Spermatophore—Small packet of sperm.

Spiracle — External opening of trachea.

Statocyst—A sense organ of balance.

Stimulus — Anything that evokes a functional reaction in living tissues.

Stridulation—Production of sounds by rubbing together modified surfaces.

Symbiont—Symbiotic organism.

Symbiosis — Association of living organisms to their mutual advantage.

Systematics — Classification of living things, with emphasis on their evolutionary relationships.

Tapetum — The reflecting

layer of trachea behind the retina.

Tarsus—The series of small segments which make up the last and fifth region of the leg.

Taxonomy—The description and naming of animals as a basis for classification.

Tegmen (plur. *tegmina*) — Term applied to the fore-wings when they are leathery and protective for the hind-wings but still function in flight, as in grasshoppers; often called 'elytra'.

Thanatosis — Hypnotic response often called 'death feigning'.

Thoracic gland — Organ of internal secretion producing the moulting hormone.

Thorax — Group of three segments behind the head bearing the three pairs of legs and two pairs of wings.

Tibia—The fourth segment of the insect leg, the long shank.

Tissue—The fabric of the body composed of cells and the products of cells.

Trachea — The cuticle-lined tubes conveying air from the 'spiracles' to the tissues.

Tracheoles — The fine endings of the trachea.

Triungulin — The newly hatched larva of *Stylops* and various insects showing 'hypermetamorphosis'. It somewhat resembles *Campodea* (Diplura).

Trochanter—The small second segment of the insect leg, between coxa and femur.

Tymbal — The sound-producing membrane of cicadas.

Tympanum—Ear drum.

Vein—Fine tubes of toughened cuticle which provide a supporting framework for the wings; they contain tracheae, nerves, and blood.

Ventral gland — Organ of internal secretion in the head producing the moulting hormone.

Viviparity—Giving birth to living young.

Index

SIGNET SCIENCE Books You Will Enjoy